# INBOARD

# MOTOR

# INSTALLATIONS

by

## GLEN L. WITT & KEN HANKINSON,

## NAVAL ARCHITECTS

## PUBLISHED BY GLEN-L MARINE DESIGNS

OTHER PRACTICAL "HOW-TO" BOATING BOOKS PUBLISHED BY GLEN-L:

"BOATBUILDING WITH PLYWOOD"
"FIBERGLASS BOATBUILDING FOR AMATEURS"
"INBOARD MOTOR INSTALLATIONS"
"HOW TO BUILD BOAT TRAILERS"
"RIGGING SMALL SAILBOATS"

FOR FREE BOOK LITERATURE, WRITE TO:
GLEN-L MARINE DESIGNS
9152 ROSECRANS
BELLFLOWER, CA 90706

COPYRIGHT 1978
GLEN-L, Bellflower, California
LIBRARY OF CONGRESS CATALOG CARD NUMBER 78-58127
ALL RIGHTS RESERVED
PRINTED IN THE U.S.A.
No part of this book may be reproduced in any form
without permission in writing from the publisher.
ISBN 0-939070-01-4

# TABLE OF CONTENTS

# PREFACE

This edition of "Inboard Motor Installations" is a complete revision of the original text entitled, "Inboard Motor Installations In Small Boats", first copyright in 1960. The original book was largely concerned with motor installations in the popular sized trailerable-type powerboat. However, over the years more and more people have been attempting their own motor installations in an ever-increasing variety of boat types and sizes. With today's emphasis on "do-it-yourself" pursuits, motor installations in small as well as the larger craft, both for sail and power use, operating over a wide range of speeds, are not beyond the abilities of most novices. Hence the reason for this new edition and resulting title modification from the original work.

While the basic format and subject area of the original text have been maintained, a considerable increase in scope has been provided to include advancements in motors, transmission methods, and other items related to the typical motor installation. Although the book is written from a "how-to" standpoint, enough information and theory has been included so that the book will provide not only the necessary guidance to perform the actual installation process, but also assure that the engine and transmission system can be the "correct" one for the boat in question.

Like the original book, the large, easy-to-read format with a long-lasting hard cover binding has been maintained. Since the text is used both in the classroom situation and at the work site, this durability has been much appreciated by previous readers. It is hoped that this book will provide the single-source reference material and guidance necessary to perform the work involved.

# ACKNOWLEDGEMENTS

Special thanks are given to amateur boatbuilders and other boat owners everywhere who have mustered up the courage and had the perserverance to install their own engines in their boats. Without them this book would probably not have been necessary. Gratitude should be given to all the GLEN-L customers who have badgered the firm with questions in their search for answers to their inboard powering problems. Without their prodding this book would have been a lot slower in coming to be.

Some very fine people and firms provided many of the photos and data included in the text, and their names are noted where applicable. If the service rendered to the authors is an example of that given to their prospective customers, the reader will no doubt receive good service and products from these firms also. To the many builders, friends, employees, and specialists who have suggested thoughts and ideas along with their time and effort, we express a very inadequate but sincere, "thank you".

# INTRODUCTION

The inboard motor, together with its power transmission system, related components, and installation requirements is a mystery to many boat owners, amateur builders, and even some boating professionals. The many types of powerplants and transmission choices available seem to complicate the picture for most novices. Yet like so many things in today's complex world, when taken a step at a time, the installation of an inboard motor in a boat is relatively simple. The parts and pieces are generally standard "off-the-shelf" items usually readily available. The only catch is how to install them, and that's the main function of this book.

It is hoped that the book will help clarify some of the problems and questions often asked in regard to inboard motor installations. Even if the reader is not in the process of installing an inboard motor, this book should give every boatowner who has an engine in his boat a better understanding of the component parts and functions involved. The book emphasizes motor installations in all types of pleasure craft, whether they be in sail or power craft, of either diesel or gasoline power.

Every effort has been made to keep technical material and professional jargon to a minimum. By using the illustrations, photos, and charts together with the text, even the neophyte should be able to grasp the subject. For the more experienced person in motor installations, many of the figures and plates will serve as a ready reference. Whether installing power in a new boat, or repowering an existing boat, it is hoped that this book will simplify the task and help provide the optimum performance for your craft.

# CHAPTER 1 — MATCHING POWER & BOAT

The type of motor that is installed in a boat is all-important, and it should be chosen with great care. Any inboard motor represents a considerable expense, and installing the wrong motor in a boat can be even more costly. If the motor is not properly matched to the hull it may waste fuel, wear out sooner than need be, or require more maintenance and parts. If the installation is not correct, performance could suffer, parts could fail, reliability might be questionable, and safety hazards could develop. Naturally the best method of determining the motor to be used is through professional advice. Check with the manufacturer of the boat or the designer for the power recommendation, and believe him! While a specific make of motor will probably not be recommended, the power requirements should be provided. Such a decision will usually be based on practicality; he isn't trying to overpower or underpower your boat, so don't try to second guess professional advice. It's based on experience.

If professional advice is not available, the problem is generally relegated to the field of good old common horse sense. Unfortunately, when the average person thinks about powering his boat, his sense of logic often seems to disappear. The common tendency with so many people seems to be to overpower their boats, not only beyond what speeds the boat will normally be operated at, but in many cases beyond what it is even possible or practical to drive a given hull. A typical example is the case of John Doe who hears a glowing report that Tom Jones has a boat that will do 65 miles per hour. Not to be outdone, John Doe has to have a boat that will do 70 miles per hour! Of course, when Tom Jones is asked if he has actually run his boat over a measured mile in both directions, his reply is something like this: "No, I haven't done that, but my buddy drove his car along the river while I went along with him in the boat, and he said that's what his car's speedometer registered." In short, few individuals have the faintest notion of what their REAL speeds on the water are, and exaggeration is common.

An actual case was an individual who occupied an adjacent slip some time ago. This person had a stock cruiser powered with a 100 horsepower motor. The author's boat was the same relative size and was powered with a slightly smaller motor. With everything running right, the author's boat could attain a speed of 20 miles per hour when run over the measured mile. The other individual claimed that his cruiser would go 35 miles per hour. In order to check this difference in top speeds, a 20 mile cruise was made under ideal conditions, with an agreed upon rendezvous point at the end. As the two cruisers reached the outer harbor limits, both throttles were opened, and lo and behold! The author's 20 mile per hour cruising speed was faster than the other person's 35 mile per hour boat! The author's cruiser waited at the rendezvous point for quite some time before the other boat arrived. After arriving, the other person INSISTED that the author's boat surely did 40 miles per hour since it went faster than his boat. Trying for diplomacy, the author tried to point out that he had timed his crossing at just one hour, and "just perhaps" the other boat's speed was slightly "over rated"? He would have none of that! He KNEW his speed and surely the author's boat was faster.

The moral of this story is to not be concerned with reputed or advertised speeds. The only REAL way of knowing the speed of ANY boat is to actually check the time over a measured mile run in BOTH directions in order to average out wind and tide effects. The speed of most boats and the distance of most measured mile runs are considered in NAUTICAL designations, and consequently, a boat's speed is usually given in KNOTS. While the distance of a mile on shore is 5280', a NAUTICAL MILE is longer at 6080'. If a boat's speed in miles per hour is known, multiply this by .869 in order to find the boat's speed in knots.

To run a boat over the measured mile, an accurate time piece must be used, either a stopwatch with sweep second hand, chronometer, or other similar watch. Several runs in each direction will give better accuracy. By making runs at different RPM settings, an RPM/Speed curve can be developed which can be useful in estimating cruising times and fuel consumption figures for varying speeds. The chart given in Fig. 1-1 can be used to determine the actual speed in knots of any boat over the measured mile up to 60 knot speeds. Using this chart can also allow a check to the boat's speedometer. Unless properly checked and calibrated, boat speedometers are frequently inaccurate.

## HULL TYPES

One of the greatest factors affecting speed and boat performance is the actual design of the boat's hull. It is a common tendency among boatowners to install the wrong powerplant in their boats, particularly from the standpoint of overpowering their boats in the hopes of increasing speed. In order to properly match the engine to the boat, the boatowner must have some understanding of hull designs and their limitations.

Basically, there are generally three types of hull designs:
1. Displacement hulls
2. Planing hulls
3. Semi-displacement hulls

## DISPLACEMENT HULLS

Displacement hulls can easily be identified underway, as they are the ones that "plow through" rather than ride on top of the water. In other words, they operate at relatively slow speeds. One basic fact about true displacement hulls should be kept in mind: A displacement hull has a limited top speed which, in theory, CANNOT be exceeded no matter how much power is applied. How is this limited speed determined? By the use of a rather simple formula known as the SPEED/LENGTH RATIO. Without trying to be

| Secs. | 1 min. | 2 min. | 3 min. | 4 min. | 5 min. | 6 min. | 7 min. | 8 min. | 9 min. | 10 min. | 11 min. | 12 min. | 13 min. | 14 min. |
|---|---|---|---|---|---|---|---|---|---|---|---|---|---|---|
| 0 | 60.000 | 30.000 | 20.000 | 15.000 | 12.000 | 10.009 | 8.571 | 7.500 | 6.667 | 6.000 | 5.455 | 5.000 | 4.615 | 4.286 |
| 1 | 59.016 | 29.752 | 19.890 | 14.938 | 11.960 | 9.972 | 8.551 | 7.484 | 6.654 | 5.990 | 5.446 | 4.993 | 4.609 | 4.281 |
| 2 | 58.054 | 29.508 | 19.780 | 14.876 | 11.921 | 9.945 | 8.531 | 7.469 | 6.642 | 5.980 | 5.438 | 4.986 | 4.604 | 4.275 |
| 3 | 57.143 | 29.268 | 19.672 | 14.815 | 11.881 | 9.917 | 8.511 | 7.453 | 6.630 | 5.970 | 5.430 | 4.979 | 4.598 | 4.270 |
| 4 | 56.250 | 29.032 | 19.565 | 14.754 | 11.842 | 9.890 | 8.491 | 7.438 | 6.618 | 5.960 | 5.422 | 4.972 | 4.592 | 4.265 |
| 5 | 55.384 | 28.800 | 19.459 | 14.694 | 11.803 | 9.863 | 8.471 | 7.428 | 6.606 | 5.950 | 5.414 | 4.965 | 4.586 | 4.260 |
| 6 | 54.545 | 28.571 | 19.355 | 14.634 | 11.765 | 9.836 | 8.451 | 7.407 | 6.593 | 5.941 | 5.405 | 4.959 | 4.580 | 4.255 |
| 7 | 53.731 | 28.346 | 19.251 | 14.575 | 11.726 | 9.809 | 8.431 | 7.392 | 6.581 | 5.931 | 5.397 | 4.952 | 4.574 | 4.250 |
| 8 | 52.941 | 28.125 | 19.149 | 14.516 | 11.688 | 9.783 | 8.411 | 7.377 | 6.569 | 5.921 | 5.389 | 4.945 | 4.568 | 4.245 |
| 9 | 52.174 | 27.907 | 19.048 | 14.458 | 11.650 | 9.756 | 8.392 | 7.362 | 6.557 | 5.911 | 5.381 | 4.938 | 4.563 | 4.240 |
| 10 | 51.428 | 27.692 | 18.947 | 14.400 | 11.613 | 9.730 | 8.372 | 7.347 | 6.545 | 5.902 | 5.373 | 4.931 | 4.557 | 4.235 |
| 11 | 50.704 | 27.481 | 18.848 | 14.343 | 11.576 | 9.704 | 8.353 | 7.332 | 6.534 | 5.892 | 5.365 | 4.925 | 4.551 | 4.230 |
| 12 | 50.000 | 27.273 | 18.750 | 14.286 | 11.538 | 9.677 | 8.333 | 7.317 | 6.522 | 5.882 | 5.357 | 4.918 | 4.545 | 4.225 |
| 13 | 49.315 | 27.068 | 18.653 | 14.229 | 11.502 | 9.651 | 8.314 | 7.302 | 6.510 | 5.873 | 5.349 | 4.911 | 4.540 | 4.220 |
| 14 | 48.648 | 26.866 | 18.557 | 14.173 | 11.465 | 9.626 | 8.295 | 7.287 | 6.498 | 5.863 | 5.341 | 4.905 | 4.534 | 4.215 |
| 15 | 48.000 | 26.667 | 18.461 | 14.118 | 11.429 | 9.600 | 8.276 | 7.273 | 6.486 | 5.854 | 5.333 | 4.898 | 4.528 | 4.210 |
| 16 | 47.368 | 26.471 | 18.367 | 14.062 | 11.392 | 9.574 | 8.257 | 7.258 | 6.475 | 5.844 | 5.325 | 4.891 | 4.523 | 4.206 |
| 17 | 46.753 | 26.277 | 18.274 | 14.008 | 11.356 | 9.549 | 8.238 | 7.243 | 6.463 | 5.835 | 5.318 | 4.885 | 4.517 | 4.201 |
| 18 | 46.154 | 26.087 | 18.182 | 13.953 | 11.321 | 9.524 | 8.219 | 7.229 | 6.452 | 5.825 | 5.310 | 4.878 | 4.511 | 4.196 |
| 19 | 45.570 | 25.899 | 18.090 | 13.900 | 11.285 | 9.499 | 8.200 | 7.214 | 6.440 | 5.816 | 5.302 | 4.871 | 4.506 | 4.191 |
| 20 | 45.000 | 25.714 | 18.000 | 13.846 | 11.250 | 9.474 | 8.182 | 7.200 | 6.429 | 5.806 | 5.294 | 4.865 | 4.500 | 4.186 |
| 21 | 44.444 | 25.532 | 17.910 | 13.793 | 11.215 | 9.449 | 8.163 | 7.186 | 6.417 | 5.797 | 5.286 | 4.858 | 4.494 | 4.181 |
| 22 | 43.902 | 25.352 | 17.822 | 13.740 | 11.180 | 9.424 | 8.145 | 7.171 | 6.406 | 5.788 | 5.279 | 4.852 | 4.489 | 4.176 |
| 23 | 43.373 | 25.175 | 17.734 | 13.688 | 11.146 | 9.399 | 8.126 | 7.157 | 6.394 | 5.778 | 5.271 | 4.845 | 4.483 | 4.171 |
| 24 | 42.857 | 25.000 | 17.647 | 13.636 | 11.111 | 9.375 | 8.108 | 7.143 | 6.383 | 5.769 | 5.263 | 4.839 | 4.478 | 4.167 |
| 25 | 42.353 | 24.828 | 17.561 | 13.585 | 11.077 | 9.351 | 8.090 | 7.129 | 6.372 | 5.760 | 5.255 | 4.832 | 4.472 | 4.162 |
| 26 | 41.860 | 24.658 | 17.476 | 13.534 | 11.043 | 9.326 | 8.072 | 7.115 | 6.360 | 5.751 | 5.248 | 4.826 | 4.468 | 4.157 |
| 27 | 41.379 | 24.490 | 17.391 | 13.483 | 11.009 | 9.302 | 8.054 | 7.101 | 6.349 | 5.742 | 5.240 | 4.819 | 4.461 | 4.152 |
| 28 | 40.909 | 24.324 | 17.308 | 13.433 | 10.976 | 9.278 | 8.036 | 7.087 | 6.338 | 5.732 | 5.233 | 4.813 | 4.455 | 4.147 |
| 29 | 40.450 | 24.161 | 17.225 | 13.383 | 10.942 | 9.254 | 8.018 | 7.073 | 6.327 | 5.723 | 5.225 | 4.806 | 4.450 | 4.143 |
| 30 | 40.000 | 24.000 | 17.143 | 13.333 | 10.909 | 9.231 | 8.000 | 7.059 | 6.316 | 5.714 | 5.217 | 4.800 | 4.444 | 4.138 |
| 31 | 39.561 | 23.841 | 17.062 | 13.284 | 10.876 | 9.207 | 7.982 | 7.045 | 6.305 | 5.705 | 5.210 | 4.794 | 4.439 | 4.133 |
| 32 | 39.130 | 23.684 | 16.981 | 13.235 | 10.843 | 9.184 | 7.965 | 7.031 | 6.294 | 5.696 | 5.202 | 4.787 | 4.433 | 4.128 |
| 33 | 38.710 | 23.529 | 16.901 | 13.187 | 10.811 | 9.160 | 7.947 | 7.018 | 6.283 | 5.687 | 5.195 | 4.781 | 4.428 | 4.124 |
| 34 | 38.298 | 23.377 | 16.822 | 13.139 | 10.778 | 9.137 | 7.930 | 7.004 | 6.272 | 5.678 | 5.187 | 4.774 | 4.423 | 4.119 |
| 35 | 37.895 | 23.226 | 16.744 | 13.091 | 10.746 | 9.114 | 7.912 | 6.990 | 6.261 | 5.669 | 5.180 | 4.768 | 4.417 | 4.114 |
| 36 | 37.500 | 23.077 | 16.667 | 13.043 | 10.714 | 9.091 | 7.895 | 6.977 | 6.250 | 5.660 | 5.172 | 4.762 | 4.412 | 4.110 |
| 37 | 37.113 | 22.930 | 16.590 | 12.996 | 10.682 | 9.068 | 7.877 | 6.963 | 6.239 | 5.651 | 5.165 | 4.756 | 4.406 | 4.105 |
| 38 | 36.735 | 22.785 | 16.514 | 12.950 | 10.651 | 9.045 | 7.860 | 6.950 | 6.228 | 5.643 | 5.158 | 4.749 | 4.401 | 4.100 |
| 39 | 36.364 | 22.642 | 16.438 | 12.903 | 10.619 | 9.023 | 7.843 | 6.936 | 6.218 | 5.634 | 5.150 | 4.743 | 4.396 | 4.096 |
| 40 | 36.000 | 22.500 | 16.364 | 12.857 | 10.588 | 9.000 | 7.826 | 6.923 | 6.207 | 5.625 | 5.143 | 4.737 | 4.390 | 4.091 |
| 41 | 35.644 | 22.360 | 16.290 | 12.811 | 10.557 | 8.978 | 7.809 | 6.910 | 6.196 | 5.616 | 5.136 | 4.731 | 4.385 | 4.086 |
| 42 | 35.294 | 22.222 | 16.216 | 12.766 | 10.526 | 8.955 | 7.792 | 6.894 | 6.186 | 5.607 | 5.128 | 4.724 | 4.379 | 4.082 |
| 43 | 34.951 | 22.086 | 16.143 | 12.721 | 10.496 | 8.933 | 7.775 | 6.883 | 6.175 | 5.599 | 5.121 | 4.718 | 4.374 | 4.077 |
| 44 | 34.615 | 21.951 | 16.071 | 12.676 | 10.465 | 8.911 | 7.759 | 6.870 | 6.164 | 5.590 | 5.114 | 4.712 | 4.369 | 4.072 |
| 45 | 34.286 | 21.818 | 16.000 | 12.632 | 10.435 | 8.889 | 7.742 | 6.857 | 6.154 | 5.581 | 5.106 | 4.706 | 4.364 | 4.068 |
| 46 | 33.962 | 21.687 | 15.929 | 12.587 | 10.405 | 8.867 | 7.725 | 6.844 | 6.143 | 5.573 | 5.099 | 4.700 | 4.358 | 4.063 |
| 47 | 33.644 | 21.557 | 15.859 | 12.544 | 10.375 | 8.845 | 7.709 | 6.831 | 6.133 | 5.564 | 5.092 | 4.693 | 4.353 | 4.059 |
| 48 | 33.333 | 21.429 | 15.789 | 12.500 | 10.345 | 8.824 | 7.692 | 6.818 | 6.122 | 5.556 | 5.085 | 4.687 | 4.348 | 4.054 |
| 49 | 33.028 | 21.302 | 15.721 | 12.457 | 10.315 | 8.802 | 7.676 | 6.805 | 6.112 | 5.547 | 5.078 | 4.681 | 4.343 | 4.049 |
| 50 | 32.727 | 21.176 | 15.652 | 12.414 | 10.286 | 8.780 | 7.660 | 6.792 | 6.102 | 5.538 | 5.070 | 4.675 | 4.337 | 4.045 |
| 51 | 32.432 | 21.053 | 15.584 | 12.371 | 10.256 | 8.759 | 7.643 | 6.780 | 6.091 | 5.530 | 5.063 | 4.669 | 4.332 | 4.040 |
| 52 | 32.143 | 20.930 | 15.517 | 12.329 | 10.227 | 8.738 | 7.627 | 6.767 | 6.081 | 5.521 | 5.056 | 4.663 | 4.327 | 4.035 |
| 53 | 31.858 | 20.809 | 15.451 | 12.287 | 10.198 | 8.717 | 7.611 | 6.754 | 6.071 | 5.513 | 5.049 | 4.657 | 4.322 | 4.031 |
| 54 | 31.579 | 20.690 | 15.385 | 12.245 | 10.169 | 8.696 | 7.595 | 6.742 | 6.061 | 5.505 | 5.042 | 4.651 | 4.316 | 4.027 |
| 55 | 31.304 | 20.571 | 15.319 | 12.203 | 10.141 | 8.675 | 7.579 | 6.729 | 6.050 | 5.496 | 5.035 | 4.645 | 4.311 | 4.022 |
| 56 | 31.034 | 20.455 | 15.254 | 12.162 | 10.112 | 8.654 | 7.563 | 6.716 | 6.040 | 5.488 | 5.028 | 4.639 | 4.300 | 4.018 |
| 57 | 30.769 | 20.339 | 15.190 | 12.121 | 10.084 | 8.633 | 7.547 | 6.704 | 6.030 | 5.479 | 5.021 | 4.633 | 4.301 | 4.013 |
| 58 | 30.508 | 20.225 | 15.126 | 12.081 | 10.056 | 8.612 | 7.531 | 6.691 | 6.020 | 5.471 | 5.014 | 4.627 | 4.295 | 4.009 |
| 59 | 30.252 | 20.112 | 15.063 | 12.040 | 10.028 | 8.592 | 7.516 | 6.679 | 6.010 | 5.463 | 5.007 | 4.621 | 4.291 | 4.004 |

FIG. 1-1 — Time/Speed chart used to determine the speed of a boat when run over a measured nautical mile course. For accuracy, the boat should be run in both directions to equalize the effects of wind and current.

3

too technical, the speed/length ratio equals the speed of the boat in knots divided by the square root of the waterline length (note that we did NOT say the overall length of the boat!). In other words, if a boat has a waterline length of 25′, and a speed of 5 knots, its speed/length ratio would be 1.0, since the square root of 25′ is 5, and when this figure is divided by the speed, the result is 1.0.

On the other hand, a boat that has a waterline length of 36′ and a speed of 6 knots also has a speed/length ratio of 1.0. Similarly, a boat with a waterline length of 49′ and a speed of 7 knots would likewise have a speed/length ratio of 1.0. The point is that if all three of these boats are displacement hulls, and all operate at the same speed/length ratio, the effect is that the longer the waterline length, the faster the boat will go, UP TO A POINT! Through testing and experimentation done a long time ago, it was found that if a displacement hull was pushed to its maximum hull speed, it would build up a huge bow wave forward and a deep trough along its length. If more power was added, the boat would not go any faster and would quite literally sink into this trough. Fuel economy suffered drastically also. The results of these experiments showed that in just about all cases, the point where the addition of more horsepower failed to provide a subsequent increase in speed corresponded to a speed/length ratio of 1.34. This is the ultimate number for all displacement hulls. In order to EXCEED this speed/length ratio, the hull form of the boat must be changed, and this can usually only be done during the design and construction phases; not afterwards. So in terms of maximum speed/length ratios for our first example of the 25′ boat, if it were a displacement type hull, the maximum possible speed of the boat regardless of horsepower would be: Square root of the waterline length = 5 x 1.34 = 6.7 knots MAXIMUM.

With displacement hulls, knowing this maximum potential speed together with the weight of the boat, the naval architect can very accurately specify the horsepower required to drive the boat in order to reach this speed. While winds and tides could be grounds for some additional power, attempting to power the boat beyond this speed by the addition of more horsepower would be a pure waste of money.

How does a boat owner know if his boat is of the displacement type or not? Usually the displacement boat will have rounded longitudinal running lines, especially in the aft sections (see Plate 1). In fact, a bathtub in the water would be a good example that everyone can relate to that would operate as a displacement hull. Most monohull sailboats, tugboats, ocean liners, canoes, and barges are displacement-type hulls. In other words, hulls which have rounding longitudinal lines below the water that sweep up at the ends, especially at the stern, are usually displacement hulls (see Fig. 1-2). Many boat owners are quite satisfied with the slower displacement-type boats; they are economical, if slow. The owners of these boats are quick to point out that they aren't in a hurry, and in fact, that's why they have their slow boats. It's some sort of an "escape" from the hustle and bustle of everyday life. The point is, they are on the water enjoying themselves, and that's all that matters. Their greatest

FIG. 1-2 — This photo shows a typical displacement type hull. Note the bow wave forward with the corresponding hollow or "trough" midway along the hull side. Because of the shape of the hull, the speed of this boat is limited, but little power is required.

glory is passing up fuel docks as they chug off into the sunset.

## PLANING HULLS

On the other hand, if the form of the hull is changed so that the addition of more power allows the boat to ride up and over its own bow wave and EXCEED its limited displacement hull speed, the boat becomes the planing type. Generally, full planing is considered to be occurring when a speed/length ratio of 3.0 is reached. In other words, in our example of the boat with the waterline length of 25' with the square root of this figure being 5, the boat would be fully planing at a speed of 15 knots (5 x 3.0). However, an important element enters into the speed capabilities when this speed/length ratio is reached: In theory, the boat's speed is limited ONLY by the amount of power available. In other words, boat speed can be increased almost infinitely. To many, this may sound too good to be true, and it is! In most boats a point is reached where hull resistance, coupled with the additional weight of added engine and fuel necessary to drive the hull, will impose limits to the maximum speed. However, it is anybody's guess where this limit lies! Even many naval architects can't accurately predict it. Such a boat is shown in Fig. 1-3.

Consider the case of the popular Western drag boats used in competition. These boats, which are of the planing type, achieve incredible speeds in the short distance of only a quarter of a mile, which at one time was said to be "impossible" by certain naval architects. These boats are a perfect example of what may occur when a boat is powered for extremely high speed/length ratios. In effect, the speed/length ratio at these high speeds becomes academic because there is so much power available that the boat becomes virtually airborne, leaving the boating science of hydrodynamics, and entering the threshold of aerodynamics. In other words, given enough power, the full planing boat might probably fly, albeit quite poorly.

In the real and practical boating world, however, most boats will operate at quite conservative speeds and for good reasons. First, the cost of additional power and fuel is simply out of reach for most individuals. Secondly, sea conditions quite often limit the actual speeds of boats since the hulls simply cannot take the pounding. Lastly, even if the boat could take high speed conditions and not fail, the crew would probably give out due to exhaustion. For most boatowners, this is not what boating is all about. The boatowner with the planing type hull is generally satisfied with more moderate speeds. The question usually is, however, how much power will be required for this planing performance?

From the foregoing, there must be enough power to reach minimum planing speed, which is considered to be a speed length ratio of 3.0. As stated, the boat will climb up and over its own bow wave at this speed, and this phenomenon is quite familiar to anyone who has ridden in planing boats. The expression "getting over the hump" is the common description of the boat riding up and over the bow wave, and the sensation on many boats is a somewhat sudden gain in speed and leveling of the boat's attitude or trim. The boat feels "free" since it actually has overcome it's own wave making resistance. With planing boats, one must pay the price for this speed, because considerably more power and fuel is necessary than that used in similar sized displacement boats.

How does one tell if he has a full planing type hull? Usually the full planing hull has a transom stern that is quite wide, and perhaps may be the widest part of the hull. Longitudinal running lines, especially in the aft section of the hull will be straight, and frequently parallel with the waterline (see Plate 1). Bottoms may be completely flat, or with some degree of vee at the transom. If the boat has a deep vee aft and is fitted with lift strakes or spray rails, you can be assured that the boat was meant to plane. There are other types of full planing hulls, such as the famous three-point hydroplanes

FIG. 1-3 — This photo shows a typical planing hull. Because of the hull shape and the power applied, the boat has literally climbed up and onto its own bow wave. In theory, the speed of this boat is limited only by the power available.

and tunnel hull types, however, these are somewhat specialized boats.

## SEMI-DISPLACEMENT HULLS

But what about that range of speed/ length ratios between the "full displacement" 1.34 figure and the "full planing" figure of 3.0? This area is reserved for those boats that are known as semi-displacement boats, or one could call them "semi-planing" boats,

since they could seem to be trying to operate in one or the other modes. Naval architects frequently design boats intended for these speed/length ratios because boat owners are often not willing to settle for slow displacement speeds in many cases. As pointed out, the shorter the waterline length of a boat, the slower the boat will be if of the displacement type. In many cases, an extra knot or two will be highly desirable, or even necessary. When this is the case, the designer must change the lines of the hull from a displacement type just enough to make speeds in this range possible.

Designing boats in the semi-displacement range requires considerable care and experience on the part of the designer since exact speeds and power requirements are somewhat harder to calculate. However, boats in this category are often nearly as economical as full displacement boats, and in many cases almost as fast as full planing boats. In fact, some semi-displacement boats can operate at maximum speed in certain sea conditions that would force a full planing hull to throttle back to slower displacement hull speeds. Hence, boats of this type are gaining in popularity among boatowners interested in a good balance of speed, economy, and comfort.

Some common characteristics of semi-displacement hulls include bottom running lines that incline upward slightly toward a transom stern, little immersion at the stern, and deadwoods or docking keels along the centerline of the hull (see Plate 1). It is probably more difficult to tell a semi-displacement hull for the novice than it is for either the full displacement or full planing types, however. Consequently, powering information is best left to the professional for hulls of this type.

## CONDITIONS AFFECTING PERFORMANCE

To most boatowners, performance means speed and economy. Just about everyone wants more speed with less fuel consumption, and the two are seldom compatible. Unfortunately, many boat owners make changes to their boats without really checking the accuracy of their results, or without considering all aspects of the boat's performance. Consequently, they live under the illusion of increased speeds and fuel economy. As pointed out previously, accurate figures are necessary to assess a boat's performance. In addition to speed, fuel usage must be correctly calculated as well. The best way to do this is with fuel flow meters for gasoline engines, or a pyrometer hooked into the exhaust manifold of diesel engines. With the diesel, optimum fuel economy is checked by measuring exhaust temperature. The hotter the exhaust, the more fuel that is being burned.

Many boat owners won't want to go to the trouble and expense of using the above techniques, and instead, will just want to improve or check on those factors that will insure good performance. In the following, any or all of the conditions could exist on a single boat, and therefore, they should all be checked or considered if optimum performance is desired.

Aside from hull form, the most important factor relating to speed is the ACTUAL weight of the boat. Note the emphasis on the ACTUAL weight, and not the advertised weight, or the estimated weight, or the weight as guessed at from similar boats. Regardless of the hull type, the heavier the boat, the more power it will require to achieve a given speed, and the more fuel it will use. While displacement hulls are less affected in terms of speed by increased loads, this is only relative considering the slower speeds involved. More weight still means more power or less economy, or both. Semi-displacement and full planing boats, which by the

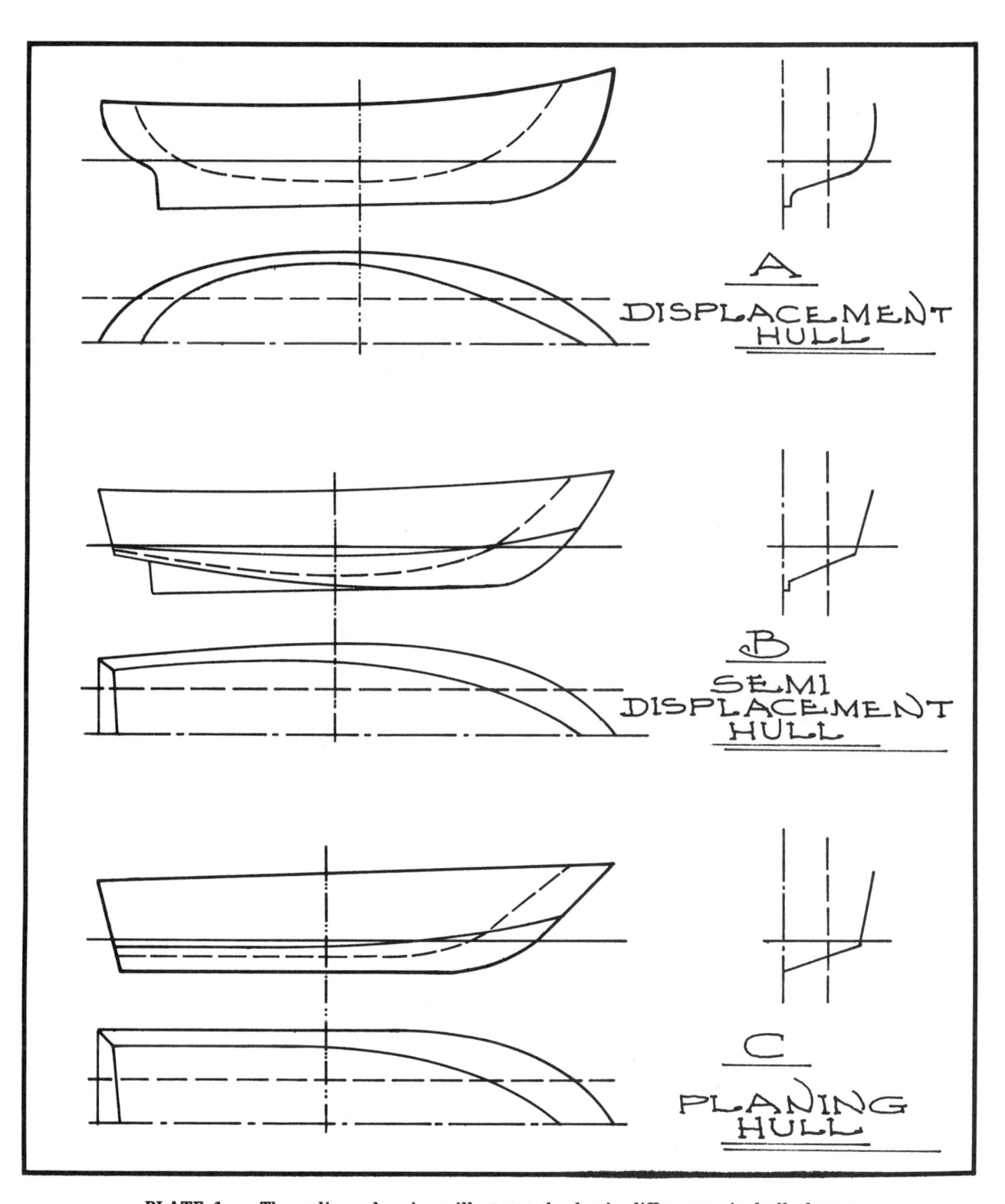

**PLATE 1** — These lines drawings illustrate the basic differences in hull shapes between displacement hulls, semi-displacement hulls, and planing hulls. Note the differences especially in the waterline shape in plan view and the running lines or "buttocks" in profile view. These lines generally show the speed capabilities of any given hull form.

9

way are excellent load carrying vessels, are even more sensitive to increases in weight. A common tendency among boatowners is to load up their full planing boats with considerable amounts of gear, and then wonder why they can't get up on plane. The simple answer in this case is that there just is not enough power available. This is why naval architects often put so much emphasis on keeping the structure as light as possible during the construction of a boat, because they know that the tendency of most boat owners is to overload their boats. When the performance suffers, the boat owner tends to blame the designer or the builder instead of himself.

Another aspect of weight is the balance or hull trim. While sometimes affected by the boat or hull design, improper loading can impair the performance of the hull. Placing loads at the stern may cause squatting, while loads located too far forward may similarly keep the boat from reaching its optimum performance. The location of all equipment, gear, and crew placed in the boat should be considered carefully. If heavy loads cannot be located amidships, then they should be equalized as much as possible throughout the boat. Avoid locating heavy weights in the ends of the vessel as much as possible. While heavy anchors and ground tackle are frequently located forward, ideally it would be better if such items could be located elsewhere, since the moment formed by the weight, times the distance forward of the balance point, is considerable in many cases.

Another critical element of performance, especially on faster boats, is drag. Drag can be caused by excessive marine growth on the bottom of the hull, roughness of the hull below the waterline, and the drag caused by underwater fittings and appendages. All these items should be faired as much as possible for a smooth flow of water under the boat.

Finally, for optimum performance, the power train must be considered. The engine must be in proper tune and in good mechanical condition. The proper type of fuel as specified by the motor manufacturer should also be used. All running gear should be in good condition and in proper alignment as well, including the transmission system, and connecting components. If the wrong reduction gear or wrong propeller size is used, performance and economy will suffer. Adequate air must be provided to the engine, and the heat in the engine compartment should be kept down in temperature for good engine efficiency. For just about all of these factors in this paragraph, the boat owner can tell if improvement is being made simply by comparing the figures on his tachometer. In further chapters, many of the areas related to these matters will be discussed in more detail.

# CHAPTER 2 — MOTOR LOCATION & HULL BALANCE

Naval architects are frequently asked a question such as this by amateur boatbuilders: "I have a 20' boat. Where do I put the motor?" Such a question is a lot like asking where the exact balance point will be for an irregularly shaped object. If no specific information has been provided on the plans used to build the boat, there is no one simple answer. But basically, the location of an engine is primarily a balance problem.

Every boat hull has a certain percentage of its hull volume located below the waterline in order to float or support the boat. The amount of volume below the waterline is EXACTLY equal to the amount of water that the boat "displaces" or pushes aside when it is set into the water. The weight of this displaced water will weigh EXACTLY the same as the boat in the water. This is why the weight of the boat together with a normal load of fuel, water, crew, and gear is called the DISPLACEMENT. In designing the boat, the naval architect uses various formulas to calculate this displacement together with other characteristics in order to predict how the boat will function, both at rest, and underway.

An important element of the displacement of the boat is that the displacement volume of the hull is providing the flotation capability. The water below in effect is pushing up against the hull to keep it afloat, while the weight of the boat and everything aboard is attempting to push the boat down into the water. The force of the water pushing the boat up is called buoyancy, while the force pushing downward is called gravity. The point at which the buoyancy force operates upward due to the displacement volume is called the Center of Buoyancy or "CB". The point of concentrated force of the boat's weight working downward is called the Center of Gravity or "CG".

When the boat is in the water, the location of the CB will ALWAYS be directly under the location of the CG. Because of this, the designer must calculate where the CB point is, using his displacement calculation, and also determine by close estimation through what is called a "weight study", where the CG point will be. Ideally they will fall at the same point if he has been careful in his designing process. If the points do NOT align, the laws of nature will see to it that they do once the boat is put into the water. In short, the boat will trim down by either the bow or stern to the required amount so that the two points will coincide. In order to prevent this condition, it can readily be appreciated that the designer must locate and "fix" certain items that will be located aboard the boat to assure a reasonable degree of hull balance to prevent undue trimming after launch-

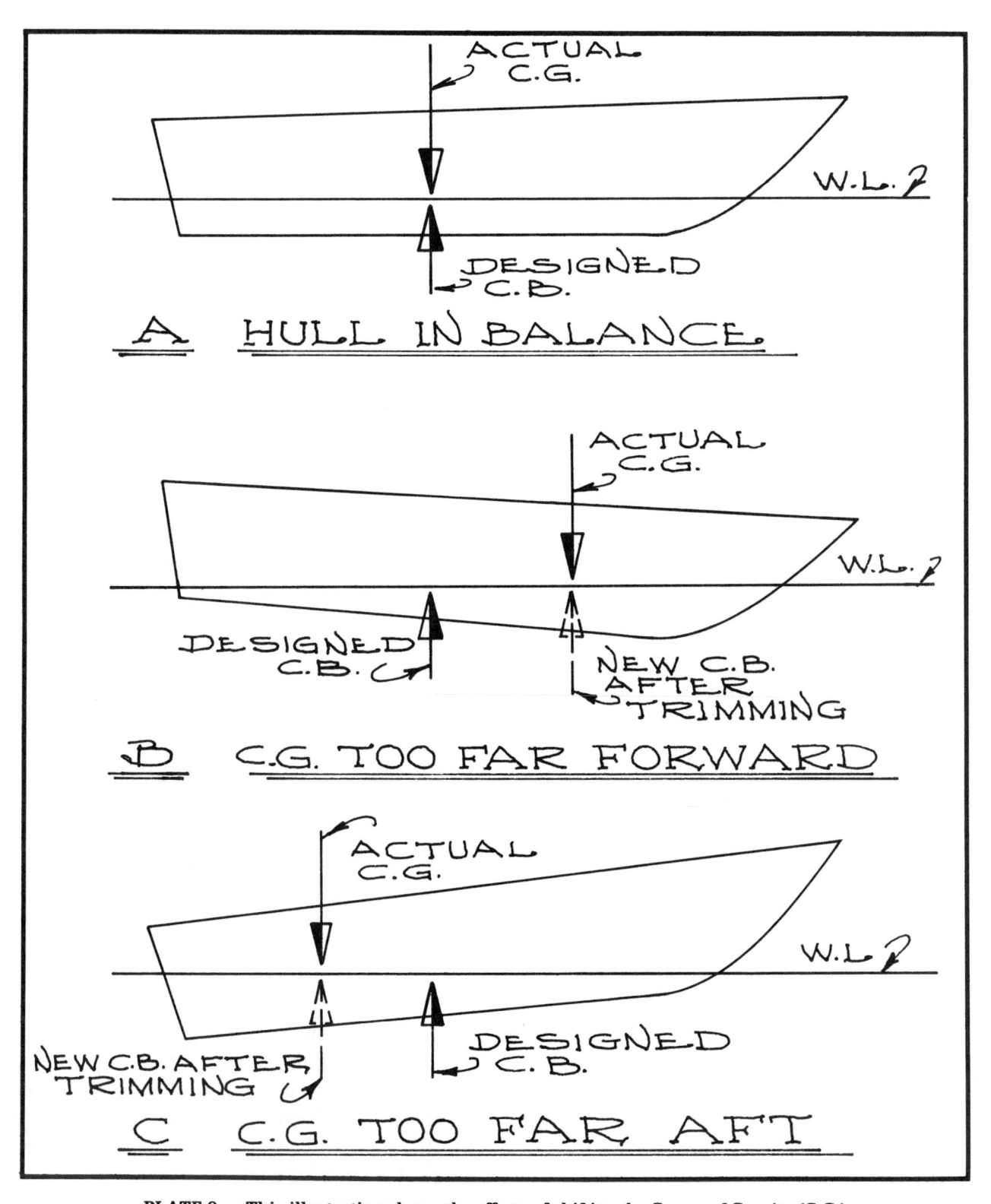

**PLATE 2 — This illustration shows the effects of shifting the Center of Gravity (C.G.) to either side of the Center of Buoyancy (C.B.). For the hull to balance, the C.G. must be over the designed C.B. If it is not, the boat will go down or "trim" either at the bow or the stern, depending on which side of the C.B. the C.G. is located.**

ing. In other words, the boat must balance. If it does not balance, the performance results could be questionable at the least, and if carried to an extreme, the boat could be dangerous.

While the foregoing may seem to be rather technical, it is important for the novice to understand what takes place, since the motor is one of the prime factors in the balancing problem. To simplify the problem, compare it to the typical child's teeter-totter. The pivot point for the teeter-totter is called the "fulcrum" point. If the teeter-totter includes a 50 lb. child on each end, and their distance apart from each other is 10 feet, it can readily be seen that if the fulcrum point is 5' from each child, the teeter-totter will be in perfect horizontal balance. If we shift one child toward the fulcrum point a distance of 1 foot, however, the weight of the child on the opposite end will cause the teeter-totter to go down on his end. The reason for this reaction is because the "moments" have been changed and are no longer in equilibrium.

What are moments? If we take the child's weight of 50 lbs. and multiply it times the distance from the fulcrum, the result is the moment, or in this case 50 lbs. x 5' = 250 ft. lbs. It is easy to see that if we have 250 ft. lbs. on either end, the teeter-totter will balance. However, as soon as one child moves in a foot, his moment is decreased to only 200 ft. lbs. (50 lbs. x 4'). The only way to balance out this change is to either shift the other child in a foot, or to add weight so that the SAME moment of 250 ft. lbs. is on BOTH ends. The question is how much weight? Since we know that the moment required for balance is 250 ft. lbs., and that the child is located 4' from the

fulcrum, we divide the moment by the distance and this gives us the required ADDITIONAL weight, or 250 ft. lbs. divided by 4' = 62.5 lbs. Thus the 50 lb. child located 4' from the fulcrum would need to be weighted with 12.5 lbs. (62.5 − 50). In other words, for every shift in distance or weight, a corresponding shift or weight change will be necessary to the opposite side so that the moments on both sides of the fulcrum point are virtually the same.

This is the same situation for a boat. The CB can be considered the fulcrum point, while the CG can be considered the combined force of the weights acting on either end of the boat to affect its balance. In many cases, the designer will note the location of the CB on his plans. From this reference point, known weights on either side of the CB can be multiplied times their distance fore or aft of the CB in order to find moments. This is what the designer does in his weight study; he literally figures each and every weight of EVERYTHING in or aboard the boat as it will be normally equipped so that the moments will balance. It is easy to see that if weights are shifted from what is shown, the hull could be thrown out of balance. Consequently, the boat owner should not make any major changes in the locations of any items of considerable weight without the advice of a naval architect or other competent person who is familiar with the particular boat, and this especially applies to the engine and its related components.

If all the foregoing seems confusing and technical, our point has been made. The location of the motor in a boat is a rather scientific and mathematical problem. There is no "by-guess and by-gosh" method involved, even

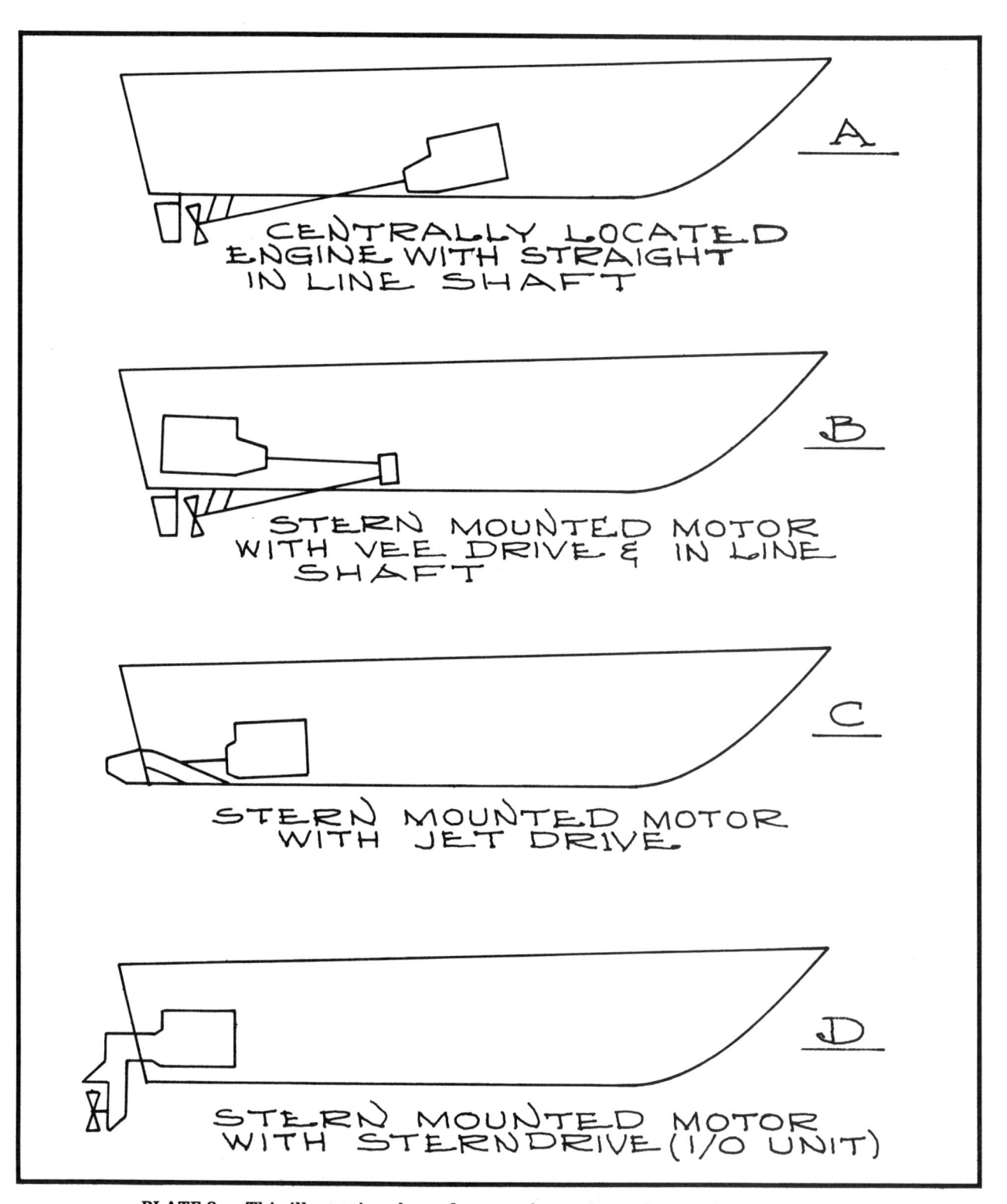

PLATE 3 — This illustration shows four popular engine and transmission configurations. With stern-mounted engines, the hull must be designed to carry the weight of the engine and gear, yet still maintain a reasonable degree of hull balance. Weight of the engine with the central location is not usually as critical since the engine is closer to the boat's designed center of buoyancy.

though some people have made lucky guesses. Because of the wide variety of possible boat shapes and underwater volumes, there is no way that a person can tell where a motor should be located in a certain boat without having a rather intimate knowledge of its design, or at least a lot of experience with similar types of boats.

One of the major advantages of the centrally located motor using a straight propeller shaft layout is that the motor, which is a considerable weight concentration, may be directly over or near the CB of the boat. Because of this, the weight of the motor will have little or no moment which could upset the balance of the boat. In addition to this, the weight of the motor could vary over a wide range in all but the smallest boats without upsetting the balance or ruining the trim of the boat to any large degree. Consequently, power changes such as adding twin engines where only one existed before, or vice versa, are not as likely to change the boat, other than perhaps sink it in the water deeper if more weight is added. Even still, such changes should only be made on competent advice.

However, many people want to change the location of a centrally mounted motor to the stern for one reason or another. Rarely should this be done, and the simple reason is the balance problem just described in the foregoing. Most boats specifically in-

tended for a centrally located engine will not have sufficient hull volume aft to provide the necessary buoyancy to support the added weight aft without affecting the balance of the hull. Similarly, a boat specifically intended for a stern mounted motor should not be changed to a central location since there may not be sufficient hull volume in the forward areas, which could put the bow down considerably and affect the performance. Many neophytes are quick to point out that if the engine is relocated, corresponding shifts in the tanks, which are another major weight in most boats, could be made to bring the moments into balance. However, the problem with this is that tanks are a variable weight, and the moments will change considerably between full tanks and near empty tanks. Such changes are therefore questionable.

The problem of engine location and balance is more critical with stern mounted motors. Often the designer will place a limit on the weight of engine which can be used at the stern. Many boatbuilders want to exceed this minimum, and sometimes this is possible to some degree. As will be covered in Chapter 5, any additional weight over the maximum recommended should be kept to a minimum. As noted in Chapter 21, there are some ways that minor unbalancing can be compensated for.

# CHAPTER 3 — MOTOR SELECTION & TYPES

## GASOLINE VS. DIESEL

The various virtues and disadvantages of both gasoline and diesel engines have been widely discussed in the boating press to the point where what follows is somewhat a repeat of well-known and common information. It is not the purpose of this text to promote one type of engine over another, even though the diesel powerplant has gained an ever increasing percentage of the inboard engine market, mainly because of the safety aspect. Although diesel fuel will ignite and burn, it will not explode the way gasoline will under normal marine conditions, and this fact alone is enough to convince many boat owners that the diesel engine is the only way to power a boat. However, there is no reason why a gasoline engine and power system can't be safe as well, assuming that proper installation, maintenance, and suitable marine equipment are used.

Many people feel that a diesel engine has potentially more power for a given rating. One often hears reference to so-called "diesel horsepower" as opposed to ordinary gasoline engine horsepower as though a horsepower was not a horsepower. Theoretically, a unit of horsepower is the same regardless of what kind of fuel makes the engine turn. However, part of this problem stems from the fact that diesel engine makers tend to rate their engines more realistically for marine conditions, probably because diesels have normally been associated with heavy-duty workboat applications where more precise ratings are necessary. On the other hand, gasoline engine manufacturers, whose engines are often converted automotive engines where high rated horsepowers may be a carry-over from the auto business, tend to give horsepower ratings that are not intended for continuous operation, and hence are more "optimistic". In fact, naval architects commonly "derate" gasoline engine horsepower ratings to around 75% of the rated power for powering calculations when more realistic continuous duty ratings are not noted.

For a given horsepower, the diesel engine will always be heavier than a gasoline engine, however, the margin has decreased considerably with new technology. While a diesel engine must be built heavier than a gasoline engine due to the extra loadings caused by the compression ignition and resulting vibration, it is a popular falacy to assume that a diesel has POTENTIALLY greater longevity. The reason that diesels last as long as they do is the fact that most diesel powerplants used in boats have been specifically intended for heavy continuous duty use in commercial applications where durability and reliability are paramount. How-

FIG. 3-1 — A single cylinder gasoline powered engine rated at 5 horsepower. Such engines are commonly used for auxiliary power in smaller sailboats. (Courtesy of Medalist-Universal Motors, Oshkosh, Wis.)

## GASOLINE MARINE ENGINE SAFETY . . . . .

*While manufacturers of marine gasoline engines may use basic automotive components, they do make certain changes that usually don't apply to these engines when used in an automobile. Such changes are usually safety-related and based on federal or other standards which manufacturers adhere to. The main reason for these changes is that fuel vapors cannot be allowed to accumulate in a boat to dangerous levels which could be ignited by an electrical spark. The following describes some of these changes, however, they may vary. A check with the U. S. Coast Guard or local governing body can be made to learn of any additional applicable regulations.*

*Standard automotive alternators may have exposed electrical contacts which can spark, while marine types have sealed contacts on the inside and meet ignition protection requirements. Automotive distributors, which can create high-energy sparks that may be released through a vent used to permit the release of ozone gas, are replaced with marine types having ignition protection and a vent with a flame arrestor to prevent sparking. Starters, generators, and accessory motors for marine use are completely sealed, and marine-type starter solenoids are ignition-protected with no vent for the release of sparks.*

*Carburetors for marine use have float chamber vents which lead back into the carburetor so that fuel will not overflow into the engine space. Marine-type fuel pumps are designed so that fuel will not leak into the engine space if the diaphragm fails. Thus, while automotive and marine components fulfill the same function, the marine type are somewhat different and safer.*

FIG. 3-2 — A two cylinder gasoline powered marine engine rated at 10 horsepower. Note the manual transmission lever for shifting. (Courtesy of Medalist-Universal Motors, Oshkosh, Wis.)

FIG. 3-3 — A four cylinder gasoline powered marine engine rated at 30 horsepower. (Courtesy of Medalist-Universal Motors, Oshkosh, Wis.)

ever, there is no reason why a diesel cannot be built to wear out just as quickly as its gasoline powered counterpart. In fact, it is getting more common to see gasoline engines "dieselized" without doing too much to "beef up" the innards of the engine, and time remains to prove whether these diesel conversions live up to their past diesel reputation.

In terms of economy it is difficult to state with certainty whether or not a diesel will be cheaper than a gasoline powered engine over the long term. Diesel fuel may be cheaper than gasoline, but this varies with the locale, current marketing trends, taxes, and other variables. Diesels, because of their injection system and beefier construction, are inherently more costly to produce than most gasoline engines. However, the diesel does consume less fuel for a given horsepower. It all boils down to how much the boat will be used, and it could be that the boat may never save enough in fuel costs to overcome the additional cost of the diesel engine.

In terms of maintenance, the diesel engine requires less of it. However, when work is necessary, a diesel specialist could be required which might cost more than a regular gasoline engine mechanic. Many people are familiar with gasoline engines, and consequently, the owner of the boat may be proficient enough to perform his own mechanical work. This could change, however, as diesels become more common. There are those people who can't stand the smell of diesel fuel or the exhaust fumes from a diesel engine. But the resale value of the diesel powered boat will probably tend to be greater than the gasoline powered craft. In general, the diesel tends to be more reliable than the gasoline engine since there is no ignition system to fail or carburetor problems common with gasoline engines. However, diesels require rather elaborate filter systems in the fuel lines since diesel fuel can get contaminated and foul the injection system of the diesel engine. Diesels also tend to be noisier than gasoline engines, and in many cases are not as

FIG. 3-4 — A six cylinder gasoline powered marine engine with a 2:1 hydraulic reduction gear.

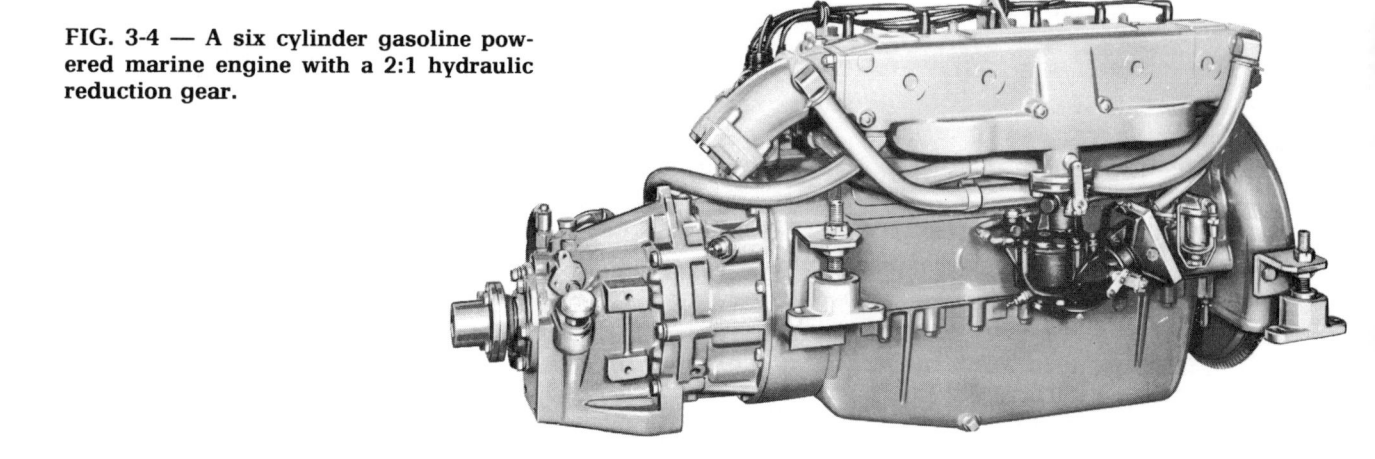

18

FIG. 3-5 — A V-8 gasoline powered marine engine with 350 cubic inches of displacement. Note the water cooled exhaust riser and connecting elbow to prevent a backflow of water into the engine from the exhaust line. (Courtesy of OMC, Waukegan, Ill.)

smooth running. And so, on goes the debate between gasoline and diesel engines! Many other factors may enter into the selection, but the final choice ends up with the purchaser.

## ENGINE SELECTION

A common question that naval architects hear is "what brand of engine do you recommend for my boat?" For some reason people who want to install an engine in their boats feel that naval architects are blessed with some innate sense about engine quality and suitability of one brand over another. Such may or may not be the case. The point is that such a question is a lot like asking a cab driver what kind of car should a person buy. Naturally, the cab driver, just like a naval architect, may have experiences he can relate about one brand or another based on very personal preferences. However, that's all that it is; personal experience. Of course, an engine is a big ticket item, and it's always desirable to get as much input as possible in pick-

ing one engine over another. But from the standpoint of the naval architect, to endorse one brand over another is not very ethical, and can be bad for his business.

Consider the case of a naval architect who insists that a client use the latest "XYZ-500" engine in a boat because he's convinced (either by advertising literature, personal experiences, or word-of-mouth) that it's the very best for the job. However, what if the boat is located and used in one part of the country, but the XYZ factory, or nearest parts supply, or nearest competent mechanic, is located thousands of miles away? Such a situation is not very practical even though the engine could be the very best, or the cheapest, or whatever. The result could be a dissatisfied client and a naval architect with a tarnished reputation. Therefore, when it comes to selecting an engine, the naval architect who has his client's interest in mind will merely state that the boat will require so much power to achieve such-and-such a speed. The selection of the engine manufacturer should then be based on the owner's requirements and where the boat will be used. An engine should be selected so that parts and service will be available wherever the boat will be used. A check with other boat owners in the area will indicate which engines are popular, why they are popular, and what to expect in the way of performance, service, and parts availability. Remember, that because so many marine engines were once automotive, industrial, or truck engines, parts may be available from other than marine suppliers. While price may be a questionable reason to buy a new engine, don't be bashful about looking for "deals" on engines. However, do remember that the best prices for engines (and anything else in the marine field in general) can often be purchased for a lower cost in the off-season when business is slow, or at a time when a dealer wants to clear out

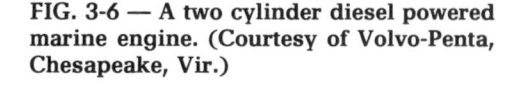

FIG. 3-6 — A two cylinder diesel powered marine engine. (Courtesy of Volvo-Penta, Chesapeake, Vir.)

FIG. 3-7 — A three cylinder diesel powered marine engine. This engine is rated at 24 horsepower. (Courtesy of Medalist-Universal Motors, Oshkosh, Wis.)

his inventory for one reason or another. Don't expect any bargains in the spring when everyone else is trying to get their boats ready for the new season.

## AIR COOLED & WATER COOLED

The overwhelming majority of marine engines are cooled by water or water-based liquid coolants. Some air-cooled marine engines are manufactured, however, their application is limited. The beginning small boat novice often would like to equip his boat with an air-cooled engine for various reasons. However, two key factors preclude the use of an air-cooled engine in most boats; insufficient airflow

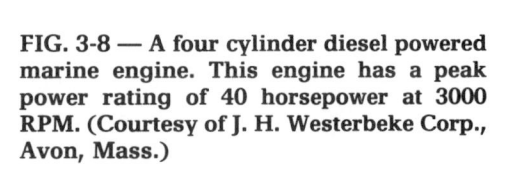

FIG. 3-8 — A four cylinder diesel powered marine engine. This engine has a peak power rating of 40 horsepower at 3000 RPM. (Courtesy of J. H. Westerbeke Corp., Avon, Mass.)

FIG. 3-9 — A six cylinder diesel powered marine engine. (Courtesy of Volvo-Penta, Chesapeake, Vir.)

to the motor for cooling, and too much heat in what could be a potentially hazardous environment.

An inboard engine is often located in tight, crowded conditions below hatches or an engine box where there is not the continual forced circulation of cooling air commonly found in automobiles, even though their engines are working much harder, and consequently giving off more heat. The heat passing through the exhaust manifolds is so intense, and the cooling volume of air so limited in most boats, that cooling of the manifolds and exhaust system with water jacketed components is virtually mandatory for safety, engine longevity, and efficient engine operation.

Because of the confined quarters for most boat engines, a potentially explosive or flammable condition exists if a component of the fuel system should fail. Because the water cooled engine heat can be more closely controlled, this danger is minimized. Then to, the extra cooling requirements for an air-cooled engine, such as greater intake air volume, thick insulation, and lagging of heat-producing surfaces would take up considerable room in the engine compartment and probably add weight. Additional ducting and fans may also be necessary to provide cooling air.

Because there are few marine air-cooled engines, many novices want to convert an air-cooled engine from shoreside use, such as from a car or truck. The problem with this is that few if any conversion parts will exist for such a conversion, and the job of making such parts is usually beyond the abilities of most people. While some air-cooled installations have been

made taking the above facts into consideration, longevity of the engine is always questionable. One must consider that any engine in a boat is running under conditions that in an automobile would be comparable to driving uphill in first gear at high RPM's all day long. Duty of this type is best done by an engine specifically intended or converted to marine use.

## SINGLE VS. TWIN ENGINES

Many boats can be equipped with either single or twin engines, and when this is possible, the pros and cons are just about as commonly heard as the arguments for and against diesel or gasoline powered engines. The most powerful argument for twin engines is the element of reliability. If one engine quits, there's at least one more left to get the boat and crew back to port. However, in many boats, it's possible to hook up a small outboard on a transom bracket, for example, that will serve for emergency power if the need arises. Or in larger boats with a single engine, many different stand-by power arrangements have been improvised, including power take-offs from the electrical generator to the propeller shaft, or a separate propeller and shaft running off the generator, or even various stand-by sailing rigs on suitable boats.

A common argument for twin screws is that they make the boat more maneuverable and easier to handle, especially in crowded conditions or in docking. A combination of twin throttles and transmissions, plus rudder action, allows instant response. With propellers turning in opposite directions, backing down the boat or turning in a tight radius can be a pleasure. The average planing-type boat does not have very good directional stability at slower speeds, and hence twin engines are common in larger planing boats. However, because twin screw planing boats are so common, a popular fallacy found among boat owners is that ALL boats are better suited to twin screws. This, however, depends on the hull configuration. In many cases, especially with slower boats of the displacement or semi-displacement type which have long deep keels, a single engine may be every bit as good from a directional stability or maneuverabil-

ity standpoint as a twin screw boat. Much depends on operator ability as well, regardless of the boat, and unfortunately many skippers would rather pay the price of an additional engine with all its gear, instead of practicing and learning how to control their vessels with single engines under a wide range of operating conditions. Such is life!

Besides the extra cost of a twin installation, many feel that there will be twice as much that can go wrong, and they're probably right. In a single installation the propeller, shaft, and rudder may be protected by a keel,

FIG. 3-10 — Some of the parts used for converting a typical automotive engine to a marine engine. Note the marine transmission with reduction gear attached and adapter housing just below. The parts required will vary depending on the particular engine being converted. (Courtesy of Barr Marine Products, Cornwells Heights, Penn.)

23

skeg, or deadwood. However, in most twin installations, these items are usually exposed and vulnerable to damage. Bent shafts, mangled propellers, and lost rudders are not uncommon, especially in debris infested water.

In many boats, twin engines will take up considerably more room, especially if the engines will be located in the cockpit area. In deep vee shaped hulls, a single engine may fit with plenty of clearance deep within the hull at the center. However, in a twin installation with the motors outboard from the centerline below the cockpit, or cabin sole, or "floor", it may be necessary to raise the sole to fit the engines in, or use smaller engines, or use engines more horizontally inclined.

Fuel economy will usually be less for a given horsepower with twin motors, however, this can vary depending on the motors. For twin engines which will be sternmounted, there must be sufficient volume for buoyancy in this area for proper hull balance. There is also more drag underwater due to the extra underwater fittings. Otherwise, installing twin engines is little different from a single engine, other than the duplication of components.

**WHAT IS A MARINE ENGINE?**

Very few engines, either gasoline or diesel, are specifically made just for marine use. While the boating industry is big business for engine manufacturers, it is not usually economically feasible to produce special engines for use on boats alone. Consequently, most engines used in boats are made using engine blocks and other components used for other purposes, such as

automobiles, trucks, busses, tractors, and other industrial applications. When an engine of this type will be used for a boat's powerplant, certain changes and modifications are necessary to make it suitable for a marine application. Engines that have been converted to marine use are said to be "marinized". Many manufacturers sell such engines, or it is possible to buy the necessary components from many sources and convert your own engine to marine use. Which is better? This is a question that can't honestly be answered since suitable powerplants exist of either type. From a convenience point of view, buying an engine "ready-to-go" may be easier for many individuals, plus the reputation and guarantee of the manufacturer could be an important factor in making an engine decision. However, these marine engines are costly. If the boat owner already has an engine or can purchase a used one in good condition at a favorable price, and he feels that he can do the conversion work using one of the numerous conversion "kits" available, then there is a chance to realize a considerable savings.

**THE "MARINIZING" PROCESS**

Converting an engine to marine use can involve several aspects. In some cases, the engine must be made stronger in certain areas to withstand the prolonged duty use common to marine conditions. The engine must also be made to be safe in the marine environment. In many cases, it may be necessary to make the engine more responsive to the power requirements of boat use. Whether using an engine from a marine engine manufacturer that has

FIG. 3-11 — This converted marine engine was originally a six cylinder Chevrolet automotive engine. Note the manual marine transmission. (Courtesy of Barr Marine Products, Cornwells Heights, Penn.)

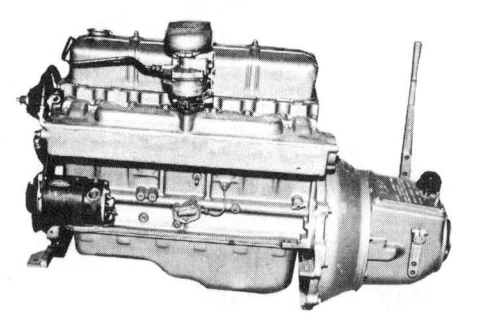

FIG. 3-12 — A converted Pontiac V-8 automotive engine is shown with a hydraulic marine transmission. Upper right and lower left photos show a 1:1 direct drive gear, while the upper left and lower right show the engine with a 2:1 reduction gear. (Courtesy of Barr Marine Products, Cornwells Heights, Penn.)

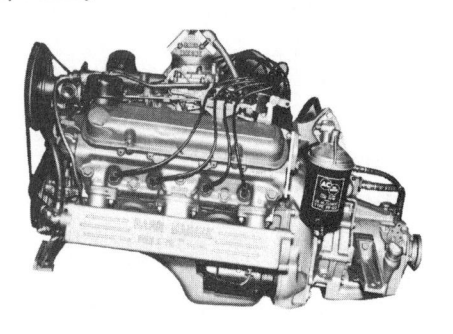

already been "marinized", or converting your own, three factors are usually used in determining what basic engine block to use; availability, durability, and cost.

Generally, the more common and popular engines tend to be converted to marine use, since they are both cheaper and more readily available. However, in some cases, these engines (which are usually of the automotive type) may not be as rugged as other types (such as those used in trucks, tractors, and heavy duty industrial applications). While a basic engine block may be used for several applications, there is a chance that for some applications, certain modifications may be made for heavy-duty use. For example, many industrial blocks which are the same as those used in some automobiles, may have heavier valve springs, or bigger valves and connecting rods, or huskier bearings. Such an engine will obviously be better suited to a marine application than the more lightly equipped automotive counterpart, if available.

Marine motor manufacturers (those who are in the business of selling ready-to-go "marinized" engines) often make additional modifications that aren't as easy for the individual converting his own engine. For example, cams may be changed or re-ground in order to change torque and horsepower characteristics so they will be more suitable for boat use. Carburetors may also be changed or modified, since on a boat the carburetor may operate at half or full throttle most of the time, which may be unlike an automotive carburetor that must operate over a variety of settings.

For those who want to convert their own gasoline engine to marine use, the following will outline the process. Note that this process is basically the same one that a marine motor manufacturer will use in "marinizing" a motor that will end up as a so-called "marine" motor. Basically, the conversion process involves adding, deleting and changing parts, many of which are external or "bolt-on" in nature. A typical marine conversion "kit" may consist of:

1. Water cooled exhaust manifolds
2. Marine water pump
3. Carburetor tilt shim or angle plate (perhaps)
4. Carburetor flame arrestor or "backfire" trap
5. Brass freeze plugs (for saltwater use)
6. Engine mounts

In addition to these components, depending on the engine, other parts might include an oil filter relocation kit, oil coolers, water cooled exhaust risers or elbows, various cover plates, various hose and plumbing assemblies, various brackets and pulleys, starter shaft extensions, lifting rings, and other items. In some cases the oil pan will be replaced because of shape or material. Ordinarily, automotive pans are stamped sheet metal, which can corrode quickly if in contact with seawater in the bilge. Heavier cast iron pans are better in this respect. Also, a pan of greater capacity may be required for marine use, or a reshaped pan may be necessary due to the boat's structure interfering, or because the shaft angle is so severe that the oil sump will be poorly located to provide positive lubrication.

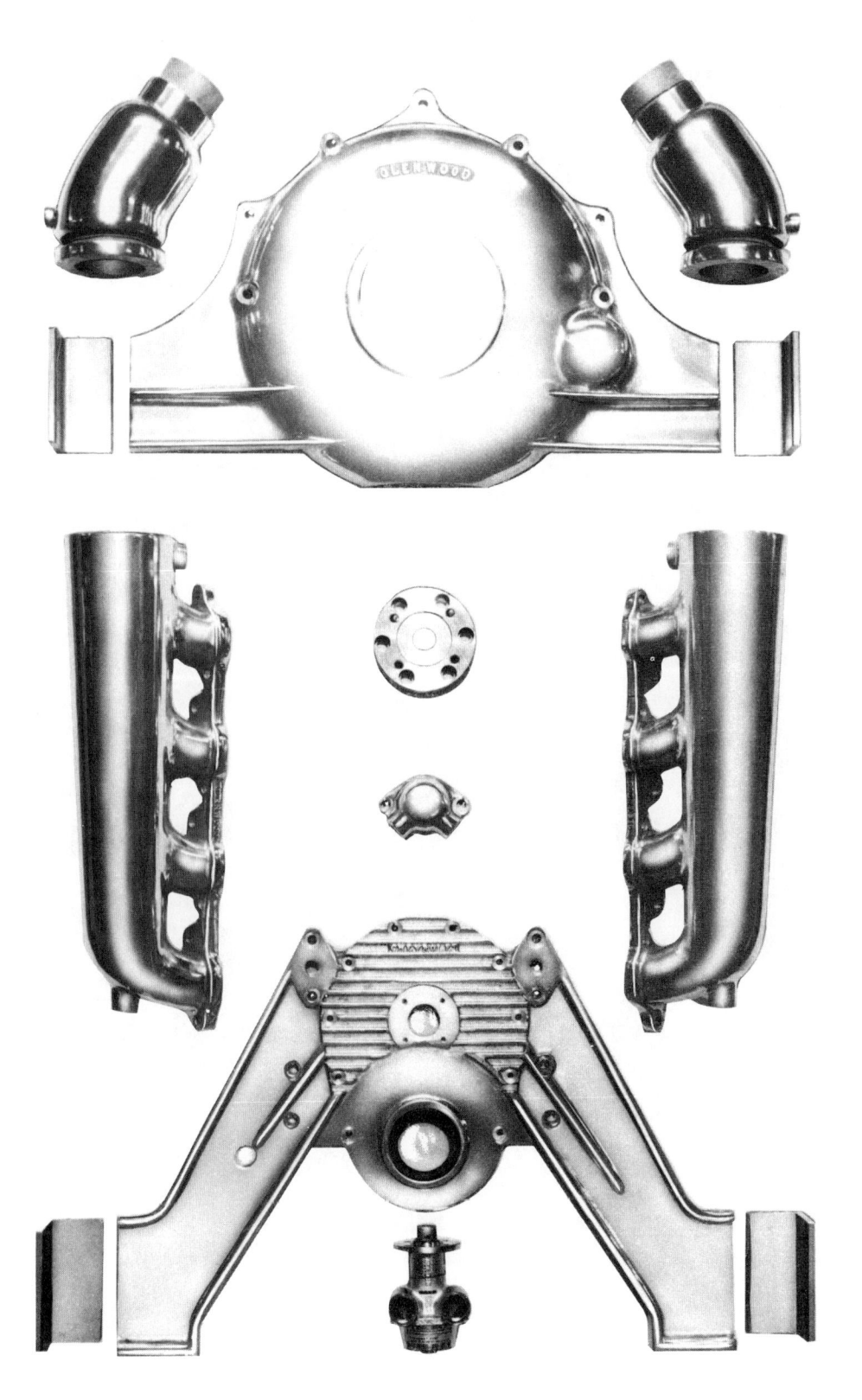

FIG. 3-13 — A typical "bob-tail" marine engine conversion kit. With this type of engine, a marine transmission is not used. (Courtesy of Glenwood Marine Equipment)

## 1 — WATER COOLED EXHAUST MANIFOLDS

In the typical engine used for shore-side purposes, the exhaust manifolds are cooled by air alone. However, in a boat where the engine is often confined within closed spaces, this heat is hazardous. Also, the heat may cause the engine to overheat and hamper engine breathing. Consequently, the

FIG. 3-14 — A completed "bob-tail" conversion of an automotive V-8. This engine will be used in a stern-mounted vee drive installation without a marine transmission. Note the hoses connecting to the exhaust elbows from the top of the engine block, and the water pump on the end driving off the camshaft. (Courtesy of Nicson Engineering, Santa Fe Springs, Calif.)

exhaust manifolds must be cooled, and this is done with water jacketed manifolds. These are perhaps the most obvious aspect of the marinized engine. In some limited uses, especially for competition boats where weight is important, and the engine is not completely confined, air cooled manifolds (or "dry stacks" as they are called) may be used (see Chapter 15). In normal boats, however, this practice is not safe.

## 2 — MARINE WATER PUMP

The automotive-type engine uses a water pump that is the recirculating type. It is not intended to pump water, but to circulate it instead. On the other hand, the marine water pump must be capable of pumping water into the engine's cooling system. Furthermore, it must be able to stand up to marine conditions, such as salt water, without corroding. Most marine water pumps are of the "Neoprene" hard rubber impeller type that can stand up to sand and silt. The water pump may be fitted on special brackets or fitted in the allotted space for the automotive type it replaces. The pump may be driven with pulleys and vee belt, or directly off the engine cam. Usually the marine pump runs at a considerably slower speed than the motor.

## 3 — CARBURETOR TILT SHIM

In many marine motor installations, the engine is often set at some angle from the horizontal. This is quite unlike, for example, an automotive installation where the engine is basically level most of the time. Since gasoline engine carburetors are intended for lev-

el operation, the tilt shim is used to bring the carburetor back to its correct plane of operation. Tilt shims are available for many different angles depending on the installation angle. They are also available for a wide range of carburetors and number of barrels or throats. If the engine is mounted horizontally, a tilt shim is not necessary.

## 4 — CARBURETOR FLAME ARRESTOR

An air cleaner is not required on a marine motor because it operates in basically clean air surroundings. Since a gasoline powered engine can backfire on occasion, this presents a potential hazard of fire or explosion aboard a boat, especially if there is no air cleaner. Consequently, the air cleaner is replaced with an approved-type flame arrestor that prevents this condition from being dangerous. These units are available in a wide range of types and sizes to adapt to various carburetors. Always allow ample clearance above downdraft carburetor flame arrestors for sufficient air to reach the engine.

## 5 — BRASS FREEZE PLUGS

Automotive and other similar type engines have machined holes in the block or cylinder head for use in fabricating the engine. These holes are plugged with freeze or expansion plugs usually made from steel. When engines are used in salt water, these steel plugs will rust and fail rapidly, and consequently should be replaced with solid brass plugs (but not brass plated steel plugs!). Only those plugs which will be in contact with corrosive conditions need be replaced, however.

FIG. 3-15 — A typical water cooled exhaust manifold as used in a marine engine conversion. This unit is made from polished cast aluminum for light weight. (Courtesy of Glenwood Marine Equipment)

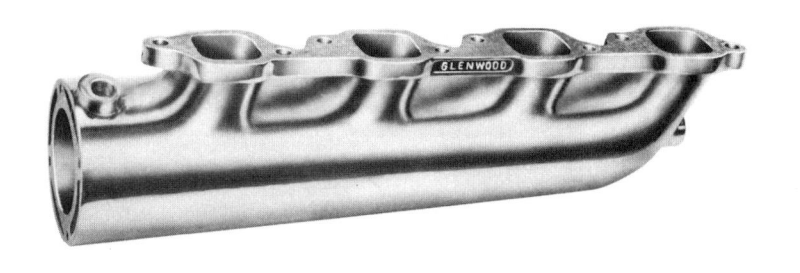

FIG. 3-16 — A header-type water cooled exhaust manifold made from polished cast aluminum. These manifolds are often used on high speed sport and competition boats. (Courtesy of Glenwood Marine Equipment)

FIG. 3-17 — A carburetor backfire flame arrestor is a necessary part of gasoline engine conversions for safety. Such units prevent flames from the engine during backfiring which could ignite volatile gasoline fumes that might accidentally enter the engine compartment. (Courtesy of Glenwood Marine Equipment)

## 6 — ENGINE MOUNTS

Because the engine will usually fit to motor stringers or similar mounting members, special mounts are required for most conversions. Such mounts may be separate components, or built in as part of other components, such as the flywheel cover. Either rigid or rubber type flexible mounts may be used, with the four-point mounting being common.

## 7 — OIL FILTER RELOCATION KIT

With many converted engines, the standard location for the oil filter could make it inaccessible. Therefore, kits are available to relocate the filter to a more convenient location. In addition to the filter, a water cooled oil cooler is frequently added in line with the filter unit. Oil temperatures often exceed those found in automobiles due to the lack of air flow.

## 8 — WATER COOLED EXHAUST RISERS & ELBOWS

Water cooled exhaust elbows or risers are usually required in conversions. The elbows direct the exhaust downward so that the cooling water can be exhausted through the exhaust line without backing up into the engine, which would damage the engine. Similarly, the elbows also provide backflow protection in the event that water enters the exhaust line from the back of the boat. If the engine is located deep in the hull or so the exhaust manifold water outlet would be too low to have a proper downward slope, risers would be used instead of elbows.

## 9 — COVER PLATES

Depending on the engine and the conversion kit, various cover plates may be required. Water cooled manifolds often have cover plates on the ends with threaded adapters where the cooling water hoses are connected. Flywheel covers are often fitted which may also serve as engine mounts, as well as being machined for mounting the starter motor. Timing gear covers are sometimes available with provisions for mounting a cam driven water pump. For safety, cover plates are often available for covering pulleys and vee belts.

## 10 — STARTER EXTENSIONS

On some conversions, the starting motor, if left in its original position, could be subjected to moisture and splashing bilge water, or may be in a position that is difficult to service due to the angularity of the motor when installed. In these cases, starter extensions are sometimes available which relocate the starter to a more forward or higher location on the engine.

## WHAT ABOUT THE TRANSMISSION?

A consideration with most marine engines is the need for some type of transmission. These are discussed in detail in Chapter 4, however, in many conversion kits, they may be part and parcel to the conversion process, and therefore may require advance thought on the part of the purchaser of an engine or conversion kit. As will be pointed out later, the standard automotive transmission is not really practical for marine use and is therefore dispensed with, together with the clutch. Automatic transmissions found on automobiles also fall into this category, although there are some exceptions. Since a boat does not have brakes, usually some sort of transmission arrangement must be provided so that reverse can be engaged to slow or stop the boat. Consequently a marine transmission is frequently coupled to the end of the engine.

If a transmission is not coupled to the engine, the engine is called a "bob-tail" engine. The "bob-tail" engine is used with sterndrive units, jet drives, and in certain vee drive installations where the transmission function is a part of the vee-drive. In certain competition boats, a "bob-tail" engine without a transmission of any type is used. In other words, the engine is started in gear and the boat takes off as soon as the engine is started. The only way to stop such boats is to shut off the engine. Obviously, such a boat is dangerous and the practice is restricted to racing boats operating under controlled conditions. Basically, the "bob-tail" engine consists of a flywheel housing for enclosing the flywheel, and usually to provide the rear mounts of the engine. A drive shaft or coupling is also necessary to connect the flywheel to the power transmission system, be it a jetdrive, sterndrive, or vee drive.

## SELECTING AN ENGINE FOR CONVERSION

Any engine that will be converted to marine use must be in good condition. If not, the engine should be rebuilt or overhauled. Of course, a new engine is ideal for converting. While it is theoretically possible to convert just about any engine to marine use, it is best to use stock conversion parts instead of attempting to make custom parts, even if the person is qualified to do the job. The stock type conversion parts are usually proven units and will no doubt be cheaper due to mass production. While stock conversion parts are available for a wide variety of engines, those engines which are most common and popular usually have the cheapest price for corresponding conversion parts simply because more of them are used. Odd-ball engines or those which are no longer made could cause problems not only in locating conversion parts to complete the job, but also when replacement parts are needed. Some conversion parts manufacturers specialize in high-performance engine conversions, while others concentrate on the more standard types of engines. Most conversion kits are for the popular automotive gasoline engines.

Conversion parts are available in both iron or steel and aluminum. For fresh water use, either material is suitable. In salt water, especially if sea water is used for cooling of water jacketed manifolds and components, corrosion can be a problem. The engine heat added with salt water can precipitate salt from the water and build up deposits that can damage metal parts. Aluminum is especially susceptible. However, if the engine is flushed out with fresh water after every use in salt water, corrosion can be greatly minimized. This is especially easy to do on trailerable type boats, and many owners actually rig garden hose adapters to their boat's cooling system just for this purpose. Otherwise, fresh water cooling can be used as discussed in Chapter 14.

32

FIG. 3-18 — Typical automotive engine ready for conversion. The transmission has been removed and the engine set on blocks for easy accessibility.

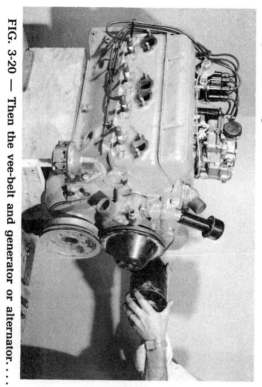

FIG. 3-20 — Then the vee-belt and generator or alternator....

FIG. 3-19 — The parts not required for marine service are removed, starting with the exhaust manifolds....

FIG. 3-21 — And the water pump....

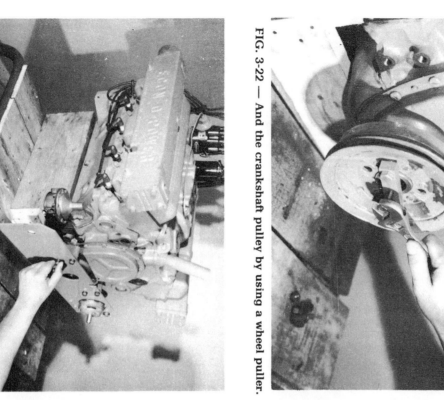

FIG. 3-22 — And the crankshaft pulley by using a wheel puller.

FIG. 3-23 — Now the engine is ready for the conversion parts. Start off with the water cooled exhaust manifolds.

FIG. 3-24 — In this case the front motor mount supports the water pump and is installed on the front of the engine block.

FIG. 3-25 — The crankshaft pulley is re-installed in its original position.

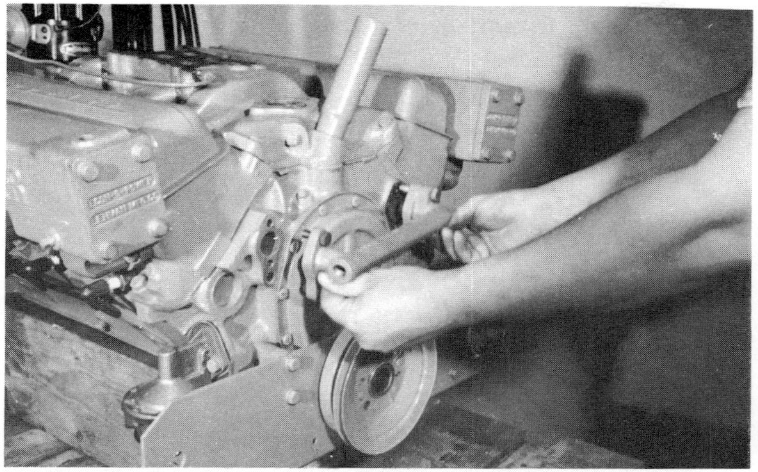

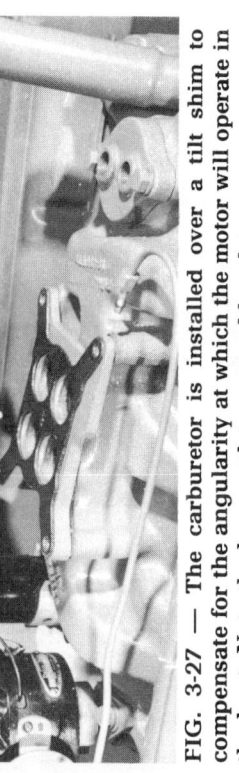

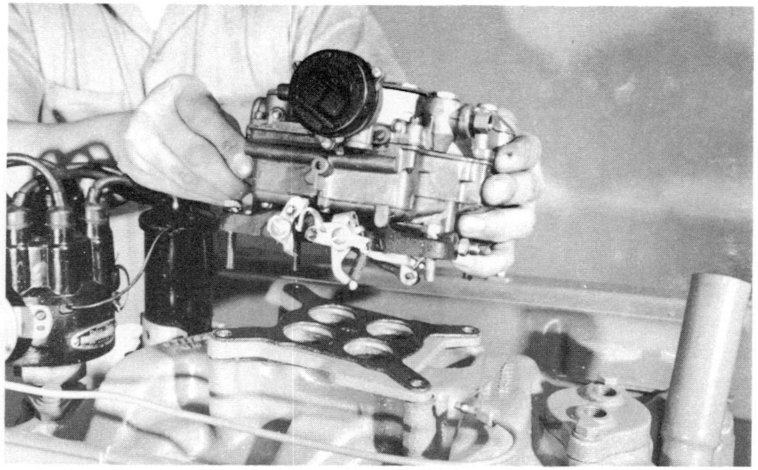

FIG. 3-27 — The carburetor is installed over a tilt shim to compensate for the angularity at which the motor will operate in the boat. Note the hose outlets covered by plates.

FIG. 3-29 — The driving belt for the water pump and generator is placed in position.

FIG. 3-26 — The water inlet header is bolted to the block.

FIG. 3-28 — The generator or alternator is installed in position.

35

FIG. 3-30 — Lifting rings to facilitate handling the completed engine are bolted in place.

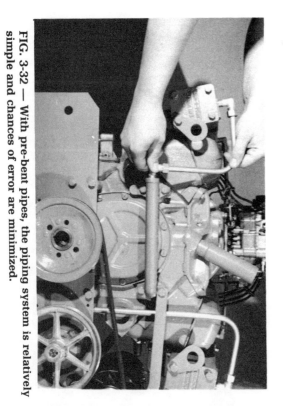

FIG. 3-32 — With pre-bent pipes, the piping system is relatively simple and chances of error are minimized.

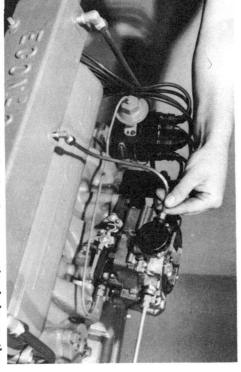

FIG. 3-31 — Pre-bent water piping is installed next.

FIG. 3-33 — The special tube for the automatic choke on the carburetor is fastened in place.

FIG. 3-34 — The piping is completed by the installation of the water outlet tubes that will pass the cooling water into the exhaust pipe.

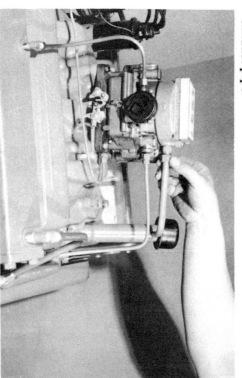

FIG. 3-36 — The flame arrestor is installed on the carburetor. An attachment is provided to withdraw smoke and fumes from the engine crankcase.

FIG. 3-35 — A safety cover is bolted in position over the belt linkage for safety.

FIG. 3-37 — The standard vent tube is sealed off with a special expansion plug.

FIG. 3-38 — The drive flange for the reverse gear is bolted to the flywheel.

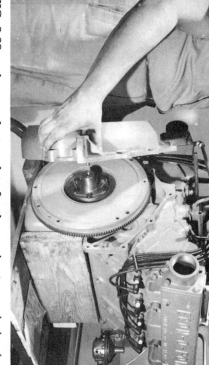

FIG. 3-39 — A new adapter plate for the marine transmission is bolted in place.

FIG. 3-40 — Since the reverse gear contains its own lubrication system, an "oil dam" is installed to retain oil in the reverse gear case.

FIG. 3-41 — The reverse gear driving drum is installed.

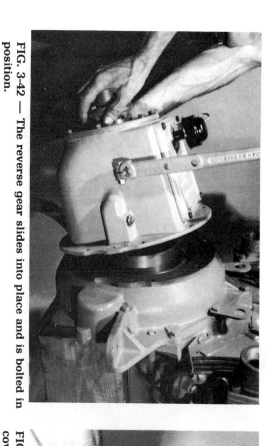

FIG. 3-42 — The reverse gear slides into place and is bolted in position.

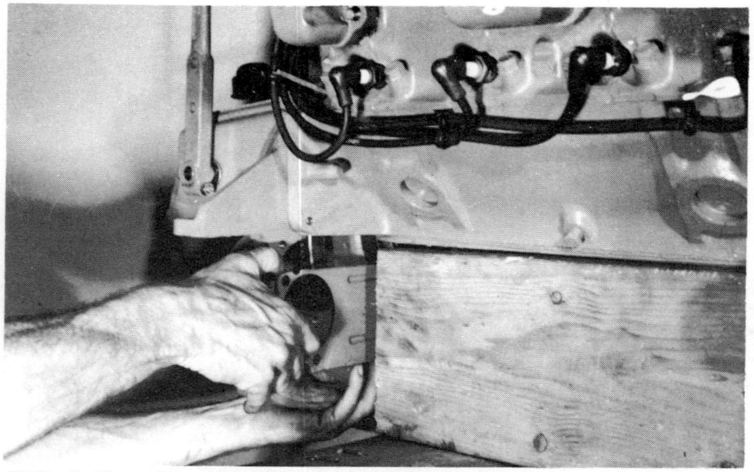

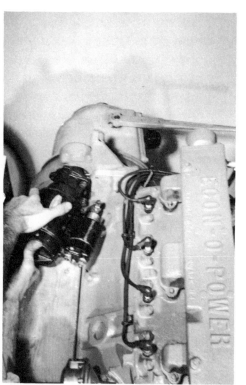

FIG. 3-44 — The starting motor is then installed.

FIG. 3-43 — The opening remaining in the flywheel housing is covered by use of the regular automotive parts.

FIG. 3-45 — The completed automotive conversion ready for the marine installation.

(FIG. 3-18 thru FIG. 3-45 courtesy of Barr Marine Products, Cornwells Heights, Penn.)

# CHAPTER 4 — POWER TRANSMISSION

In order to transfer the power provided by the inboard engine to propulsive force that will move the boat, some sort of power transmission system is required. With the exception of jet drive units, propulsive force is usually provided by a propeller located towards the stern in the water, either under or aft of the boat. Since the power provided by the engine may not be efficiently adaptable to the propeller; and in order to provide forward, neutral, and reverse control; some sort of transmission is necessary between the propeller and the engine. In this chapter several types of power transmission systems will be discussed. The first type of system discussed will be referred to as the conventional straight shaft arrangement, using a centrally located motor coupled to a transmission driving a straight shaft through the bottom of the boat with a propeller.

## THE MARINE TRANSMISSION

Unlike the standard shift automobile transmission, the marine transmission does not use nor require a clutch. In boating, the boat must be able to have quick and positive control between forward, neutral, and reverse directions. If an automotive type clutch were used, there would be a considerable time lag between changes in direction which could be hazardous, especially when operating in crowded conditions. Fur-

thermore, the ability to shift from forward to reverse, and vice versa, is in effect, the brakes of the boat. Consequently, most boats use and require some sort of marine transmission. Unlike the automotive type transmission, the conventional marine gearbox is a single speed gearbox that is turning at about the same speed as the engine in either forward or reverse gears.

In the conventional marine installation, the propeller, when moving the boat forward, is trying to force itself forward, together with the propeller shaft, into the boat. Similarly, when backing, the propeller and shaft are trying to pull themselves out of the boat. These forces which are "thrust" loads, must be taken by the marine transmission, and hence thrust bearings are usually provided in the marine transmission. If a thrust bearing is not a part of the boat's transmission system, it must be provided separately. While separate thrust bearings and housings were once fairly common, they are seldom used in most boats simply because thrust protection is built into most transmissions.

Marine transmissions are generally of two types; manual or hydraulic. The manual type is a band-type transmission that requires the operator to physically move a lever either forward or back to activate forward or reverse directions. The bands on this transmission require periodic adjustment, and activating the lever to shift the transmission requires some degree of force. The hydraulic transmission, on the other hand, uses multiple-disc clutch packs instead of bands and is therefore adjustment-free. The hydraulic feature of the transmission allows for quick, smooth, finger-tip shifting ease and a quieter transmission.

Transmission adapters are available to fit or adapt to a wide range of automobile flywheel housings for those de-siring to convert their own engines. Some transmissions are also available to connect to the crankshaft end (the end opposite the flywheel end) of the engine. This can be advantageous in lowering the height of the engine in the conventional straight shaft installation since the engine with the flywheel at the forward end will allow it to be set lower in the hull. Swapping ends by turning the engine also effectively changes the rotation of the engine.

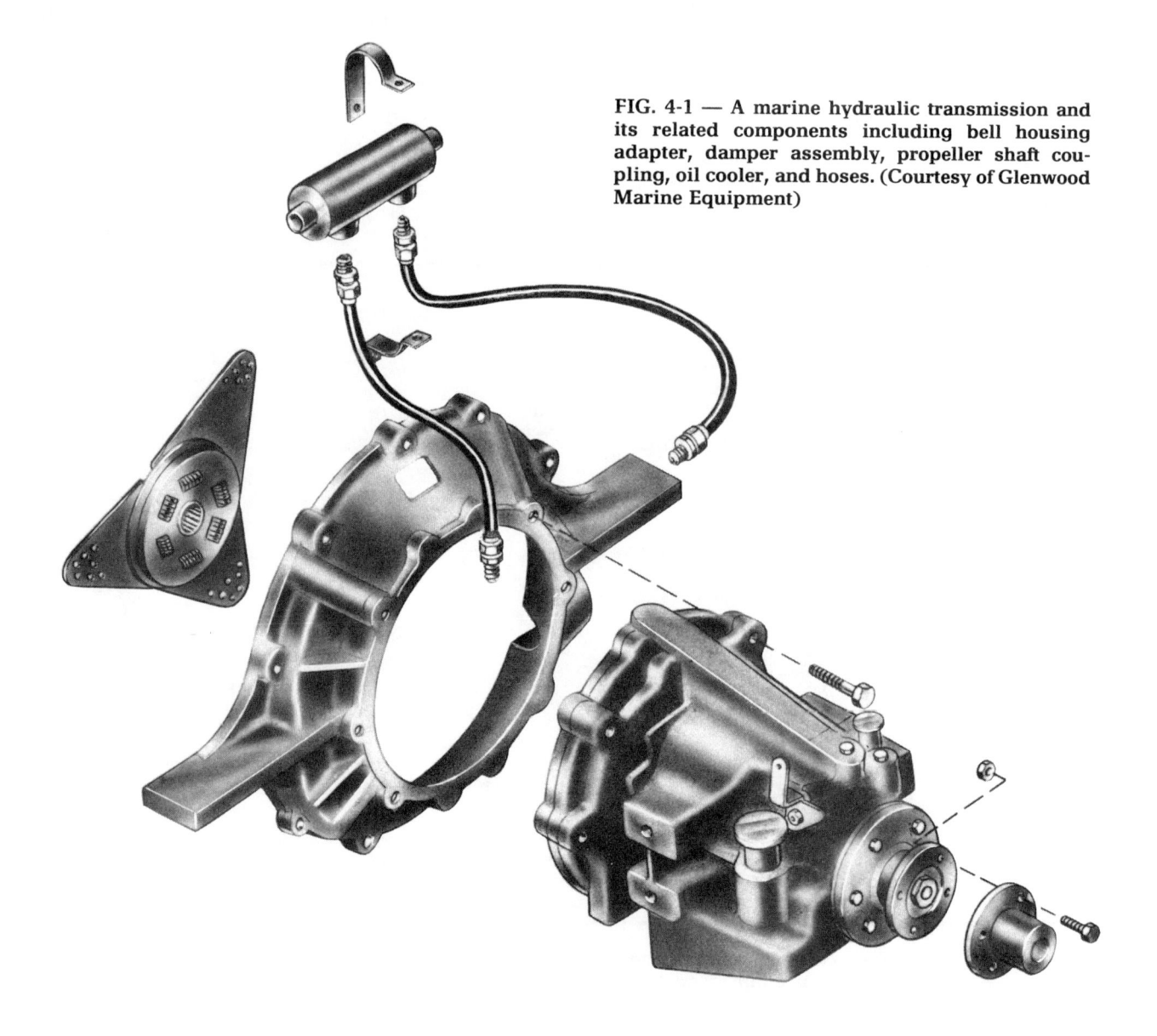

FIG. 4-1 — A marine hydraulic transmission and its related components including bell housing adapter, damper assembly, propeller shaft coupling, oil cooler, and hoses. (Courtesy of Glenwood Marine Equipment)

Note that most engines rotate counter-clockwise or left handed when viewed from the flywheel or aft end of the engine.

In engine conversions, the hydraulic transmission can be used with the standard shift automotive flywheel coupled by a damper plate. A damper, which is usually included with the transmission, is generally mounted to the flywheel to prevent torsional and rotational vibrations of the engine from reaching the power transmission system. In addition, most hydraulic transmissions require a separate oil cooler. A typical marine transmission with its related components is shown in Fig. 4-1.

## REDUCTION GEARS

In addition to directional control and thrust protection, the marine transmission may also serve the function of changing the RPM between the engine and the propeller. While many boats can get by without varying the propeller shaft speed in relation to engine speed, or otherwise use a direct drive gearbox, other boats will require a reduction gear that will reduce the propeller shaft speed from that of the engine speed in order to multiply the twisting force or "torque" available at the shaft. The ability of the transmission to provide this change in propeller shaft RPM is important in order to

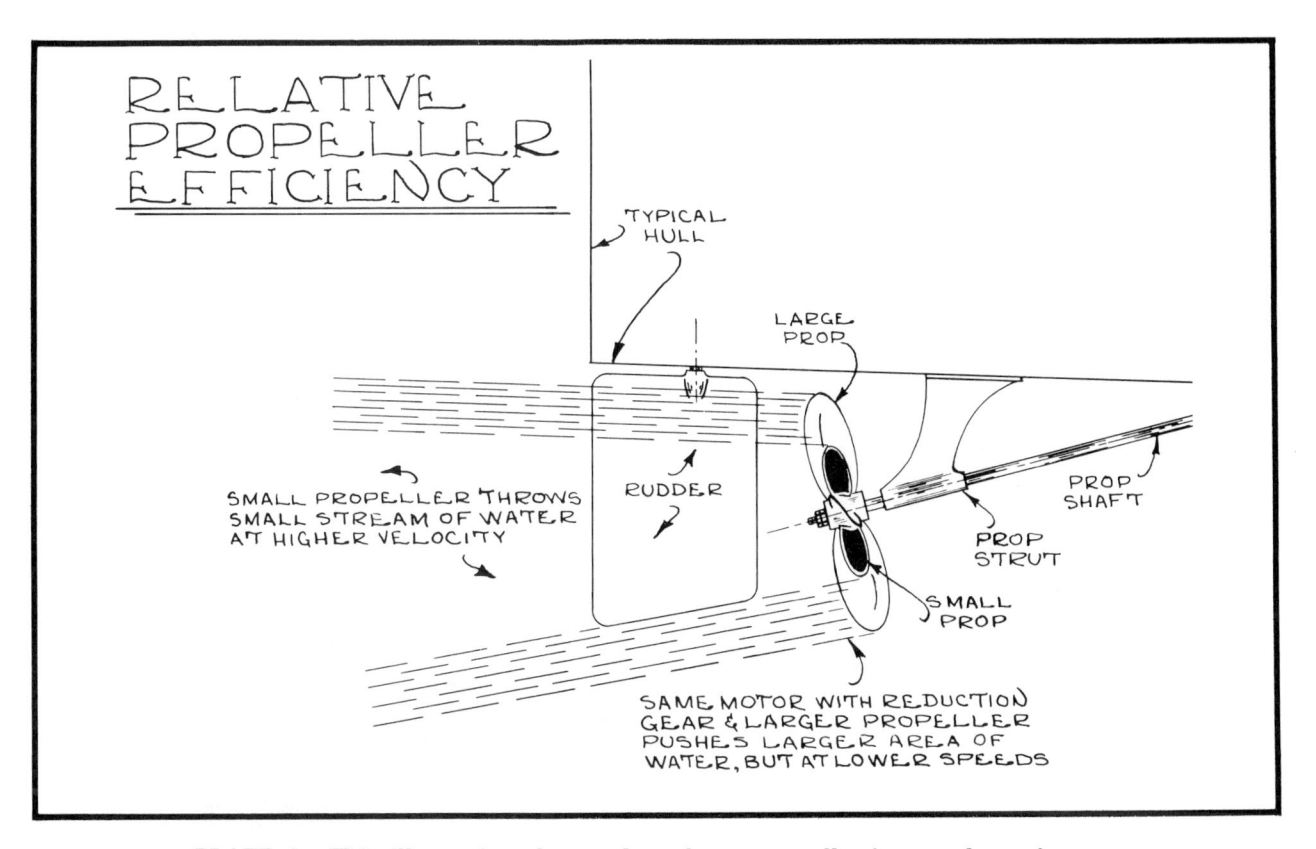

**PLATE 4 - This illustration shows why a larger propeller in most boats is more efficient than a smaller one. Depending on the boat and power system, a reduction gear may be required in order to use the larger propeller effectively.**

use the most efficiently sized propeller.

Generally, the smaller, lighter, and faster a boat is, the smaller will be the reduction gear ratio. In fact, small runabouts and cruisers often will not require a reduction gear since high RPM will be desirable at the propeller. Consequently, engines aboard such boats will have direct drive gear boxes turning out a 1:1 ratio. As will be discussed, there are many boats which require even less than a direct drive gear, in which case an overdrive or "step-up" gear ratio is required. In these cases, the propeller shaft will actually be driven at a higher speed than that provided by the engine. Such boats, however, are usually of the high speed sport or competition craft with very fast turning propellers.

FIG. 4-2 — A marine hydraulic transmission of a type used on larger boats. This unit is available in reduction ratios of from 1.5:1 to 6:1, with power ratings to 610 horsepower. (Courtesy of Twin Disc, Inc., Racine Wis.)

Regardless of the horsepower of the motor at its rated RPM's, it is seldom that the marine engine is run at top speed. Furthermore, it is seldom that the maximum rated horsepower is that which is available at the propeller shaft. As in an automobile, if the engine were run wide-open for long periods of time, it would simply not hold up. That's why it is best to assume that the power to be used, at least in continuous duty use, be about two-thirds to 75% of the given maximum. In other words, if an engine were peak rated at 4800 RPM, it would be preferable to operate at about 3200 to 3600 RPM. With diesel engines, continuous duty ratings are often listed, and these should be adhered to except for intermittent periods.

## MATCHING ENGINE & GEAR

In many cases, people are horsepower-crazy, or crave maximum RPM from their boat engines. Their sole aim is to cram in as much horsepower as possible, and gear the boat to turn as high an RPM as the engine is capable of. Actually, the motor in a boat is used to twist the propeller shaft, with this "twist" rotation better known as torque. Torque is expressed in pounds/feet. To clarify this, assume for a moment that the propeller shaft has a crank handle fastened on the driving end. If a force of 10 lbs. were imparted at a point 1 foot from the turning axis, there would be a twisting motion imparted to the shaft of 10 pounds feet. Torque is therefore a measurement of the force transmitted to turn a propeller shaft, and can be easily figured on any engine as long as horsepower and corresponding RPM's are known.

To find the torque of a motor, multiply the horsepower rating times the number, 5252. Then divide this by the rotating speed, and the result is the torque. The formula would read:

$$\text{Torque} = \frac{\text{BHP x 5252}}{\text{RPM}}$$

As an example applied to this formula, check the chart shown by Fig. 4-3. This chart represents a typical gasoline powered engine, which in this case develops 275 BHP at 4000 RPM. Using the formula above, the result is approximately 361 pound feet of available torque or twisting energy at this engine's maximum horsepower and RPM (275 x 5252 divided by 4000 = 361.075 pounds feet). However, checking to the chart again it will be noted that the PEAK torque rating (the highest point on the torque curve) occurs at a much lower RPM rating. The horsepower available at this peak rating is approximately 212. Translating this in the formula provides a torque rating of 212 x 5252 divided by 2800 = 397.65 pounds feet. In other words, this engine has more turning force available for the propeller at the lower RPM even though horsepower would be less. Consequently, for best efficiency and economy, the engine should be turned at the lower RPM in order to realize its maximum torque.

Going back to the recommendation of using only ⅔ to 75% of an engine's rated power, this example above makes the point. Even though this engine is top rated at 275 horsepower, the actual optimum power available occurs at just about 70% to 75% of the rated figures. This situation is common with gasoline powered engines. The above example debunks the popular notion that a very high horsepower motor may be used, operating at low throttle settings to get the desired speed so that the engine will "loaf" along while still attaining good efficiency and economy. Instead the engine should be operated at its optimum power rating regardless of the RPM at which it is attained. As can be seen from the chart, if the torque curve were a straight horizontal line, or "flat", then all the foregoing would be academic. Indeed, engine designers would love to have such a situation and they often try to make engines with these characteristics. However, most engines are far from ideal, and the torque characteristics should be known in order to suit the engine to the boat.

The foregoing will apply to just about any boat in which no reduction gear is used. But what happens when a reduction gear, such as a 1.5:1, is attached to the same motor? In order to determine the shaft speed, the RPM at the peak torque rating must be divided by the reduction gear ratio: 2800

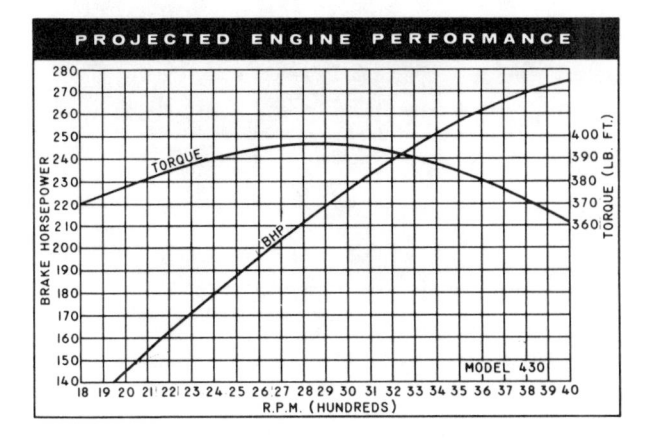

FIG. 4-3 — A typical engine performance chart showing horsepower and torque curves at corresponding RPM's. This chart is for a gasoline powered engine.

44

RPM ÷ 1.5 = 1867 RPM. Applying these new figures to the previous formula gives: 212 x 5252 divided by 1867 = 597.67 pounds feet of torque. Observe that by adding a reduction gear, considerable increase in torque has been gained. While an increase in torque may be important, it should not be assumed that an even greater reduction gear would be preferable for all cases. There is a desirable shaft speed for every boat, and this shaft speed has a direct relationship to the speed of the boat. Increases in torque usually translate to increases in thrust. However, thrust alone is not always the prime objective in all boats. Planing boats, for example, will require less torque to get on plane than slower, heavier, boats where added torque will be necessary to get a firm "bite" on the water. Then too, high speed racing

FIG. 4-4 — **This automotive conversion is intended for use on slower, heavier type boats since it is coupled to a husky 2.5:1 reduction gear.**

boats which depend on high rotative propeller speeds, may have little need for great amounts of peak torque. Such boats often operate with the hull frequently airborne so that high propeller speed is more important than torque.

As can be seen, reduction gear ratios vary considerably and may range from about 1.5:1 to 5:1. Generally, the heavier the boat, the larger the reduction gear ratio should be. Also, the larger the propeller that will be turned, the slower it will usually turn and the larger will be the reduction gear. For example, tugboats, freighters, and commercial fishing craft have relatively huge, but slow turning propellers, in order to provide the necessary thrust to do their jobs.

It should be impressed upon the reader that propellers and reduction gears depend on the boat and its use. It is not possible to figure the correct motor, reduction gear ratio, or propeller unless all the characteristics are known. These factors include the horsepower of the engine over a wide range of RPM's, waterline length of the boat, displacement or weight of the boat, type of hull, reduction gear choices available for a given engine, whether the boat is single or twin screw, maximum possible propeller diameter that will fit, and other factors.

How do you determine if a reduction gear is necessary for a given installation beforehand? As a general rule of thumb for pleasure boats, the propeller should turn about 100 RPM for each mile per hour of boat speed. For example, a boat powered with a motor rated at its optimum power at 3000 RPM should be capable of attaining a speed of 30 miles per hour if using a direct drive without any reduction. However, what if the boat were only capable of achieving a maximum speed of just 10 miles per hour? According to our rule, the propeller should then be turning at just 1000 RPM (10 miles per hour x 100 RPM). In this instance, a 3:1 reduction gear would be required to achieve the 1000 RPM propeller speed while the engine turns at its ideal 3000 RPM rating. From the preceding it should be obvious that the speed potential of the boat must be rather carefully estimated in relation to the power available in order to select the proper reduction gear. In some cases, especially on high speed sport and competition boats, an overdrive gear could be advantageous.

The designer or manufacturer of the boat probably has a vast amount of experience behind him that dictates the sensible motor, propeller, and reduction gear ratio that should be used (if any), and what the performance results will be. In many cases with pleasure boats, this experience is desirable, since often the ideal sized propeller or reduction gear in theory, cannot be practically applied due to propeller size limitations, lack of a suitable gear ratio being available, or other factors. In such cases a compromise must be made, and this is where professional advice will prove valuable.

In general, except under competent advice, the boat owner is advised NOT to use a reduction gear when repowering unless the boat has one in the first place, nor to change the reduction gear ratio from an existing one. It is simply too complicated a problem to give any set method that will cover all boats. If you have a boat that you feel could perform better, get professional advice

first. Most propeller companies have a service that will provide information on the propellers or gears that could be suitably used if they have complete information on the boat. These companies have a tremendous backlog of experience and will no doubt be able to match your boat to the proper size propeller and reduction gear combination.

## CONVERTED AUTOMOTIVE TRANSMISSIONS

In an effort to cut costs, and because availability of parts is quick and easy, many individuals would like to use a converted or altered automotive "stick shift" transmission for marine use. Such transmissions can be used by altering some gears and eliminating others, but this type of transmission is considered a poor substitute for a full marine type. Cooling provisions may be necessary, thrust bearings would be required, and connecting to the propeller shaft presents a problem. Most such modified transmissions simply can't stand up under marine service where the transmission will be under full load at all times while underway. In addition, the clutch is always necessary, and there would be a momentary lag when shifting that could be dangerous if a quick stop were necessary, or in maneuvering in close and crowded quarters.

Similarly, many wish to use an automotive-type automatic transmission. In stock condition, such units are simply not up to the rigorous duty of marine conditions that most boats operate under. Over a period of years numerous attempts have been made by various companies to convert such automatic transmissions to marine use. There have been both failures and successes, however, much depends on the type of unit and the intended use. For specific conditions such transmissions offer some advantages and features not possible in the standard marine-type transmission.

Most automatic transmissions have either two or three speeds forward, in addition to neutral and reverse. In the faster boats used for sport, competition, or water skiing purposes, the torque multiplication possible by varying engine RPM is desirable. For example, low range (like first gear in a car) gives high initial acceleration on take-off by allowing the engine to "rev" at its peak torque rating instead of bogging down as often occurs with standard "one-speed" marine transmissions. As speed increases, shifting can be done into the top gear range for a potentially higher top speed. Propeller pitch (and diameter if clearances permit) can be increased since the boat has greater range of torque over all speed ranges. This can also give better economy and less engine wear. In affect, the boat would have qualities similar to a car equipped with an "overdrive" on the transmission.

In the standard automotive automatic transmission, especially earlier designs, shifting was somewhat sluggish between gear ranges, and under marine conditions, this would cause an immediate reduction in propeller RPM that was not acceptable. However, with suitable modifications, quick and positive shifting can be accomplished under full power without any significant loss in propeller RPM. In high speed boats of the vee-drive configuration where an overdrive is built into the vee-drive, such automatic transmissions will permit a larger overdrive gear ratio than would be practical with the standard marine-type transmission. In more normal types of boats, where operating speeds are more limited, the standard marine transmission usually makes a more practical system.

**VEE DRIVES**

A vee drive enables the motor to be mounted at the stern of the boat and still drive through a conventional straight line shaft arrangement as with the centrally located motor. In effect, the vee drive is a transfer case that changes the direction of the engine shaft to the opposite direction. In certain types of boats, the vee drive offers several advantages. In many cases, the vee drive will allow a decrease in the shaft angle to a greater degree than if the motor were straight coupled and more centrally located. In a cabin type boat, the stern mounted motor isolates noise and fumes to the aft end of the boat. The engine can be set into the hull to better advantage since it does not have to be parallel with the drive shaft unless of the close-coupled type. Exhaust lines can be much shorter, also. Finally, moving the motor to the stern in certain types of boats can improve speed and performance.

Note however, that not ALL inboard boats can have a stern mounted motor. There must be sufficient buoyancy at the stern to support the weight of the motor and gear so that the boat will trim level with the waterline. Basically, any boat specifically intended for a centrally mounted inboard motor should not be adapted to a stern mounted engine location except on the

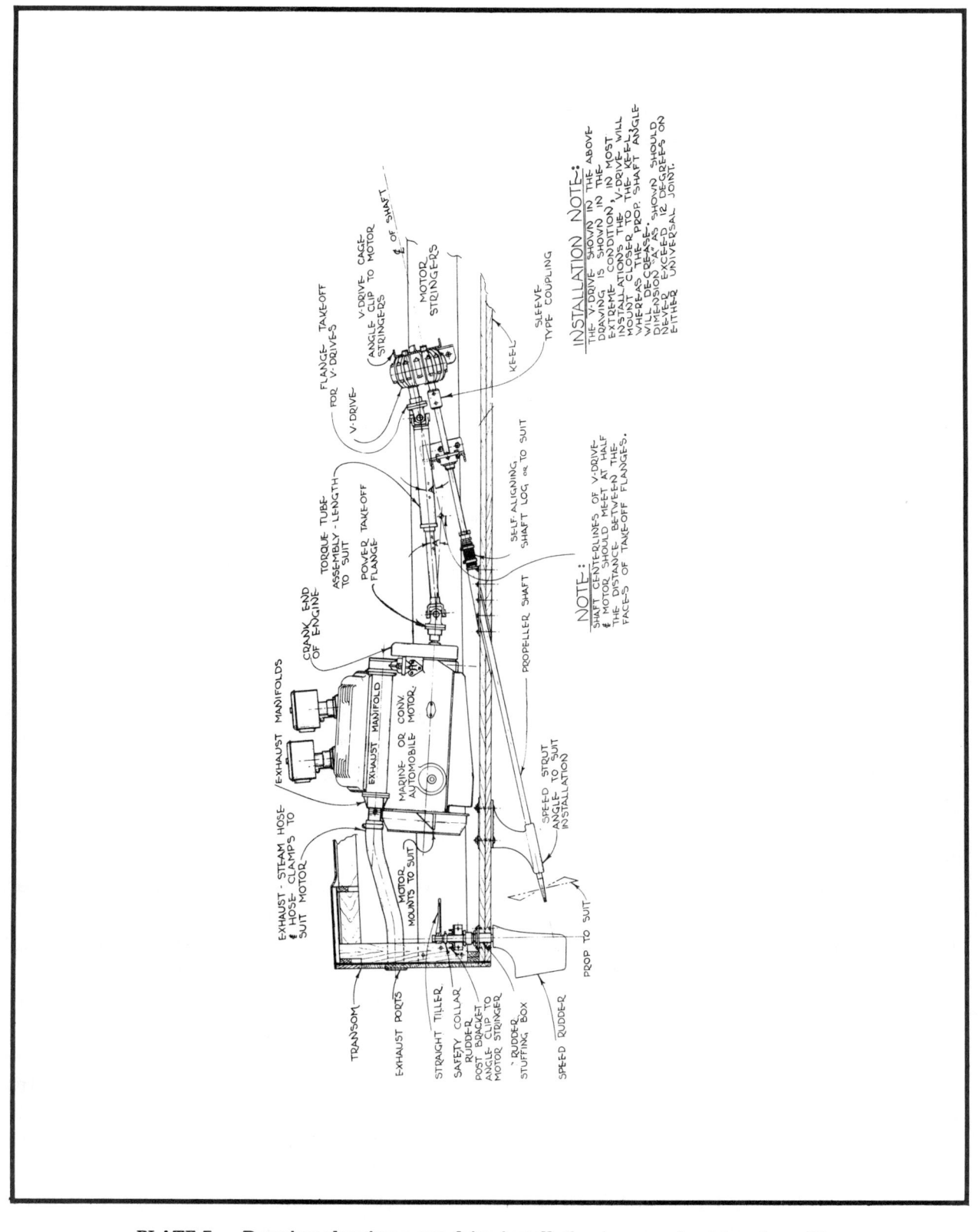

**PLATE 5 — Drawing showing a vee drive installation in a runabout type boat. Note that the angularity on either universal joint should not exceed 12 degrees.**

48

advice of a qualified naval architect or the manufacturer of the boat. While such modifications can and have been made, the results may be questionable and experience indicates that there have been numerous mistakes made with such modifications that could detract from the value of the boat, not to mention the performance.

Various types of vee drive units are

available. The basic vee drive is merely a transfer case as noted previously (see Fig. 4-5). When these are used, a marine transmission is usually connected to the engine to provide forward, neutral, and reverse control. In other cases, vee drives are available which include an integral marine transmission (see Fig. 4-7). The transmission in the vee drive may be of the forward-

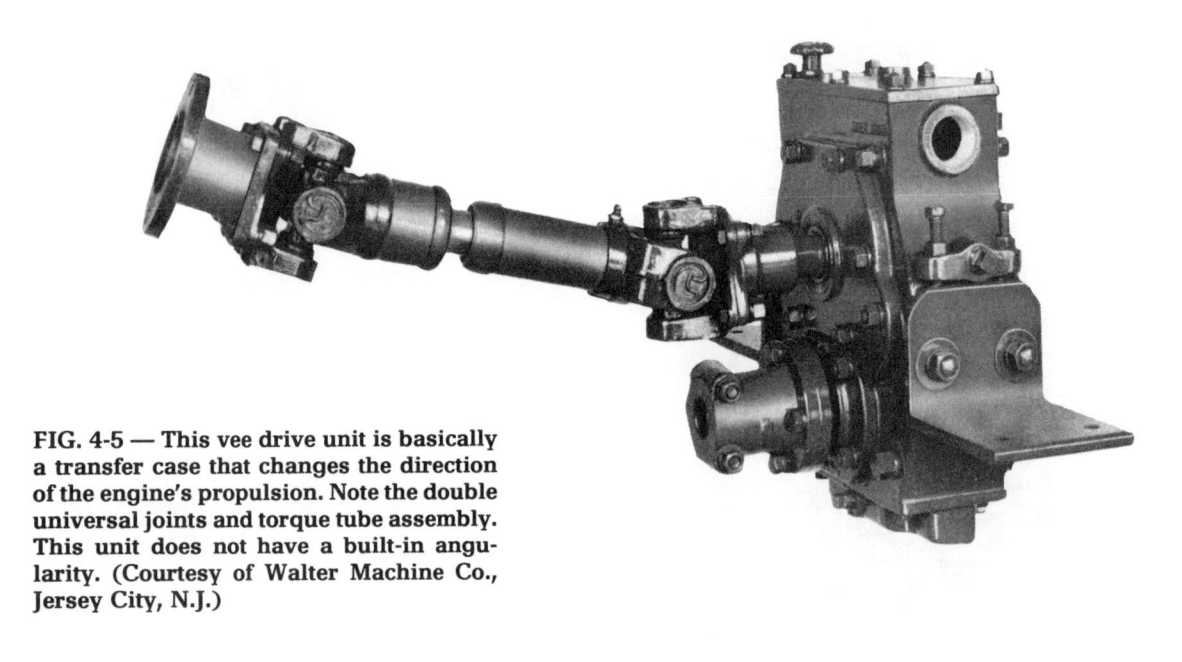

FIG. 4-5 — This vee drive unit is basically a transfer case that changes the direction of the engine's propulsion. Note the double universal joints and torque tube assembly. This unit does not have a built-in angularity. (Courtesy of Walter Machine Co., Jersey City, N.J.)

FIG. 4-6 — This vee drive unit has a built-in angularity. The second universal joint is not visible as it is built into the vee drive unit. The opening in the side is for connecting the water cooling system. (Courtesy of Walter Machine Co., Jersey City, N.J.)

FIG. 4-7 — This vee drive features a built-in angularity and integral gearbox for forward, neutral, and reverse control. (Courtesy of Casale Engineering, City of Industry, Calif.)

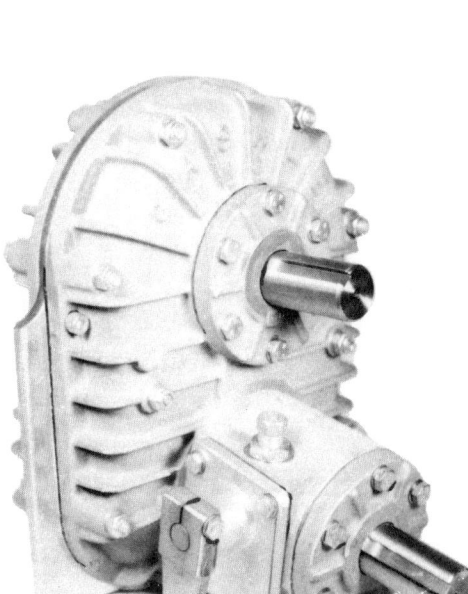

FIG. 4-8 — This vee drive is the split case type with forward, neutral, and reverse transmission, and built-in angularity. (Courtesy of Casale Engineering, City of Industry, Calif.)

FIG. 4-9 — This split case vee drive with built-in angularity is the so-called "in and out" or forward and neutral type without reversing gear. (Courtesy of Casale Engineering, City of Industry, Calif.)

neutral-reverse type, or in some cases where reverse gear is not used, such as in the smaller runabouts and competition boats, the vee drive may be the so-called "in-and-out" type having just a neutral and forward position (see Fig. 4-9). Vee drives are available which are remotely located from the engine, or which are close-coupled to the engine or marine transmission, which is in turn, mounted to the engine (see Fig. 4-10 and Fig. 4-11). Such units are quite compact and are ideal where space is at a premium. If a re-

duction gear or overdrive is necessary, this can usually be incorporated in the vee drive instead of in the marine transmission. Another variation available with vee drives is the split case type (see Fig. 4-12). This allows relatively quick changes to be made to the gears, thereby changing the ratio. Such vee drives are often used on high speed boats that will be used for a variety of conditions, such as water skiing and racing, or where weather and sea conditions make the gear change feature desirable for efficiency.

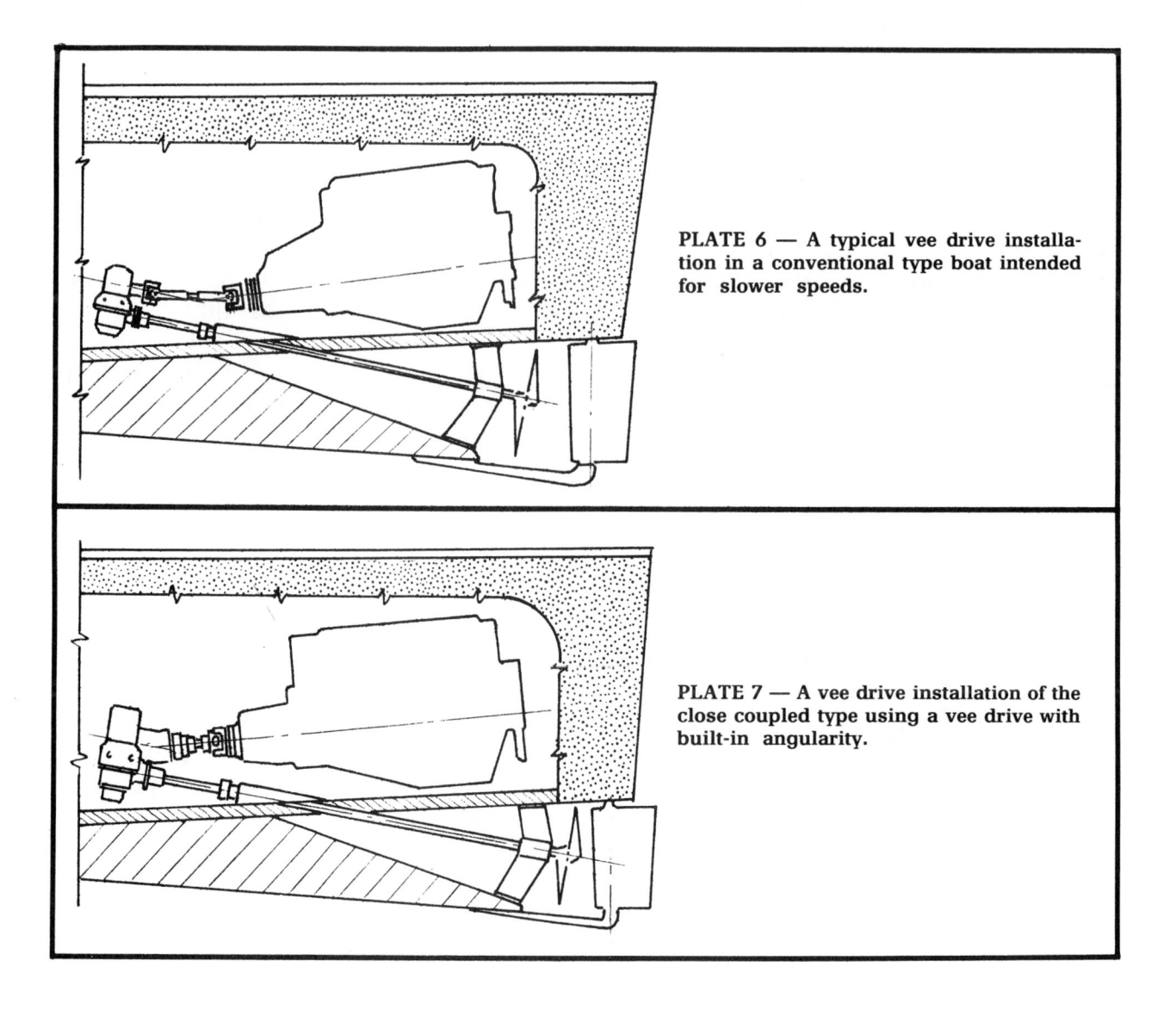

PLATE 6 — A typical vee drive installation in a conventional type boat intended for slower speeds.

PLATE 7 — A vee drive installation of the close coupled type using a vee drive with built-in angularity.

On vee drives which are located remotely from the engine, the propeller thrust must be taken by the vee drive if it has built-in thrust bearings. If not, a separate thrust bearing and housing must be provided aft of the vee drive (see Fig. 4-14). Most vee drives have built-in shaft angularity at some fixed degree, usually 10 or 12 degrees. Vee drives may sometimes be air cooled, however, most modern units are water cooled. Many vee drives tend to be noisy in operation, however, this varies with the unit and the type of gears used.

A common question with prospective amateur boatbuilders is which is the cheapest power system; the conventional centrally located motor with straight shaft, the vee drive with stern mounted inboard, the stern mounted inboard using a sterndrive, or the stern mounted motor using a jet drive? This is a difficult question to answer because there are so many variables, assuming that the boat could take any

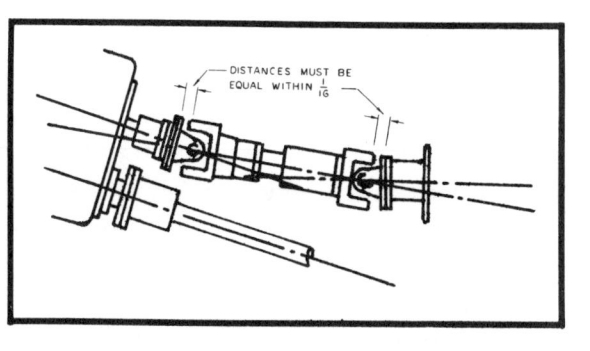

PLATE 8 — The angularity difference between the vee drive and the engine must be equally "split" between the universal joints in the torque tube installation as shown by the dimensional tolerance. If not, wear will be taken on one joint and cause it to fail prematurely.

or all of these systems. Much depends on if the individual has a motor and will convert it himself, what type of shifting arrangement he is willing to settle for, how much of the installation work he will do himself, and on the prices for the various items of equipment. With vee drives alone there is a wide variety of units which results in a wide range of prices. Consequently, each situation must be checked through with all the possible alternatives to arrive at the lowest cost for a given type of power installation.

## INSTALLING THE VEE DRIVE

Installing a motor with a separate vee drive is simpler than installing a conventional centrally located motor and transmission. The reason, to a great extent, is the fact that close alignment is not required for the engine. Often the motor is separated from the vee drive by some distance. For this reason a double universal joint with torque tube is usually used to connect the motor to the vee drive (see Fig.

FIG. 4-10 — This marine engine features a direct close-coupled vee drive with marine transmission. Such a unit saves valuable space in many types of boats. (Courtesy of Medalist-Universal Motors, Oshkosh, Wis.)

4-15). It must be understood that two universal joints are required. A single universal will take up differences in angularity on one plane only. Because there are two angles, one for the vee drive and one for the motor crankshaft centerline, compensation for the angularity in both planes requires the use of two universal joints. Best practice calls for the angularity difference between the motor and vee drive to be equally taken by the universal joints. In other words, the angle is split 50/50 between the two universal joints. Putting all the action on one will not only cause excessive wear, but may also set up excessive vibration (see Plate #8).

With engines that have the vee drive coupled to the engine or to the transmission directly, the use of the torque tube and double universals is not re-quired. Such engines are installed similarly to the centrally located inboard with straight shaft, which will be covered later. Otherwise, the vee drive is mounted to the motor stringers or other structural hull members, using mounts or a "cage" provided with the unit, or purchased separately (see Fig. 4-14). Alignment to the propeller shaft must be accurate. Connection to the propeller shaft may be made by either a flange coupling or a split sleeve coupling. Various couplings are discussed in Chapter 7. If the flange coupling is used, alignment of the vee drive flange coupling to the shaft flange coupling is done the same way as with the standard straight shaft centrally located inboard motor described in Chapter 8. If a split sleeve coupling is used, the coupling con-

FIG. 4-11 — Another example of a marine engine directly coupled with a vee drive. In this case, the engine is a large displacement V-8. Note the oil cooling hose from the vee drive to the oil cooler, and the water cooling hose connecting both ends of the oil cooler to the engine. (Courtesy of OMC, Waukegan, Ill.)

nects to the propeller shaft and to the stub shaft on the vee drive. Alignment is quite simple. With the coupling on the propeller shaft, the connection is made to the vee drive. When the propeller shaft will spin freely when connected, alignment is true.

A recommended safety option for vee drive assemblies is the addition of a guard over the torque tube. In high speed operation, universal joints have been known to fail. The whipping shaft can cause severe damage to the hull as well as injury to crew members. This guard may simply be a ring protector over the torque tube shaft. With some vee drives, a power take-off vee-belt pulley can be used on the vee drive upper shaft to drive certain accessories such as generators and alternators.

FIG. 4-12 — This vee drive is a split case transfer unit without transmission although the angularity is built-in. (Courtesy of Casale Engineering, City of Industry, Calif.)

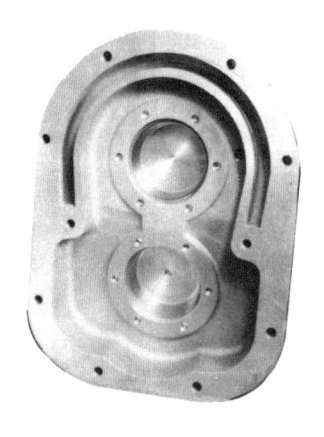

FIG. 4-13 — The split case vee drive is often used on sport and competition craft where it is desirable to change the gear ratios to match the engine to the conditions of use. (Courtesy of Casale Engineering, City of Industry, Calif.)

FIG. 4-14 — Although most vee drives have a built-in thrust bearing, if not it must be provided separately as shown in this installation between the vee drive and shaft log. A bracket or "cage" is used to transfer the thrust to the motor stringers. A similar "cage" is used to secure the vee drive. (Courtesy of Glenwood Marine Equipment)

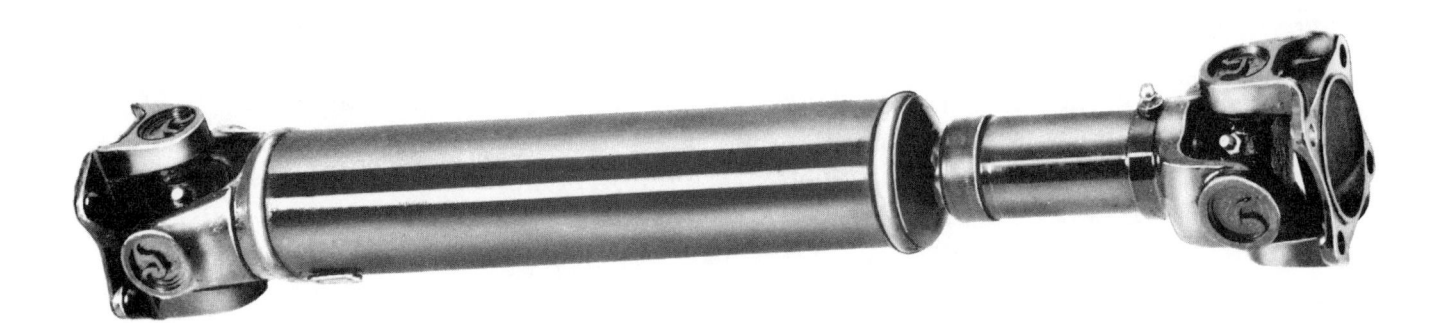

FIG. 4-15 — A typical torque tube and universal joint assembly used to connect the engine to a vee drive unit. This unit allows for compensating the angularity difference between the engine and the vee drive. (Courtesy Glenwood Marine Equipment)

FIG. 4-16 — A typical vee drive installation showing the torque tube connecting the vee drive to a "bob-tail" engine. Note the guard over the torque tube as a safety precaution in the event that the universal joints fail.

## VARIATIONS OF MARINE TRANSMISSIONS

Besides the standard marine and vee drive transmissions, there are other types of transmissions and transfer cases which offer certain variations for specialized situations. For example, installations which require a "bob-tail" engine, such as with certain stern drive and jet drive systems which do not require a forward, neutral, and reverse transmission, may need some reduction or step-up gearing to slow down or speed up the shaft speed. Such a step-up gear for a jet drive is shown by Fig.

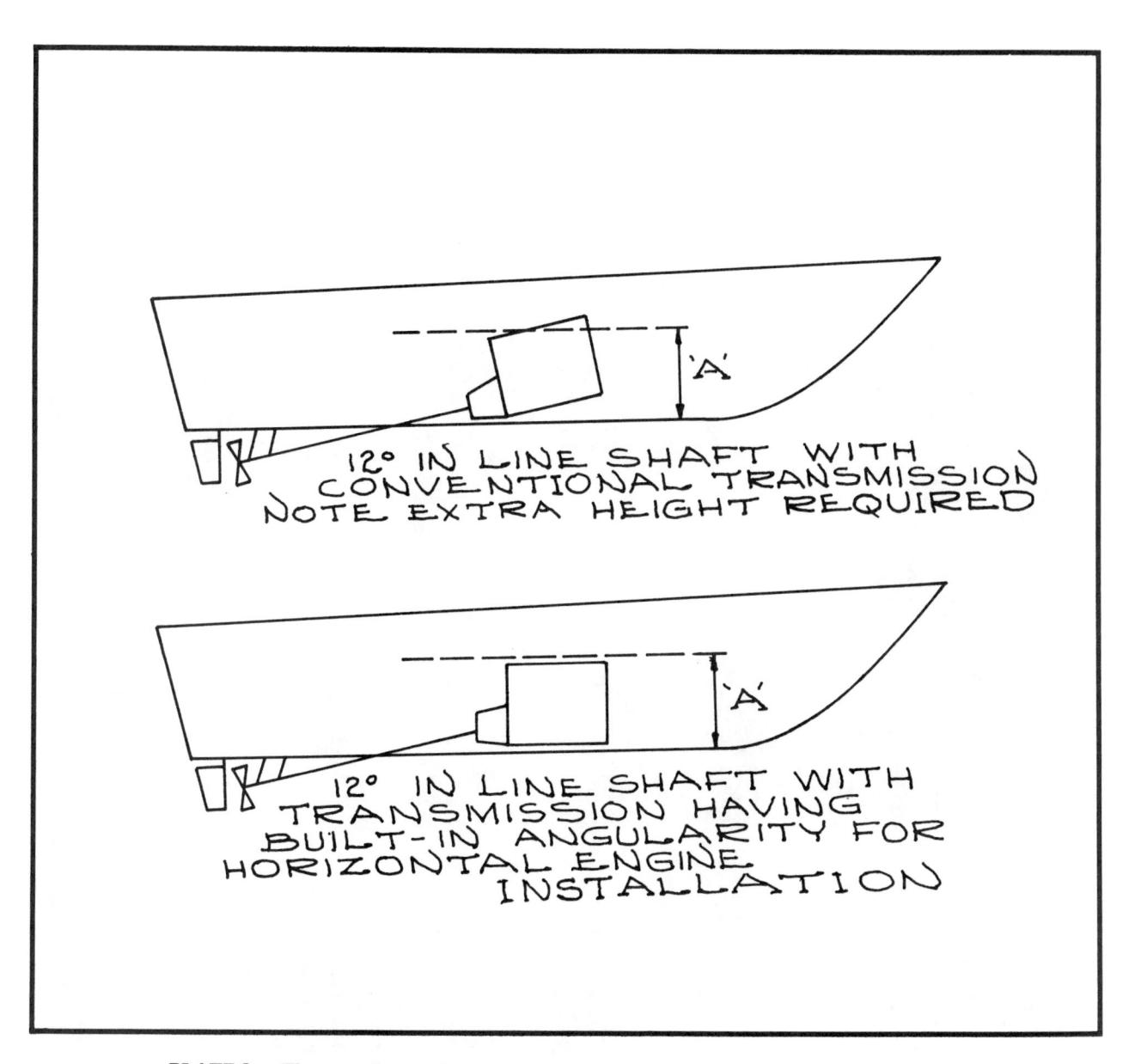

PLATE 9 — The use of a marine transmission with built-in angle will allow the engine to be mounted more-or-less horizontally while still allowing a suitable shaft angle. More space would be required for the same engine, if mounted in line with the shaft angle.

FIG. 4-17 — A jet drive "step-up" gear used to increase the RPM at the jet unit from that of the engine. Note the yoke connector to receive the universal coupling from the jet drive. (Courtesy of Casale Engineering, City of Industry, Calif.)

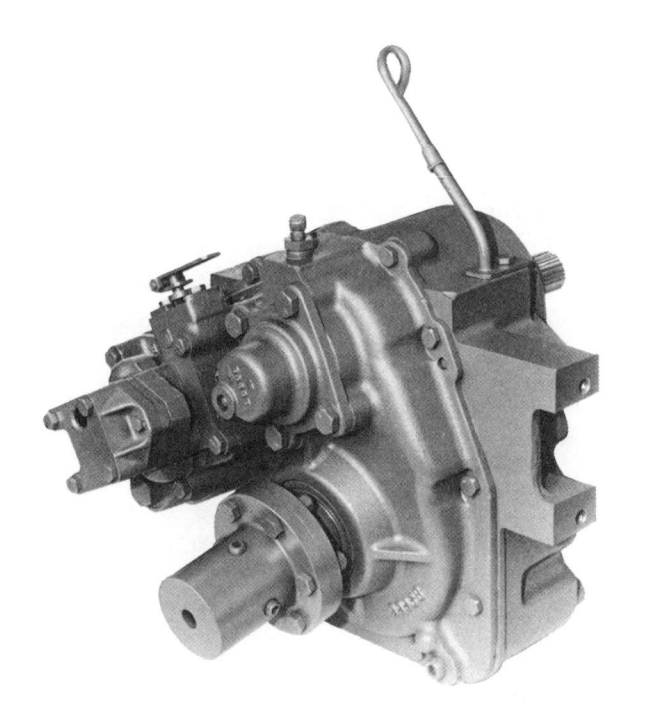

FIG. 4-18 — This marine hydraulic transmission features a built-in 10 degree down angle which allows the engine to be mounted more-or-less horizontally in the boat in the central location while still maintaining an angled shaft. Such an installation can reduce the space required for the engine by a considerable amount and increases the efficiency of the engine. (Courtesy of Twin Disc, Inc., Racine, Wis.)

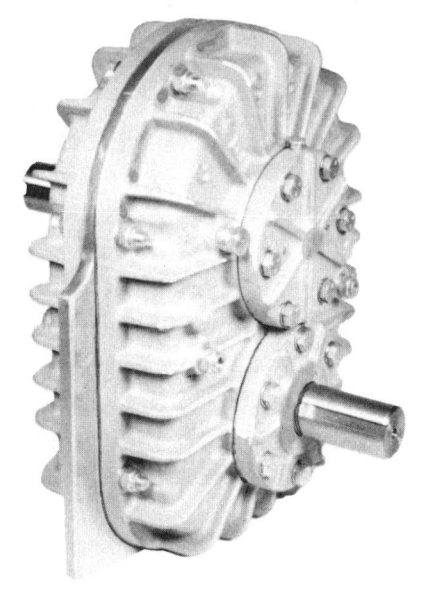

FIG. 4-19 — An independently mounted in-line gearbox of the split case type. The engine would be mounted to the left via a double universal joint connection which would allow it to mount horizontally in the boat while maintaining a suitable shaft angle. (Courtesy of Casale Engineering, City of Industry, Calif.)

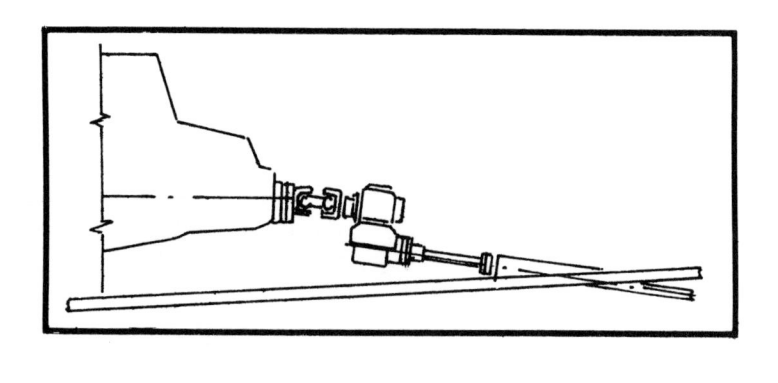

PLATE 10 — Another method for mounting the engine more horizontally is to use an in-line independently mounted transmission, coupling to the engine with double universal joints.

4-17. Also, gearboxes are available that mount directly to the "bobtail" engine flywheel housing the same way as other marine transmissions in order to provide step-up or reduction gear ratios.

In the conventional centrally located engine installation, the engine is often mounted at quite an angle from the horizontal. While most engines will, or can be modified, to operate at angles often up to 16 degrees, a smaller angle would be desirable. Consequently, some marine transmissions are available which have a built-in angularity (see Fig. 4-18 and Plate 9) which will still allow the propeller shaft to be angled, but also permit the engine to be installed more-or-less level. Another way that this can be accomplished is to use a marine transmission independently mounted to the propeller shaft at the shaft angularity (see Fig. 4-19 and Plate 10). A double universal joint coupling is then used between the engine and transmission, allowing the engine to be mounted more level. Installing such a transmission is similar to an independently mounted vee drive, except that the engine goes forward of the transmission. Several other types of power transmission systems are discussed in Chapter 5.

## THRUST BEARINGS

As noted previously, most marine transmissions and power transmission systems have thrust bearings built into the units so that no concern need be given to a separate thrust bearing. However, a separate thrust bearing may be required in certain cases, especially if no thrust bearing exists in the power transmission system to absorb the propeller thrust. Another example would be boats such as competition craft where a "bob-tail" engine would be used. If there is no thrust bearing in the system, the engine itself cannot be expected to take these forces; they must be transferred to the hull in some other manner. This is where a separate thrust bearing and thrust bearing mount are necessary. The bearing should be a heavy duty radial bearing capable of taking two-way thrust. The bearing must be securely mounted to a ready-made bracket or one specially made for the boat. Usually, such a bearing housing or bracket is fixed to the motor stringers so the force is transferred to the hull (see Fig. 4-20). The thrust bearing can be locked to the shaft in several ways depending on the type of bearing. The set screw type requires that counterbores be made in the shaft. An

FIG. 4-20 — A close-up shot of a thrust bearing with "cage" and similar vee drive mount. Metal angle clips are used to join the brackets to the motor stringers. In most vee drive units, thrust bearings are built in and separate units like these are not required.

eccentric type locks to the shaft, while others may use a collar on either side of the bearing. A collar on the forward side is often used as a safety factor regardless of the type to prevent the shaft from coming out of the boat. The typical industrial-type bearing usually has a very short life in marine conditions due to corrosion. If used, care should be taken to keep water out of the unit and to keep it well greased.

## POWER TAKE-OFFS

A wide variety of power take-offs are available to operate auxiliary systems directly from the main engine. These auxiliary systems can include generators, winches, bilge pumps, compressors, hydraulic equipment pumps, fishing reels, and similar equipment. A common power take-off system uses a vee-belt pulley fixed to a stub shaft off the crankshaft. A vee-belt joins this pulley to the power take-off assembly

located adjacently which usually consists of a series of two or more pulleys used to drive the auxiliary systems. Clutches are used to engage the power take-off pulleys, and these can be directly controlled at the power take-off or located remotely in a convenient location such as the wheelhouse or on deck. A typical power take-off system is illustrated by Plate 11.

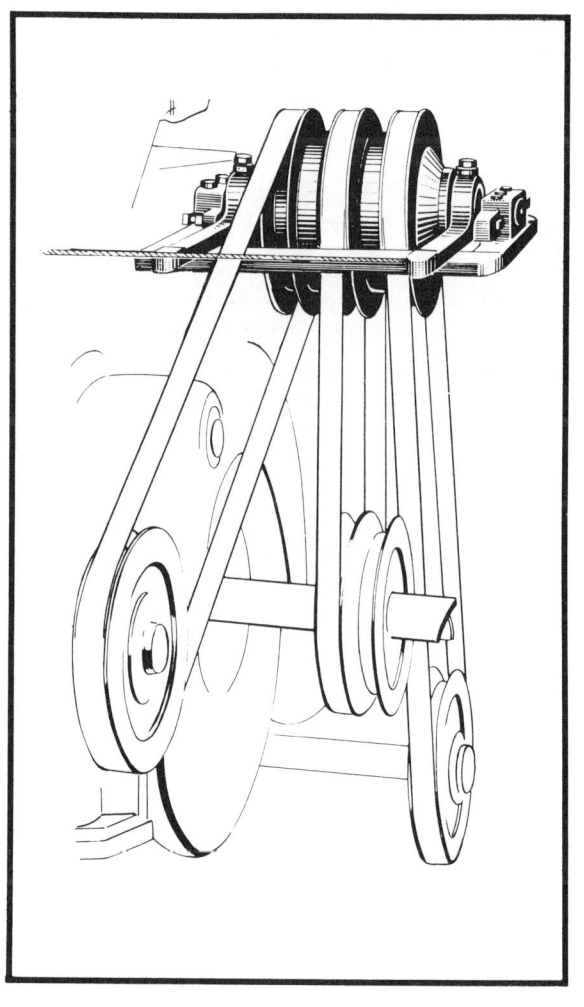

PLATE 11 — A power take-off assembly allows various accessories to be driven off of the boat's engine by way of vee-belts. Units are available with direct control at the engine, or remotely located such as at the control console. (Courtesy of R. C. Plath Co., Portland, Ore.)

It is often necessary to figure out the vee-belt pulley ratio in a power take-off system. The following formulas can be used to figure either the RPM or pulley diameter of both the driving and driven pulley.

Driving pulley:

$$RPM = \frac{\text{diameter X RPM of driven pulley}}{\text{diameter of driving pulley}}$$

$$Diameter = \frac{\text{diameter X RPM of driven pulley}}{\text{RPM of driving pulley}}$$

Driven pulley:

$$RPM = \frac{\text{diameter X RPM of driving pulley}}{\text{diameter of driven pulley}}$$

$$Diameter = \frac{\text{diameter X RPM of driving pulley}}{\text{RPM of driven pulley}}$$

Another type of power take-off is the free wheel drive unit (see Plate 12). This type of unit is especially suitable for sailboats equipped with auxiliary inboard engines. Aboard such boats, the propeller, if not of the folding type, can either be locked in position, or allowed to rotate or spin naturally as a result of forward momentum from the sail's propulsive force. However, allowing the shaft to spin freely in this manner can damage some transmissions. By installing a free wheel drive unit between the shaft and the transmission, however, the energy transmitted by the spinning propeller to the shaft can be used via a pulley and vee-belt to drive an alternator. This in turn can be used to keep the boat's batteries charged and provide electricity while sailing, all without using the main engine and wasting fuel. Because the free wheel drive unit disengages the propeller shaft from the transmission, the transmission is protected from damage and it is no longer necessary to fire up the engine to charge the batteries, which could be quite a beneficial feature on long cruises.

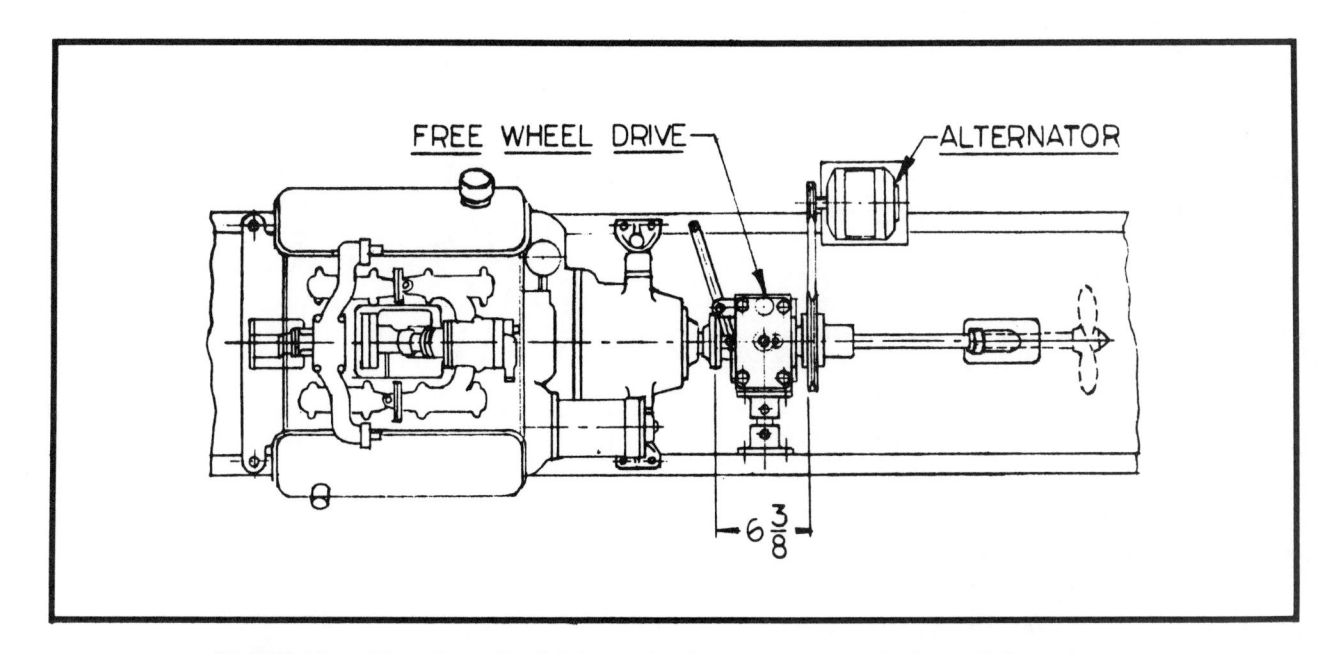

**PLATE 12 — This free-wheel drive unit allows power to be taken off the spinning propeller shaft to drive an alternator, for example. In a sail boat, such a unit keeps the batteries charged without running the engine. (Courtesy of Walter Machine Co., Jersey City, N.J.)**

# CHAPTER 5 — STERNDRIVES

One of the most popular power transmission systems is the sterndrive unit, which is sometimes referred to as an inboard/outboard drive, I/O unit, outdrive, "Z"-drive, trans-drive, or vertical drive. Basically, the sterndrive is like an underwater portion of an outboard with a shaft connecting an upper drive shaft parallel to the engine crankshaft, to a lower horizontal shaft which transmits the engine's power to the propeller. The motor is located inboard, but the propulsion unit is outboard of the transom. The engine may be directly coupled to the sterndrive with the transmission built into the sterndrive unit, or coupled to a marine transmission which is in turn coupled to the sterndrive, or the engine may be lo-

cated some distance forward of the stern in which case a torque tube or drive shaft with universal joints is used to connect to the sterndrive. In the latter instance, a marine transmission may be coupled directly to the engine, or provided as a part of the sterndrive.

Sterndrive units which are separately coupled to the engine usually are mounted onto the transom of the boat. However, with integral engine/sterndrive power units, mounting methods may vary considerably. In some cases, engines will mount to motor stringers in the conventional manner with the outdrive rigidly coupled to the engine and thereby "floating" free through the transom (see Fig. 5-1). In other cases, a front mount may be provided on the

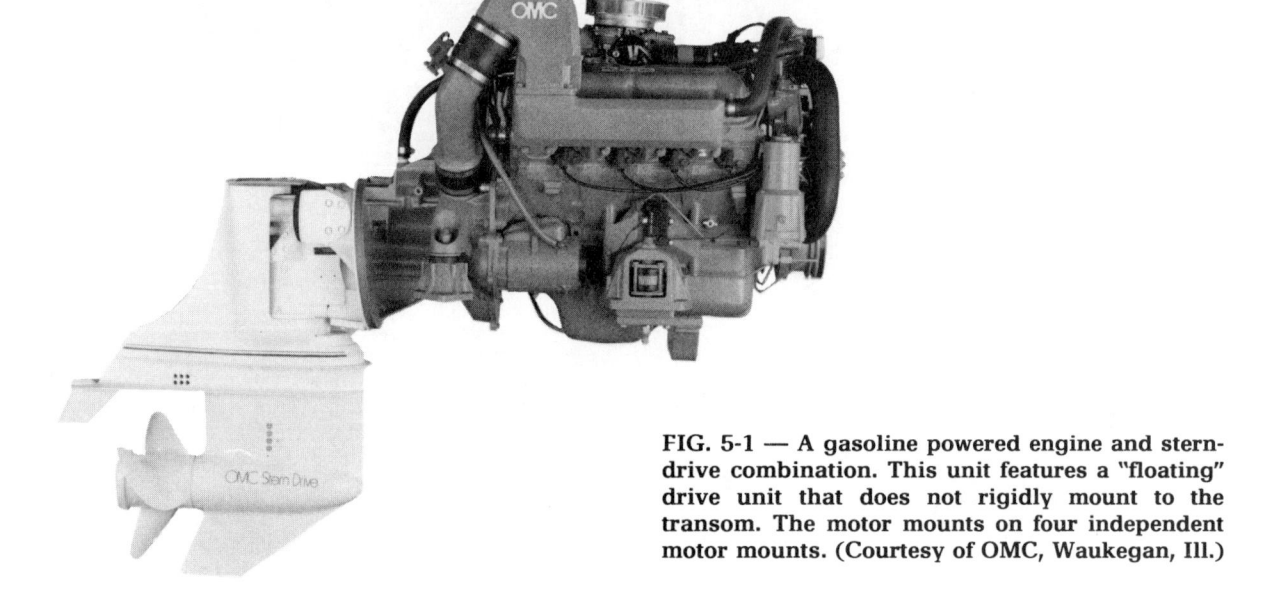

FIG. 5-1 — A gasoline powered engine and sterndrive combination. This unit features a "floating" drive unit that does not rigidly mount to the transom. The motor mounts on four independent motor mounts. (Courtesy of OMC, Waukegan, Ill.)

engine with the sterndrive forming the rear mount by bolting to the transom (see Fig. 5-2). Still another method sometimes used in lightweight units is to cantilever-mount the entire power system, including engine and sterndrive, from the transom without any other support (see Fig. 5-3).

When the sterndrive unit incorporates the transmission, the shifting mechanism and action is usually much like that of an outboard motor using so-called "dog"-type clutches. The engine must be throttled down and positively actuated thereby producing a solid "clunking" sensation familiar

to so many outboard operators. Some sterndrive manufacturers have developed power-assist methods of shifting that do require less "muscle" with this type of shifting mechanism. For more elegant and smooth shifting, the type of sterndrive hooked to a marine hydraulic transmission or one of the converted automotive automatic transmissions can sometimes be used instead, depending on the sterndrive manufacturer. Regardless of the system, a safety interlock should be provided so that the engine can be started only in the neutral position.

The sterndrive with stern-mounted

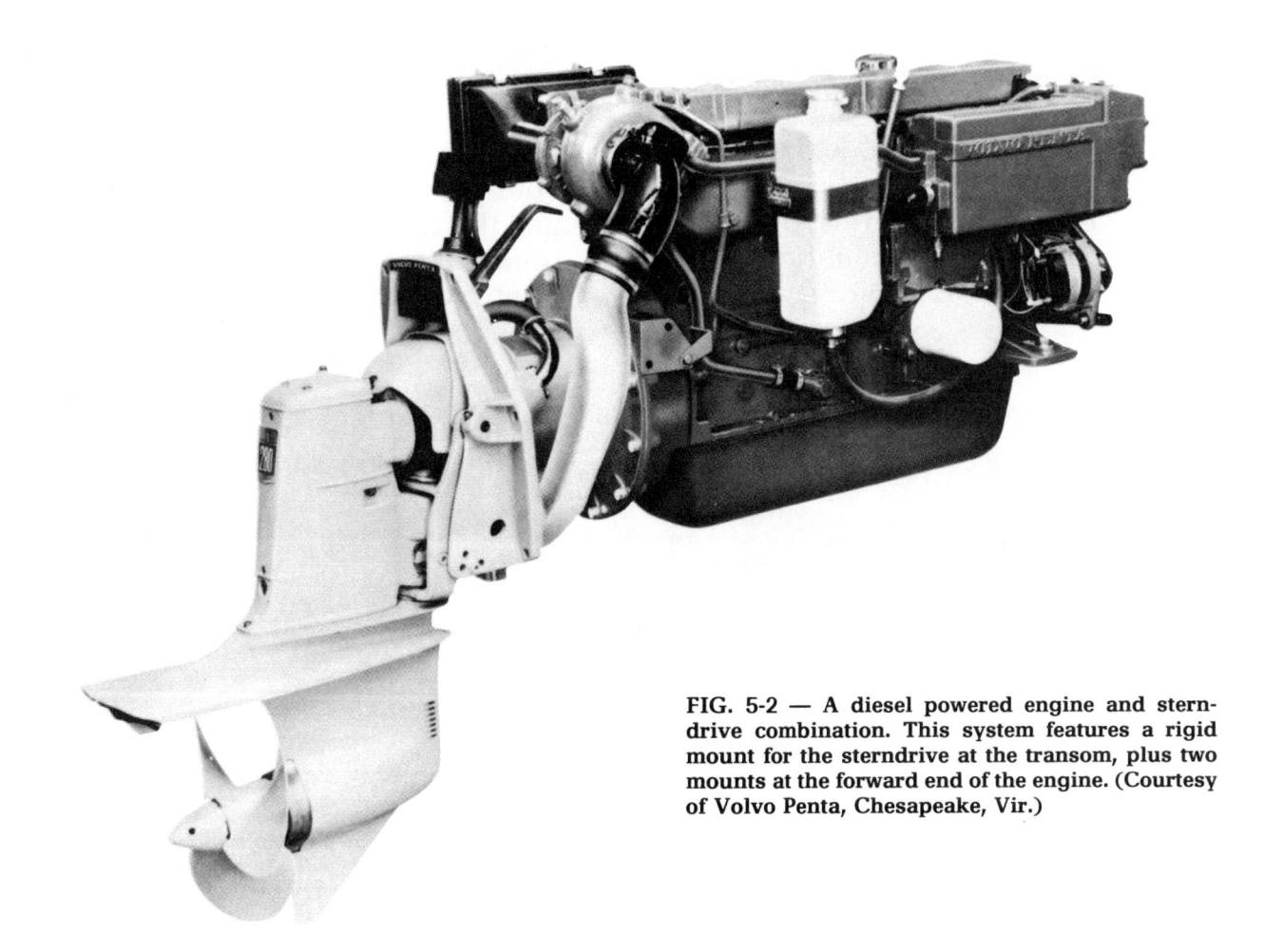

FIG. 5-2 — A diesel powered engine and sterndrive combination. This system features a rigid mount for the sterndrive at the transom, plus two mounts at the forward end of the engine. (Courtesy of Volvo Penta, Chesapeake, Vir.)

motor has been a great boon to boating. However, this does not mean that it is the ideal system for all boats. All power systems have advantages and disadvantages, and the boat owner must weigh the merits of each system with respect to the boat in question and the requirements of use. An advantage with the sterndrive is in the steering. In just about all marine power systems, steering is accomplished by varying the direction of the propulsion water flow. In the conventional inboard or vee drive power system, the water is directed to one side or the other by the rudder, which deflects the water causing the stern to turn. For the rudder to be effective, it must have sufficient area and be in the path of the propulsion stream; in other words, it should be directly behind the propeller. However, in reversing situations the rudder is behind the propulsion stream, and consequently steering in the reverse direction is not nearly as

FIG. 5-3 — **This compact lightweight engine and sterndrive combination features a transom cantilever mounting system.**

effective. With the jet drive system, efficiency in reverse is considerably less also, since the thrust must be deflected against the normal flow. However, with the sterndrive system, the entire propeller system is turned for steering so that maximum directional control is produced and the response is quick and direct (see Fig. 5-4). This results in a high degree of control in both forward and reverse.

The sterndrive has other advantages similar to outboard engines. For example, if the unit strikes an object in the water, most will "kick-up" to prevent or minimize damage to the unit and propeller, since the sterndrive is connected to the engine with universal or similar type joints. The kick-up feature also allows the sterndrive to tilt up and stay up, which makes launching, trailering, and servicing much more convenient (see Fig. 5-5). Many units come with either manually fixed or "power trim" devices which can raise or lower the drive shaft from the horizontal, or vary the angle of attack for a more level ride, or to compensate for the effects of unbalanced loading, as well as for safer operation in shoal waters (see Fig. 5-6). While the power-trim feature is often desirable, some boats, especially larger and heavier ones, will make better use of trim tabs or plates such as those described in Chapter 21, and consequently some units are available with or without the power-trim feature. Because the propulsion thrust of water is more horizontal with the sterndrive instead of angular as with the conventional inboard, the propeller thrust should theoretically be more efficient. In spite of advertising claims to the contrary, however, there is little scientific or

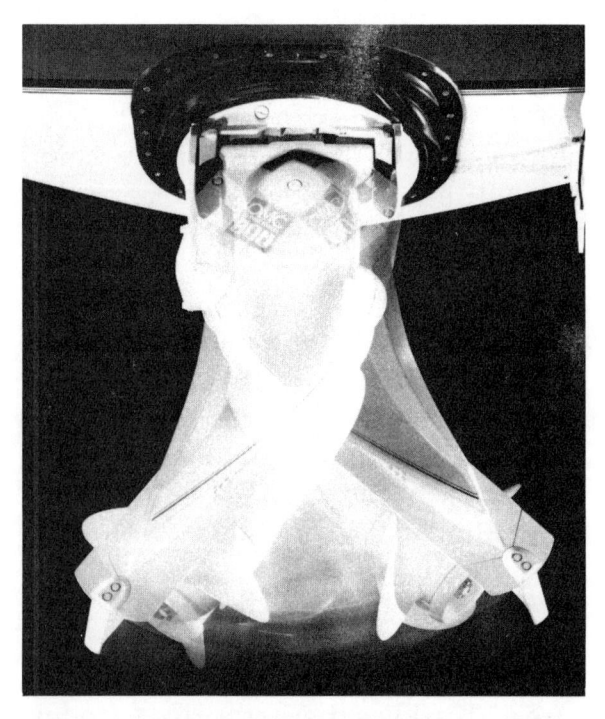

FIG. 5-4 — This top view of a sterndrive unit shows how the entire propulsion unit turns to steer the boat thereby giving excellent directional control. (Courtesy of OMC, Waukegan, Ill.)

FIG. 5-5 — Sterndrive units tilt up for easy trailer launching, and also kick-up if an obstruction is hit in the water. (Courtesy of OMC, Waukegan, Ill.)

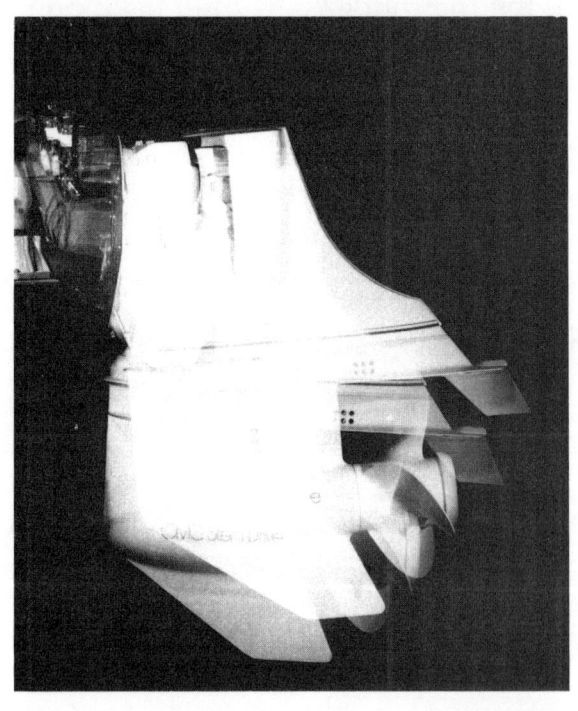

FIG. 5-6 — Many outdrive units offer trimming capabilities to balance and level out the running trim of the boat underway. This feature also compensates for variations in loads. (Courtesy of OMC, Waukegan, Ill.)

practical proof of this advantage in terms of added speed or economy for a given boat and engine combination.

Another appealing aspect of the sterndrive that may be more apparent than real is the economy and ease of installation. Since there is no propeller shaft, strut, bearing, stuffing box, rudder, or rudder port required, the costs of these items together with their installation is saved. However, the cost of the sterndrive unit can be considerable. While alignment of the engine is seldom a critical situation with the sterndrive installation, the sterndrive itself can be quite heavy and awkward to support while fitting and installing.

Sterndrive systems are available with a wide variety of options for both convenience and safety. In addition to power trim and power tilt features, systems are available with power shifting, power steering, steering angle indicators, and many other options. Naturally such features may add to the cost as well as to the complexity in what is already a complex piece of equipment, which opens the subject of some of the disadvantages of sterndrive units.

Because of inherent engineering handicaps and the additional gearing required with sterndrive units, there is some unavoidable power loss due to extra gearing, not to mention a potential for mechanical problems. Maintenance and operation of the sterndrive should be as prescribed by the manufacturer. In many cases depending on the boat and unit, a sterndrive may have greater underwater drag although great strides have been made in this area. Because of drag and engineering limitations, propeller diameter is often limited which can cause a loss of efficiency in many boats as opposed to conventional inboards where the propeller size is often only limited by the maximum practical shaft angularity. With twin screw installations, some sterndrives are not available in counter rotating units which can set up steering torque reactions. In fact, even single engine sterndrive units seem to suffer more from this problem then do conventional inboard boats (depending on hull type), and consequently most sterndrives are fitted with so-called "trim tabs" under the propeller cavitation plate behind the propeller. With this trim tab, the term "trim" refers to the directional trim in the steering as opposed to the fore-and-aft or balancing trim referred to with manual and power trim systems. The

FIG. 5-7 — A sterndrive unit that can be purchased separately and connected to a marine or converted engine. The transmission is also a separate unit and can be of many types and ratios to suit varying installations. (Courtesy of Marine Drive Systems, Edison, N.J.)

FIG. 5-8 — A sterndrive unit that is also a separate unit, but specially streamlined below the water for high speed use. Note the stainless steel cleaver or "chopper" propeller. (Courtesy of Marine Drive Systems, Edison, N.J.)

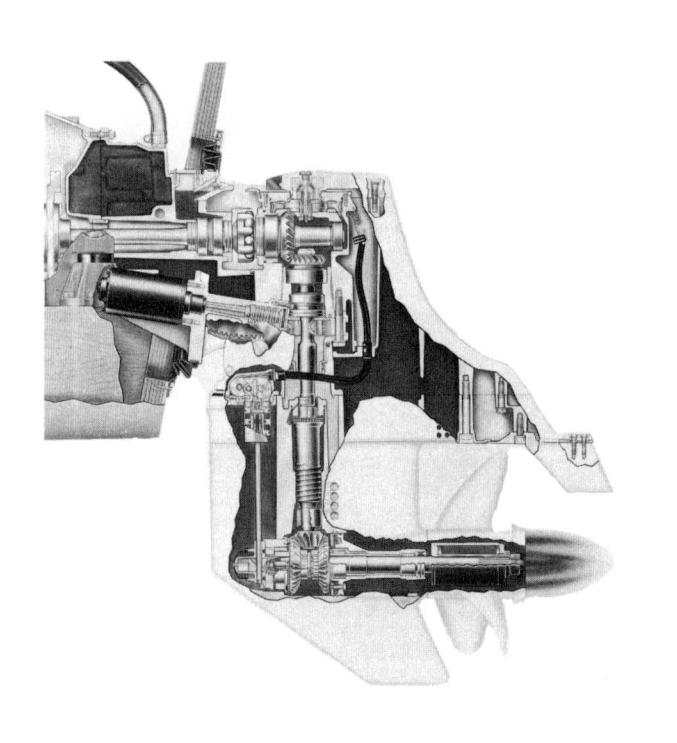

FIG. 5-9

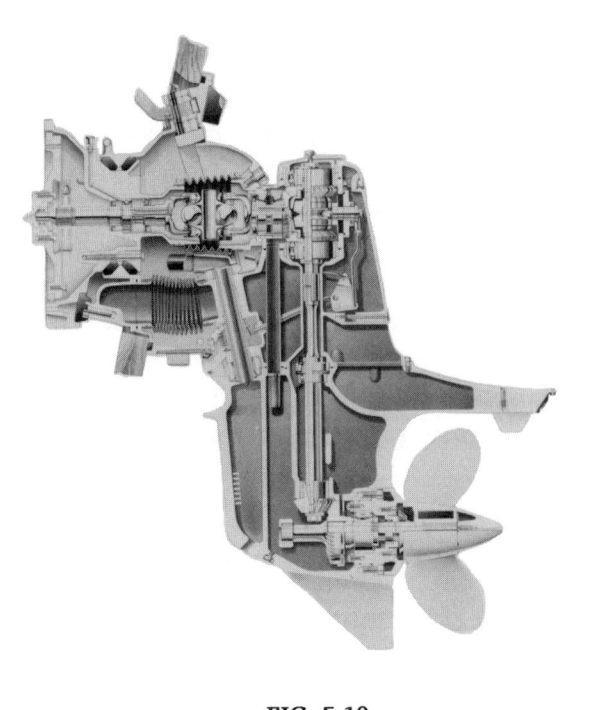

FIG. 5-10

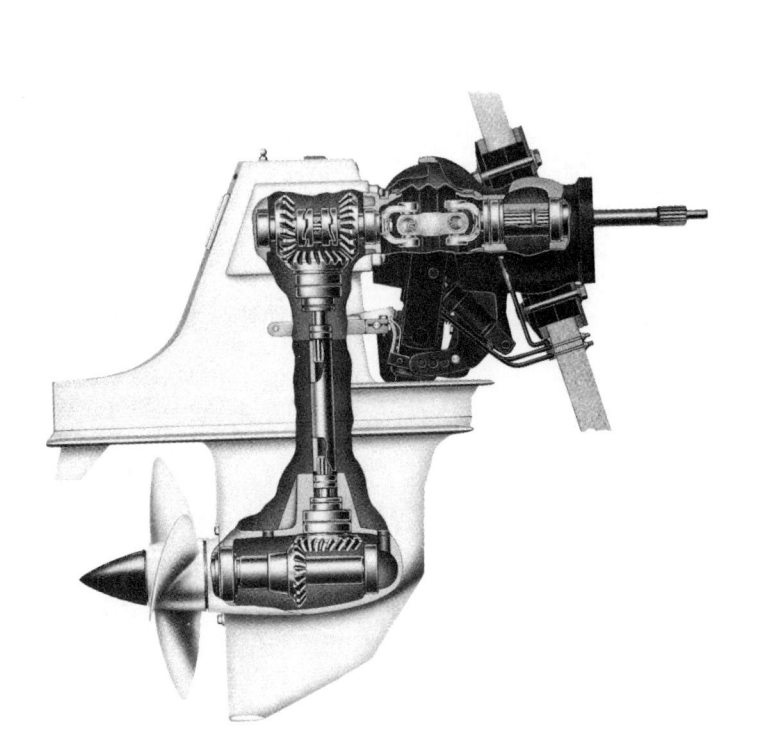

FIG. 5-11

FIG. 5-9 thru 5-11 — These photos show three different approaches to the design and engineering of sterndrive units. All have trim tabs for directional control (see text), and built-in shifting instead of separate transmissions. FIG. 5-9 shows a unit that does not use a universal joint like the other two, and the exhaust exits through the propeller hub. The units shown in FIG. 5-10 and FIG. 5-11 mount to the transom, while the unit shown by FIG. 5-9 passes through the transom and "floats" free, with a rubber boot sealing the hole. (FIG. 5-9 courtesy of OMC, Waukegan, Ill.; FIG. 5-10 courtesy of Volvo Penta, Chesapeake, Vir.; FIG. 5-11 courtesy of Marine Drive Systems, Edison, N.J.)

trim tab is located, sized, and designed to provide corrective steering action over a wide range of speed and operating conditions for many types of hulls, and hence its adjustment is entirely experimental on the part of the operator. In extreme cases steering torque problems can persist in spite of trim tab adjustment, and sometimes the hull is at fault since it may be defective in terms of being symmetrical about the centerline. Then too, propeller rotation and size may add to the problem. Corrective action to such problems can involve many steps, and most boats will need some degree of "tuning" to achieve optimum performance.

Another potential problem with sterndrive units is corrosion, especially in saltwater conditions. Through understanding of the problem and proper design and engineering, great strides have been made in current sterndrive units to minimize corrosion. However, just about all units consist of aluminum outer castings with parts of dissimilar metals within which can lead to possible corrosion, especially of the aluminum components. Special coatings and strategically located sacrificial anodes aid in corrosion protection, however, boats which will remain in saltwater at all times should retract the sterndrive free of the water if at all possible. For trailered boats, it is a good idea to wash down the sterndrive with fresh water after each use.

Steering systems for sterndrive units may be of several types, however, most adapt to the conventional steering control systems commonly used aboard boats, including the single push-pull cable, rack and pinion, and hydraulic types. In some cases, the sterndrive manufacturer has special steering and control systems specifically intended for the sterndrive in a "package" form, and these are usually available also for twin engine systems, and for connection to automatic pilot systems. Steering systems are discussed in Chapter 16.

## STERNDRIVE INSTALLATION

As previously noted there are several mounting methods used for sterndrives as well as several different sterndrive/power combination possibilities. The most important point with a sterndrive installation is that it is suitable for the boat in question. In spite of claims to the contrary, some boats are not suitable for sterndrive installations, and may be better suited for other types of power systems. If the engine will be stern-mounted, the hull must be capable of carrying the weight of the engine, as well as the sterndrive, in this portion of the hull without upsetting the balance at rest or underway. Much will depend on the weight of the units, however, this generally means that the shape of the hull must usually be full in the aft areas in order to provide the volume for the necessary buoyancy. A boat with a wide, deep, well-immersed transom may probably be suitable for a sterndrive installation. However, one that is double ended with fine lines aft or with little transom immersion will most likely not be satisfactory. As a general rule, a boat specifically intended for a centrally located inboard should not be converted to a sterndrive power installation except under good advice from a qualified person such as a naval architect. The balance of the boat could be

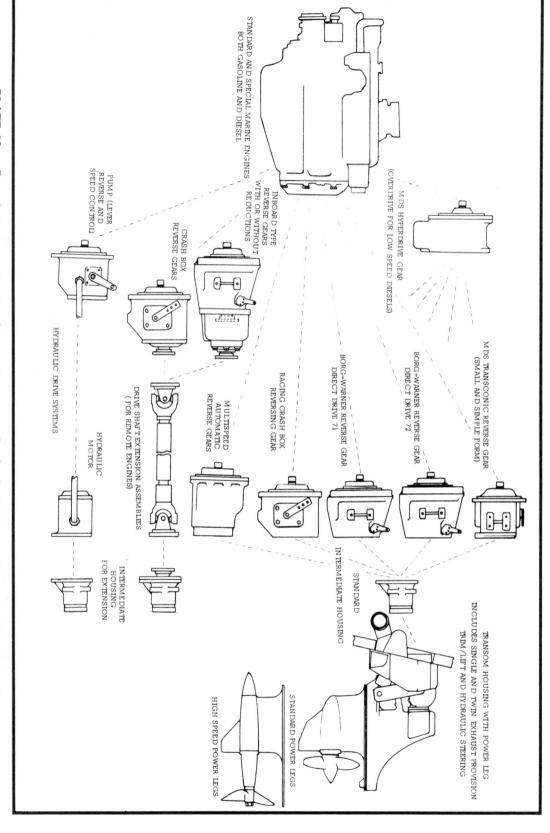

**PLATE 13** — By using a separate sterndrive unit without transmission, several options are possible. In addition to a wide selection of possible transmissions, the engine can be coupled via the transmission directly to the sterndrive in a stern-mounted installation, or it can be located forward in the hull joined with a double universal joint drive shaft or torque tube. Such a system also allows for a wide variety of both gasoline and diesel power options, including marine engines and converted automotive powerplants.

STANDARD AND SPECIAL MARINE ENGINES BOTH GASOLINE AND DIESEL

MDS HYPERDRIVE GEAR (OVERDRIVE FOR LOW SPEED DIESELS)

INBOARD TYPE REVERSE GEARS WITH OR WITHOUT REDUCTIONS

PUMP (LEVER REVERSE AND SPEED CONTROL)

CRASH BOX REVERSE GEARS

HYDRAULIC DRIVE SYSTEMS

HYDRAULIC MOTOR

DRIVE SHAFT EXTENSION ASSEMBLIES (FOR REMOTE ENGINES)

MULTISPEED AUTOMATIC REVERSE GEARS

RACING CRASH BOX REVERSING GEAR

BORG-WARNER REVERSE GEAR DIRECT DRIVE 71

BORG-WARNER REVERSE GEAR DIRECT DRIVE 72

MDS TRANSCONIC REVERSE GEAR (SMALL AND SIMPLE FORM)

INTERMEDIATE HOUSING FOR EXTENSION

STANDARD INTERMEDIATE HOUSING

TRANSOM HOUSING WITH POWER LEG INCLUDES SINGLE AND TWIN EXHAUST PROVISION TRIM/LIFT AND HYDRAULIC STEERING

STANDARD POWER LEGS

HIGH SPEED POWER LEGS

upset leading to questionable results.

In many instances with amateurs building boats from plans, the designer will specify the maximum weight that can be used with a stern mounted motor. This weight is usually the total weight, including the drive, and should be adhered to as closely as possible. However, many builders want to load on more weight in the form of larger engines or sterndrive units and wonder what will happen. This gets to be a situation like, "how many straws does it take to break the camel's back". The novice is often quick to point out that the balance problem can be solved by moving or adding tanks forward. But what happens when the tanks are only half-full, or empty? Admittedly, some degree of additional weight may not be detrimental, however, the extra weight should be kept within limits, and as an extra precaution, some type of trimming device is usually advised, either in the form of power trim of the sterndrive, or by the addition of trim plates (see Chapter 21).

As a general rule, sterndrive systems are mostly used in high speed planing boats, and with good reason. Such boats lend themselves well to the desirable hull shape suitable for stern mounted engines. Then too, large weights concentrated at the stern where pounding and motion is least go hand-in-hand with modern high speed planing designs. Another reason for sterndrive suitability for high speed use is the fact that larger, slower turning propellers associated with semi and full displacement boats cannot be used in most stern drives. Or put another way, the propeller sizes possible with many stern drive boats are not large enough for efficiency in boats of this type.

Specific installation details for sterndrive units and engines are not possible since they all vary with the manufacturer. In all cases, follow the instructions provided with the sterndrive system. However, the builder should check carefully regarding the transom angle of the boat, and what is available to match from a particular sterndrive manufacturer. In some cases, modifications may be necessary on the transom so that the angle will mate with that required for the sterndrive. In other cases, the sterndrive will adapt to several angles or infinite transom angularity. The installer should make sure that the sterndrive, when connected to the hull, will allow the recommended clearances from the back of the boat, and from the cavitation plate to the bottom of the hull, yet still be able to be connected to the engine. If structural members must be cut away within the boat to make the installation, such areas must be reinforced to maintain the structural integrity of the original hull. In some cases additional thickness must be added to the transom, especially for sterndrive units which bolt to the transom. With cantilever mounted units, extra support in the form of knee braces and gussets may be necessary to reinforce the transom. Exhaust and water intake arrangements are often made integral with the engine/sterndrive system, but in other cases, these may be separate and should be planned for in the installation. Ventilation requirements could vary from other types of installations, especially with stern mounted motors located in aft cockpits. It would seem easy to locate engine compartment vents on the engine box itself, or on the transom aft. However, these locations are not suitable (see Chapter 18). For engines located some distance forward of the sterndrive and coupled with a torque tube, the alignment procedures are similar to that required for the vee-drive installation described in the previous chapter.

## OTHER TYPES OF POWER TRANSMISSION SYSTEMS

Several other power transmission systems should be discussed, even though their use is somewhat limited. These include the thru-hull drive or so-called "sail drive" units, hydraulic drive systems, and belt drive systems. These types use an inboard engine, ultimately driving a propeller.

## THRU-DRIVE SYSTEM

The thru-hull drive unit (also called "sail drive" and sailing boat drive) is quite similar in concept to the sterndrive except that the drive unit passes through the hull and is usually located some distance forward of the transom or stern. On sailboats, the drive unit is best suited to so-called "fin keel" types where the ballast fin keel is separated from the rudder located aft. With this hull configuration the drive is located at some point between the fin keel and the rudder (see Plate 14). Such units are NOT intended for use in high speed planing hulls, and because of power and propeller size restrictions, best efficiency results in boats between 20' and 40', depending on the unit used.

Thru-hull drive units eliminate the need for propeller shafts, shaft logs, shaft struts, and bearings, as well as the job of installing such items. Propellers can be either the fixed or folding type, however, minimum drag will result with the folding type. Water pickup for engine cooling is through the drive unit thereby eliminating a thru-hull fitting and seacock for this connection.

At least two engine configurations are available. One type is similar to the typical sterndrive/engine combination, with the engine setting horizontally in the hull and driving through what amounts to a sterndrive unit which passes through the hull (see Fig. 5-12). Another type uses what amounts to an outboard engine set through the hull, with the engine on end so the crank shaft is in the vertical direction. Many of these units are virtually two-cycle outboard engines converted for inboard use in the thru-hull drive configuration. The thru-hull drive units do not tilt up or have any steering function like a sterndrive unit, however.

Many sailboat owners question the extra drag that could be caused by having a permanent appendage located below the waterline. Indeed on smaller sailboats, such as the trailerable type which might use an outboard motor on a transom bracket or in a well, there will obviously be more resistance, especially then when the outboard is retracted. However, on the conventional inboard installation driving through a shaft with a strut and support bearing, tests show that resistance is the same or lower with the thru-hull drive unit. The actual speed differential between similar boats amounts to a small fraction of a knot so that resistance is of no practical importance, however.

As with sterndrives, the lower units of the thru-hull drives are of aluminum. The manufacturers use special coatings, treated castings, and critically spaced replaceable sacrificial anodes to prevent corrosion. However, since the units could be immersed in saltwater at all times, and do include dissimilar metals inside, the potential for corrosion still exists. Careful main-tenance is mandatory on boats remaining in salt water. On trailerable boats, or boats which will not remain for long periods in salt water, corrosion should not be a major consideration.

## THRU-HULL DRIVE INSTALLATION

Because of the special nature of the thru-hull drive unit, and because each

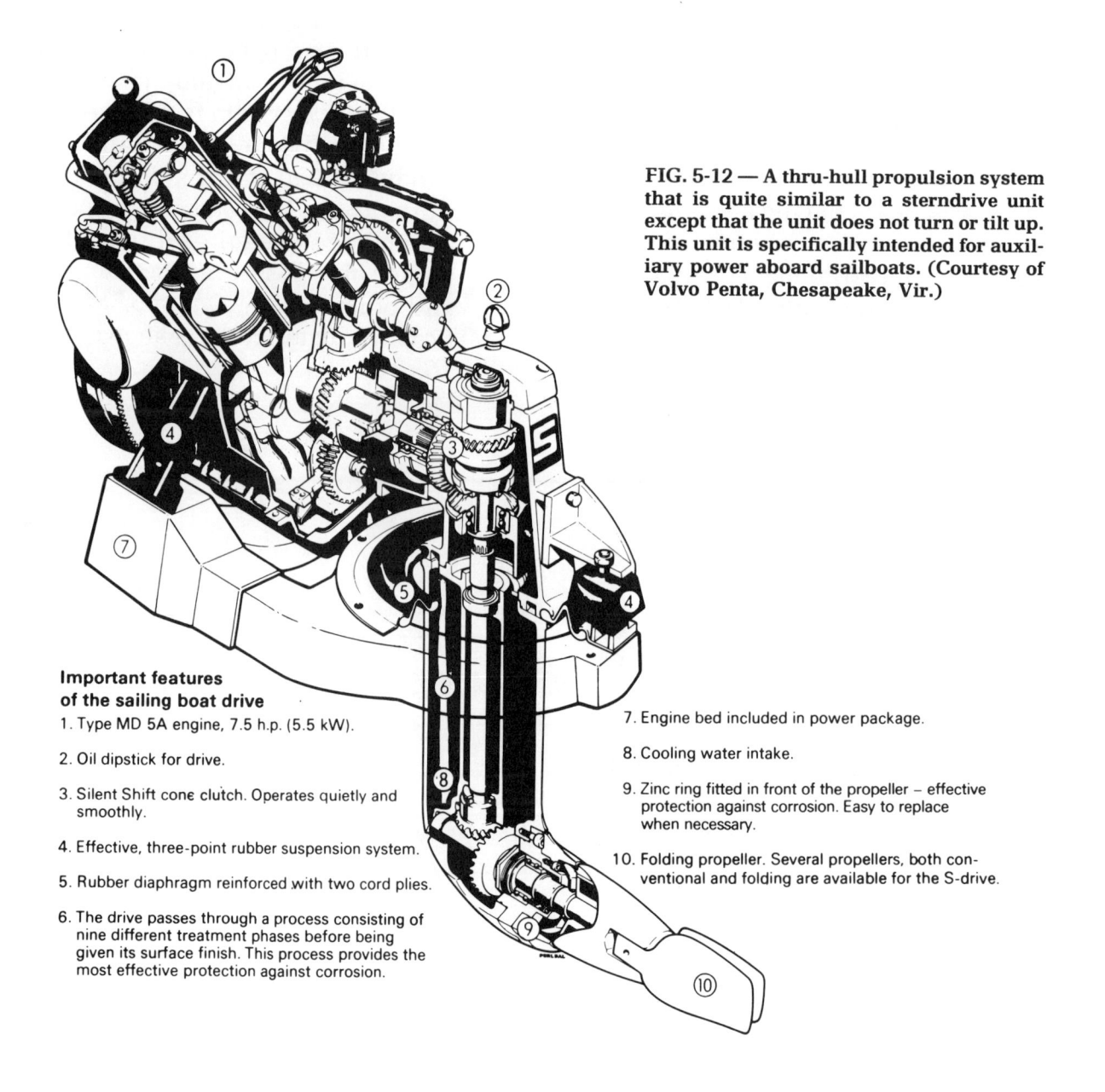

FIG. 5-12 — A thru-hull propulsion system that is quite similar to a sterndrive unit except that the unit does not turn or tilt up. This unit is specifically intended for auxiliary power aboard sailboats. (Courtesy of Volvo Penta, Chesapeake, Vir.)

**Important features
of the sailing boat drive**

1. Type MD 5A engine, 7.5 h.p. (5.5 kW).

2. Oil dipstick for drive.

3. Silent Shift cone clutch. Operates quietly and smoothly.

4. Effective, three-point rubber suspension system.

5. Rubber diaphragm reinforced with two cord plies.

6. The drive passes through a process consisting of nine different treatment phases before being given its surface finish. This process provides the most effective protection against corrosion.

7. Engine bed included in power package.

8. Cooling water intake.

9. Zinc ring fitted in front of the propeller – effective protection against corrosion. Easy to replace when necessary.

10. Folding propeller. Several propellers, both conventional and folding are available for the S-drive.

manufacturer offers quite different units, installation will vary considerably and must be per the recommendations of the manufacturer. Basically, however, a hole is cut in the bottom of the boat, and the thru-hull drive system inserted through this hole. In most cases, the motor mounting method is specified or perhaps even provided by the manufacturer (see Plate 15), and hence little can be given in the way of additional information. However, since a hole will be made in the bottom of the boat, this could cause a potential weak spot that could need additional reinforcement to restore the boat's original integrity. This would be especially true on boats having a central keel or keelson member. Otherwise, motor installation requirements would be the same as for any other inboard motor with regard to exhaust, ventilation, fuel system, etc.

## HYDRAULIC DRIVE SYSTEMS

The hydraulic drive system uses a conventional inboard marine engine, either gasoline or diesel powered, connected to a hydraulic pump. The hydraulic pump is, in turn, connected to a hydraulic motor by a series of semi-flexible hoses. The hydraulic motor is mounted to the propeller shaft just as would be done with a conventional inboard motor, and it is this motor that drives the propeller shaft and propeller. The main advantage of the hydraulic drive system is that the inboard engine coupled to the hydraulic pump can be located at any suitable location in the boat. This can be an important advantage in certain sailboats for balancing purposes, space limitations, and other factors. One type of hydraulic drive installation is shown by Plate 16.

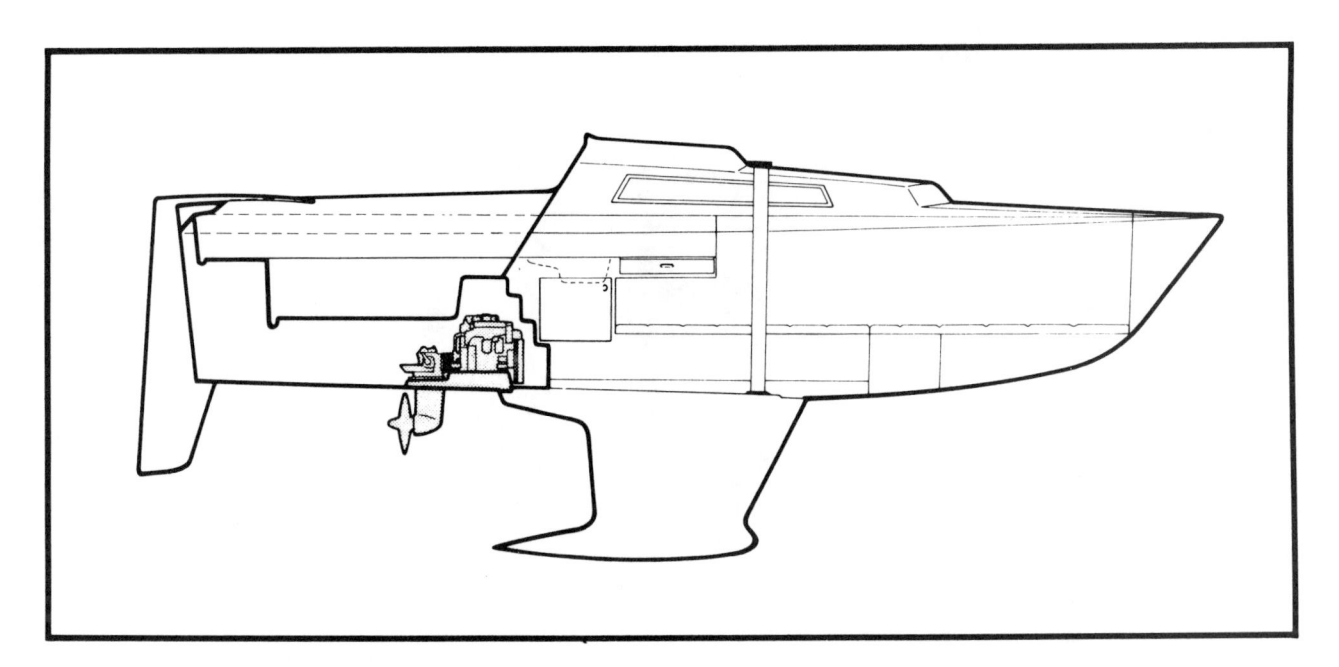

PLATE 14 — A typical thru-hull drive system installed in a sailboat. Note the fin keel with separate aft rudder recommended for this type of system. Since the drive is fixed, steering is provided by the boat's rudder. (Courtesy of Volvo Penta, Chesapeake, Vir.)

The hydraulic motor portion of the system is quite compact. Hoses joining the hydraulic pump portion can be virtually of any length. Reduction gearing can be built into the hydraulic drive system simply by varying the displacement between the hydraulic pump and the hydraulic motor. Controlling the direction of the hydraulic fluid provides forward, neutral, and reverse operation of the power system. In other words, the power transmission is basically non-mechanical. However, there is a greater loss of power as opposed to a mechanical gearbox, causing about a 15% power loss in these systems. Consequently, power would fall off as compared to a conventional system, or conversely, the engine size would need increasing to maintain the same performance.

## HYDRAULIC DRIVE INSTALLATION

Installation of the inboard engine portion of the hydraulic drive system is simple since it can be located in any area of the vessel. A typical set-up would have the engine mounted to motor stringers in the normal manner, but since there is no direct mechanical connection to the propeller shaft, the installation would be much like that of an auxiliary electrical generator. In other words, the engine would set on its mountings and be bolted down securely. Accurate alignment is not necessary for the engine. A conventional propeller and shaft arrangement would be used, connecting by a standard coupling in alignment to the hydraulic motor portion of the system. The resulting system could be quite closely

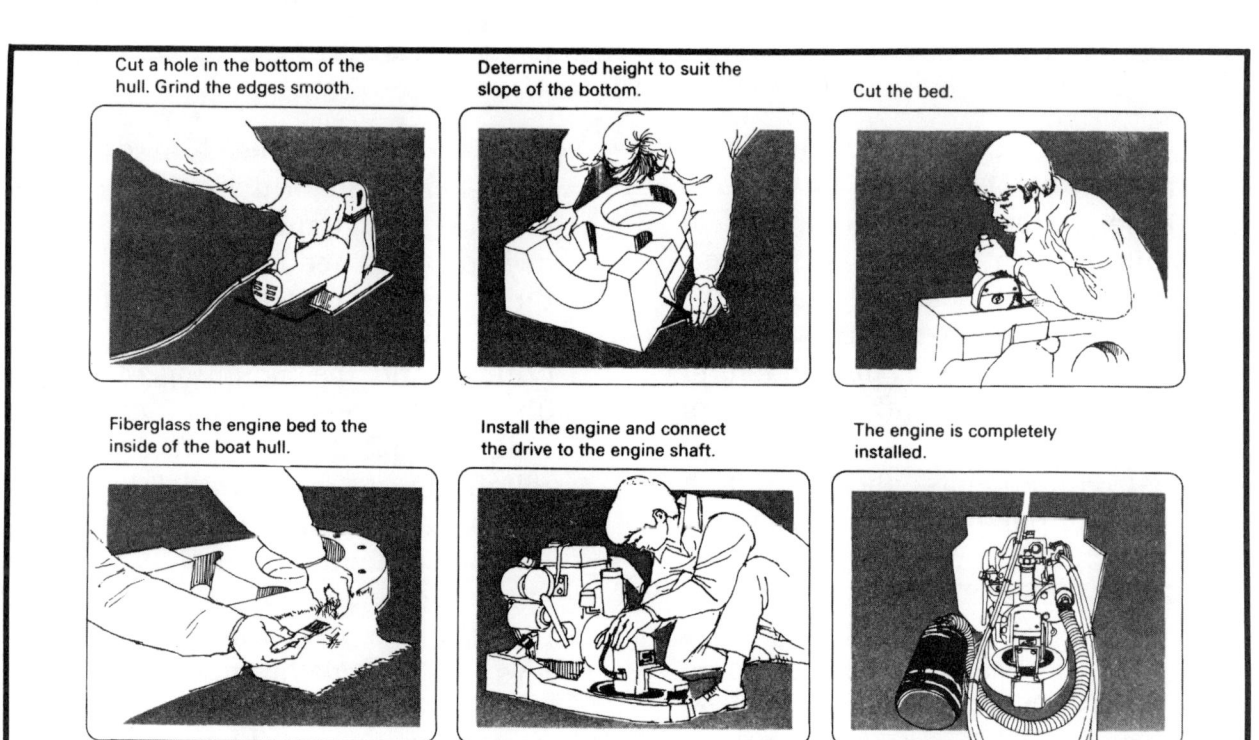

Cut a hole in the bottom of the hull. Grind the edges smooth.

Determine bed height to suit the slope of the bottom.

Cut the bed.

Fiberglass the engine bed to the inside of the boat hull.

Install the engine and connect the drive to the engine shaft.

The engine is completely installed.

**PLATE 15 — Installing the thru-hull drive unit shown in FIG. 5-12 is basically simple, partly because the manufacturer in this instance includes the specialized mounting components. (Courtesy of Volvo Penta, Chesapeake, Vir.)**

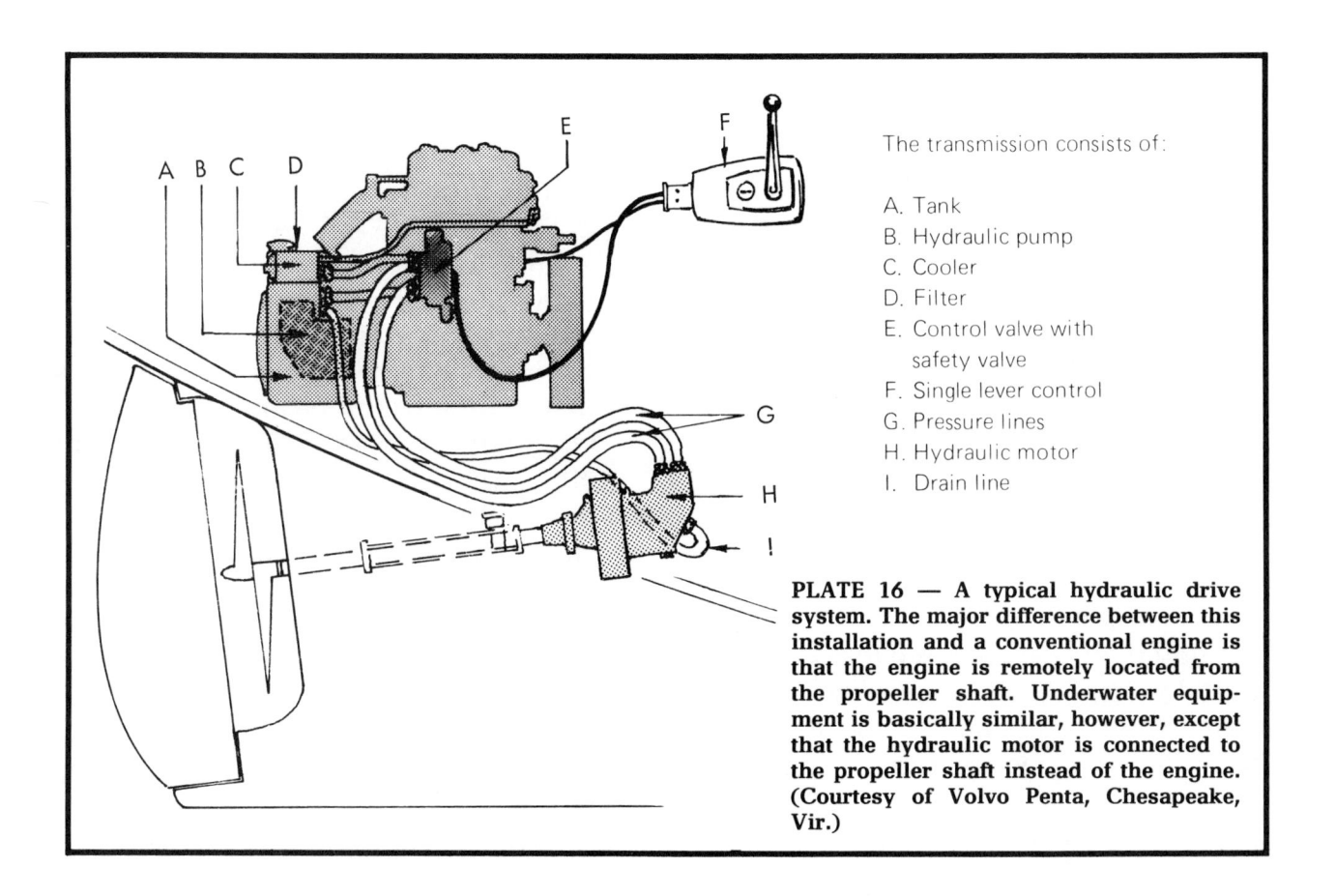

The transmission consists of:

A. Tank
B. Hydraulic pump
C. Cooler
D. Filter
E. Control valve with
   safety valve
F. Single lever control
G. Pressure lines
H. Hydraulic motor
I. Drain line

**PLATE 16 — A typical hydraulic drive system. The major difference between this installation and a conventional engine is that the engine is remotely located from the propeller shaft. Underwater equipment is basically similar, however, except that the hydraulic motor is connected to the propeller shaft instead of the engine. (Courtesy of Volvo Penta, Chesapeake, Vir.)**

coupled to save space, or the propeller shaft could be of a length as required to locate the hydraulic motor unit at any suitable location. Because systems may vary with the manufacturer, the installation recommendations provided by the particular manufacturer should be consulted. Other aspects of the installation, such as fuel systems, exhaust requirements, and ventilation would be similar to any inboard engine.

## BELT DRIVE SYSTEMS

Though not common on pleasure type boats, belt drive systems are sometimes used. Several advantages make the use of belt drive appealing. The engine can be mounted at the stern in the same manner as a vee drive engine. Belts are used to drive the propeller shaft which can be quite short. While a transmission is required of some sort, reduction ratios can be built into the pulleys by varying their sizes. Alignment of the engine is not as critical, and the mounting of the engine and the propeller shaft can be virtually horizontal. For efficiency and reliability, several parallel belts and pulleys are used. The hull must have sufficient depth for the installation, since the engine pulleys are located directly over the propeller shaft pulleys. Belt drive systems are rather specialized, and the installation of such systems should be made by a specialist in the field, or a manufacturer of the system.

# CHAPTER 6 — JET DRIVES

The jet drive is another means of transmitting the power of the engine to drive a boat. A jet drive is basically a water pump driven by the engine which sucks water from an intake located in the bottom of the boat and ejects it at high velocity through a discharge or "nozzle" in the stern or transom of the boat. Hence, the nick-name "squirt gun" is frequently heard when discussing jet pump units. The action of expelling the water toward the rear causes a reaction against the hull to move it in the opposite direction. This reaction is called "thrust" and is basically the same type of reaction as in a jet airplane, except that water is used instead of air. Diverting this "jet" of water to one side or the other causes a side thrust against the hull for turning purposes. Consequently, the steering of the boat with most jet units is accomplished by turning the nozzle or otherwise deflecting the water jet thrust instead of by using a rudder, or turning of the lower unit as with a stern drive. For operating in reverse, the water leaving the nozzle is discharged forward, allowing the reaction to push the hull to the rear. This action is usually accomplished by lowering a contoured "gate" over the nozzle which deflects the "jet" of water more or less in a forward direction. Since a jet system has no transmission as such, neutral is provided by equalizing the thrust fore and aft, as the jet pump is operating at all times the engine is running.

The jet drive system has so many appealing features that many are convinced that it is an ideal drive system. A primary advantage of the jet boat is the lack of underwater appendages. No propeller, propeller shaft, strut, or rudder is required, and consequently, the trailerable boat is not only easier to launch and trailer, but shallow water operation without damage is possible. Because there is no propeller, the jet drive boat provides a safety feature for swimmers and water skiers in the vicinity of the boat. The jet pump does away with many items normally required in other types of inboard installations, and hence is theoretically cheaper and easier to install and maintain. Not only are the various underwater appendages noted above not required, but the jet pump may also do away with the transmission, water pump, stuffing box, rudder port, and shaft bearings.

The jet drive also offers unique maneuverability and operating characteristics that can be an advantage over other power transmission systems. For example, the jet drive boat has no torque reaction commonly found on many propeller driven boats regardless of the speed, and steering effort is minimal. A jet boat at speed can turn very rapidly. In fact, turns of 180 degrees are often so rapid that the hull

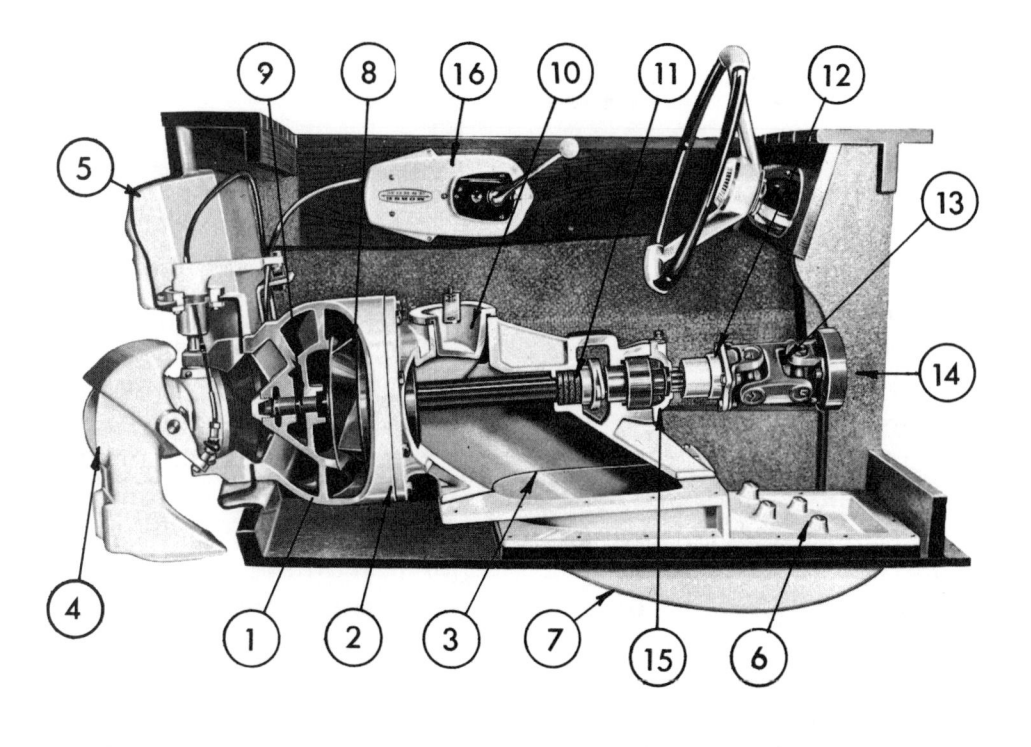

| 1 PUMP | 5 TRANSOM ADAPTER | 9 TAIL BEARING | 13 DRIVE SHAFT |
| 2 BOWL | 6 INTAKE ADAPTER | 10 HAND HOLE | 14 FLYWHEEL ADAPTER |
| 3 INTAKE | 7 GRATE | 11 STUFFING BOX | 15 THRUST BEARING |
| 4 DISCHARGE NOZZLE | 8 IMPELLER | 12 DRIVE COUPLING | 16 SINGLE LEVER CONTROL |

The Jet-Drive connects directly to the engine flywheel with the double universal drive shaft (13) which may be from 5″ to 5′ long. One end of this drive shaft attaches to the Jet-Drive with a splined coupling (12) and the other to a flywheel adapter (14) which is connected to the engine flywheel. There is no delicate alignment to worry about.

Supported by a double row thrust bearing (15) and a sleeve tail bearing (9), the Jet-Drive shaft supports the impeller (8). This impeller pumps the water from the intake (3) to the discharge nozzle (4). The stream from the nozzle propels the boat and also steers or reverses the boat, depending upon how it is directed.

Installation requires only two openings in the boat, one in the transom where the transom adapter (5) is shown; one in the bottom for the intake adapter (6). This intake adapter has a grate that keeps out debris too large to pass through the jet.

The Jet-Drive unit bolts to this intake adapter and to the transom adapter. The steering nozzle then bolts to the transom adapter and the pump (1). The installation shown here is with bowl (2) inboard. However, to save inside-hull space, the bowl may be installed outboard with equal ease.

SINGLE LEVER CONTROL — One continuous motion of this control (16) shifts and applies the throttle. Forward for speeds ahead . . . backward for speeds astern. Steer with one hand while you shift.

GRATE — This grate (7) keeps out rocks, sticks and debris too large to pass through the impeller easily. A loose finger grate is available and should be used when running in weeds with the chopper blade.

IMPELLER — Single stage, mixed flow, enclosed type.

STUFFING BOX — Adjustable and easily repacked, this stuffing box (11) prevents leakage around the shaft.

THRUST BEARING — Isolated by design and sealed from the water being pumped, this thrust bearing (15) is a double row, grease lubricated angular contact type.

HAND HOLE COVER — This cover (10) can be removed in an instant for easy access to the impeller in the unlikely event of clogging. A hand hole cover with weed chopping blade, and a loose finger grate are available.

DRIVE COUPLING — A closer engine connection is provided with this splined drive coupling (12) which eliminates the double universal shaft spline.

DISCHARGE NOZZLE — (4) Permits maximum turning efficiency and effortless steering and shifting.

**FIG. 6-1 — A typical jet drive installation (Courtesy of Berkeley Pump Co., Berkeley, Calif.)**

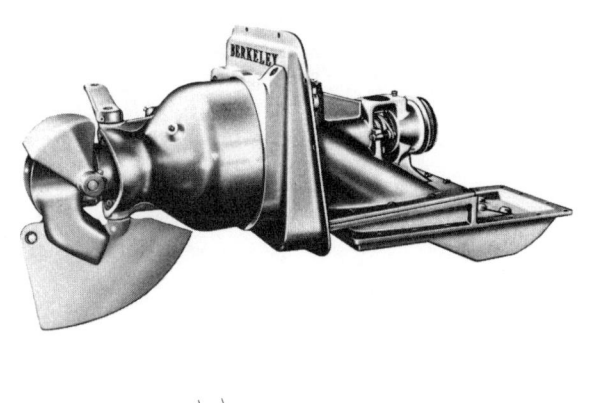

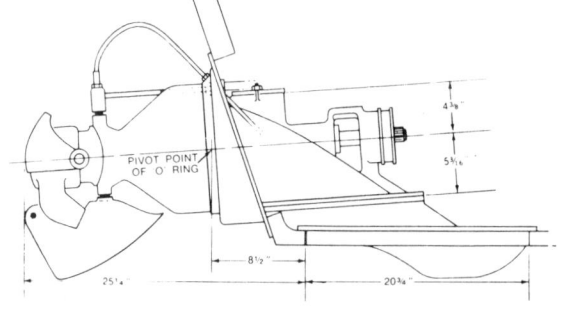

FIG. 6-2 —This is a typical jet drive unit of the "bowl outboard" type. The intake unit and transom housing each require a hole through the boat.

will swap ends, or turn in its own length. Furthermore, since there is no transmission, reverse can be applied almost instantly, giving a braking effect like no other type of boat. A jet boat at speed will "glide" a considerable distance if throttle is released. Because power transmission is smooth and vibration-free, the jet drive system is potentially quieter.

However, many of these same advantages may cause problems for the novice who is not familiar with jet boat operation. Because the jet boat's maneuverability and handling are quite different from propeller driven boats, a learning period should be required before attempting any high speed turning or reversing procedures since swamping, broaching, and capsizing could result. Slow speed handling and operation in crowded waters must be

practiced with a jet boat because the velocity of the jet at low speed is not enough for quick, positive handling. Special rudders or "steering vanes" are fitted on many jet units to aid low speed handling as well as to provide directional stability in the event of a power failure at speed.

While shallow water operation is possible and often practical with a jet boat, such practice may require special techniques. In most cases, the boat should be kept on plane in shallow draft situations and kept straight, since the draft of the hull will increase when turning or when off plane. While a jet pump will operate in only a few

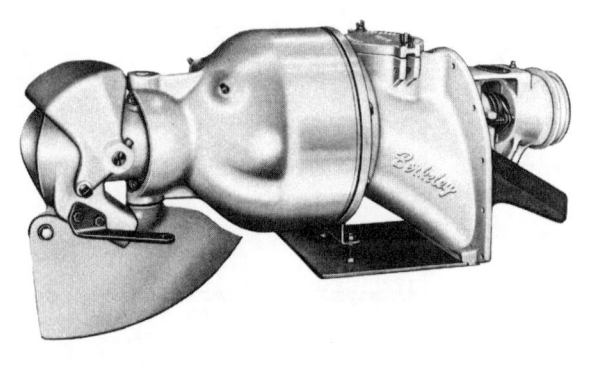

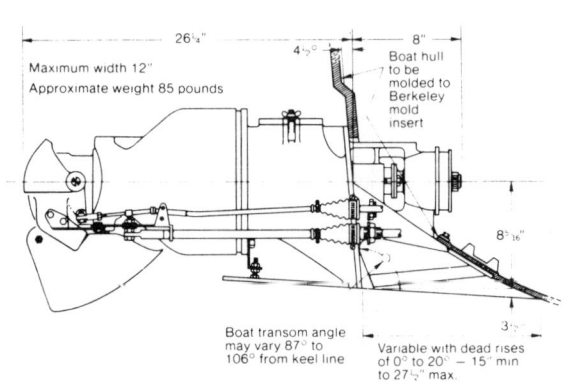

FIG. 6-3 — This jet pump is designed for "molded in" installations such as with fiberglass boats. With this unit both the intake and nozzle are actually outside of the boat, with the drive housing only passing through to the engine coupling. Note the trim plate on the bottom and the rudder or "steering vane". In this unit, the clean-out on top of the unit will be outside of the boat. (Courtesy of Berkeley Pump Co., Berkeley, Calif.)

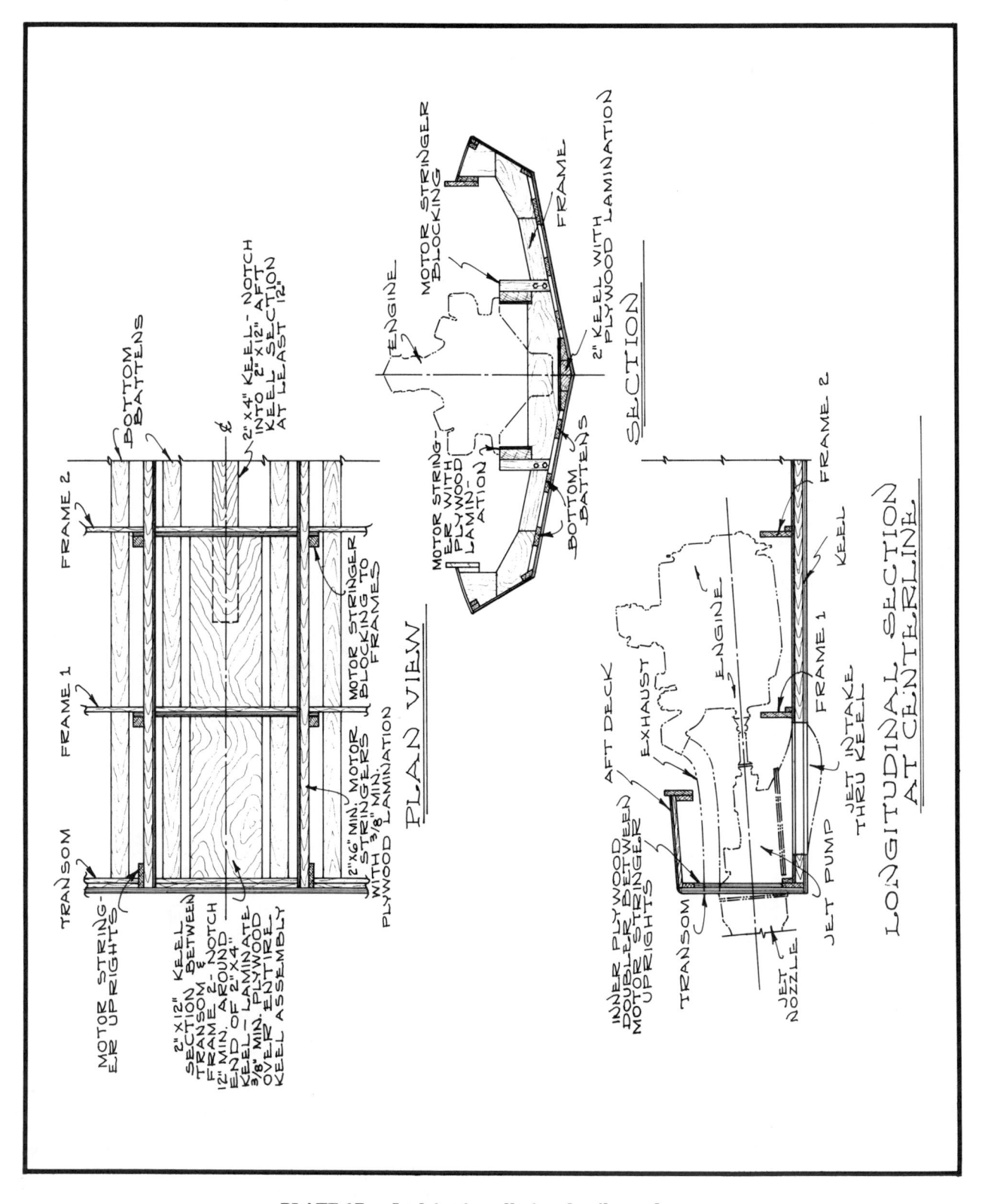

**PLATE 17 — Jetdrive installation details used on a typical plywood boat built from plans by the home builder.**

inches of water, continuous operation over sandy bottoms is hard on the jet pump and can also cause sand to get sucked into the engine's cooling system on jet units with engine cooling water intakes that are a part of the jet unit. Rocks and gravel can sometimes enter the pump and damage the impellers also. In weed infested waters, it is possible for the jet to clog even though most pumps can "ingest" a certain amount of weeds by virtue of "weed choppers" built into the pump. If clogging of the pump occurs, power will fall off and be readily noticeable. With most jet units, there are access plates or clean-out ports which can be removed to clean out any clogging

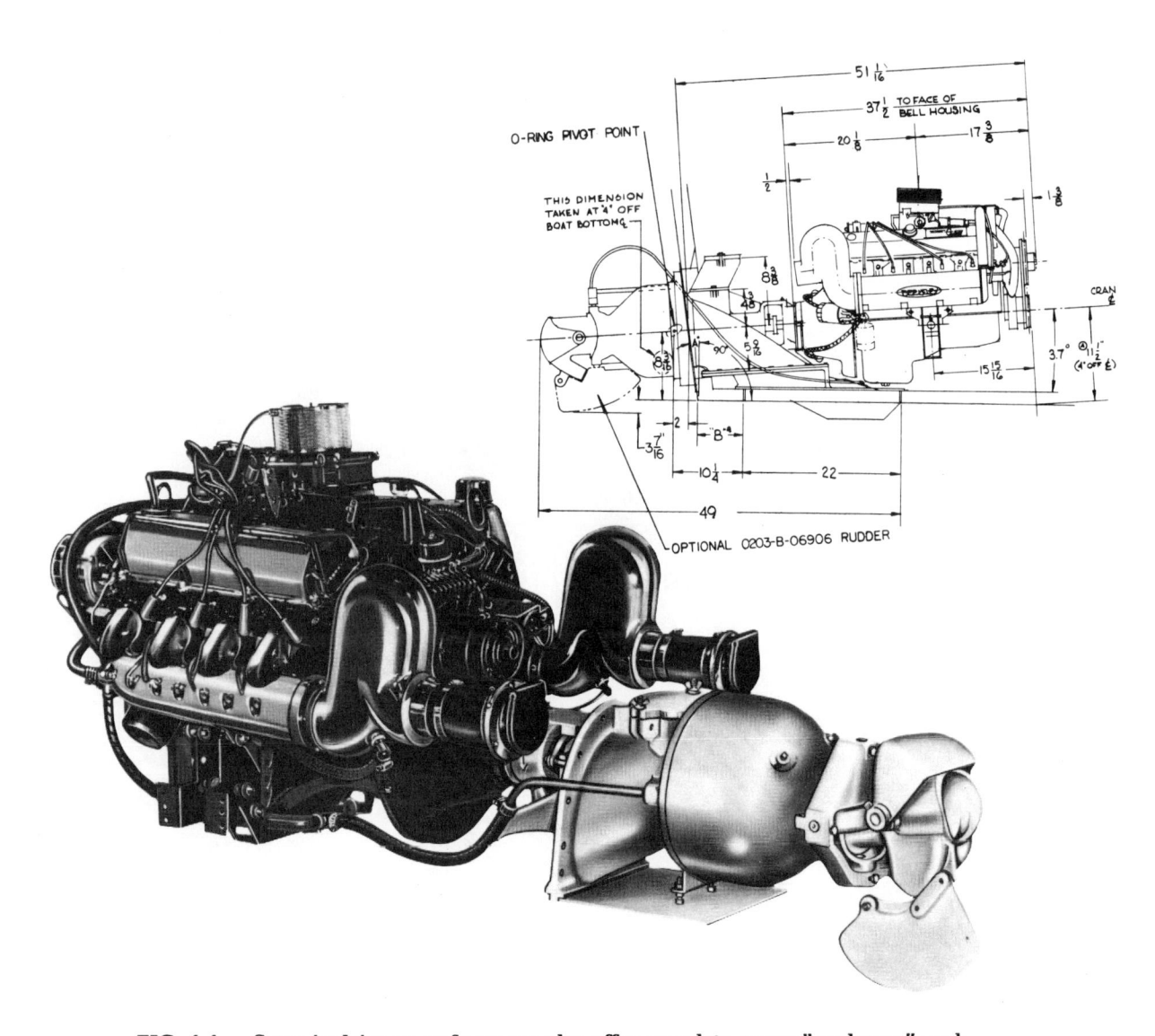

FIG. 6-4 — Some jetdrive manufacturers also offer complete power "packages" such as this unit from Berkeley. Note the risers on the exhaust manifolds together with flaps over the exhaust ports which will pass through the transom. These devices keep water from backing up into the engine when underway. (Courtesy of Berkeley Pump Co., Berkeley, Calif.)

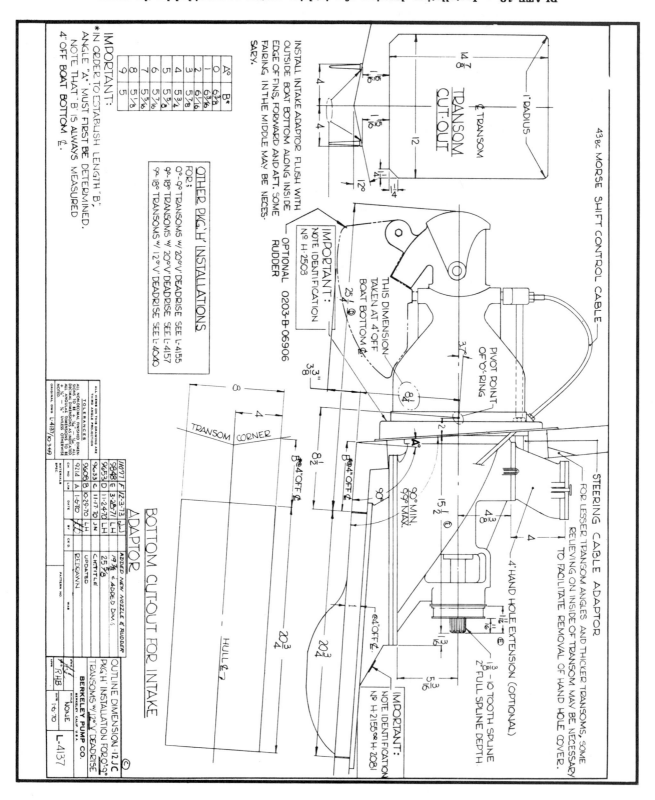

**PLATE 18** — Installation drawing of a jetdrive system as provided by the manufacturer. This unit is for a 12 degree bottom with a transom angle of 0 to 9 degrees.
(Courtesy of Berkeley Pump Co., Berkeley, Calif.)

material, although the operator must take care to check that the waterline is below the level of the clean-out port if it is within the boat. In such cases, it is a good idea to shift the crew and any other weights available to the forward portion of the boat in the hopes of raising the stern prior to removing the plate to prevent flooding the boat. In some cases, clean-out extensions are available which effectively raise the opening level.

It is imperative that the jet pump have an adequate and positive supply of water during operation. If air enters the pump causing "cavitation", power will fall off and possibly damage the pump or engine. This can be a problem especially in rough water conditions when the boat is planing and jumping free of the water. In such conditions, it is better to slow the boat down to keep the jet intake in solid water at all times, even though speed and handling may suffer.

While jet pumps may be theoretically suitable for a wide variety of boat types and sizes, present conditions limit the use of jet pumps due to efficiency and other factors. At present, jet drives are most suitable for high speed planing type inboard boats in the 15′ to 25′ range. At least some degree of "vee" or dihedral should be incorporated into the hull shape at the stern to assure a positive supply of water for the jet intake. Flat bottomed boats, especially planing types, tend to suck air and cause the pump to cavitate. For best efficiency, the hull should be shaped and powered to sustain a speed of at least 30 miles per hour. Speeds lower than this will cause a loss of economy in most cases, and make the use of a propeller type drive

more economical. Weight is also critical with jet drive boats. As a general rule, there should be at least 1 horsepower for every 30 lbs. of weight (boat weight and the load carried including fuel, passengers, gear, etc.). In other words, the lighter the boat and load, the better the performance and economy will be for the jet boat. These qualities virtually rule out the jet unit for use in heavy boats such as semi, or full displacement types, unless the special qualities of the jet unit are required above all else. If in doubt about the type of hull which would be suitable for a jet drive, check the following guide which describes common hull types:

| GOOD JET HULL (*) | FAIR-TO-POOR JET HULLS |
|---|---|
| Moderate vee bottom | Flat bottom |
| Deep vee bottom | Round bottom |
| Longitudinally stepped vee bottom (i.e. lift strakes) | Inverted vee bottom |
| | Most sailboat monohulls |
| Lapped straked vee bottom | Semi & full displacement hulls |
| Tri-hull | Catamarans with single engines |
| Catamarans with twin engines | |

(*)Note: There must be no hull appendage or "keel" from at least 2′ forward of the jet intake. If such an appendage must exist, it should be tapered in a long taper in plan view to allow solid water to enter the intake and prevent cavitation. Deep forefoots which could cause poor handling, spin-outs, and loss of speed should be avoided, as well as hooks, wedges, or other abrupt changes in the hull lines aft that could cause cavitation.

## JET PUMP INSTALLATIONS

Several types of jet pumps are available including single and multiple impeller types. While most units are made from aluminum for light weight and economy, special units are some-

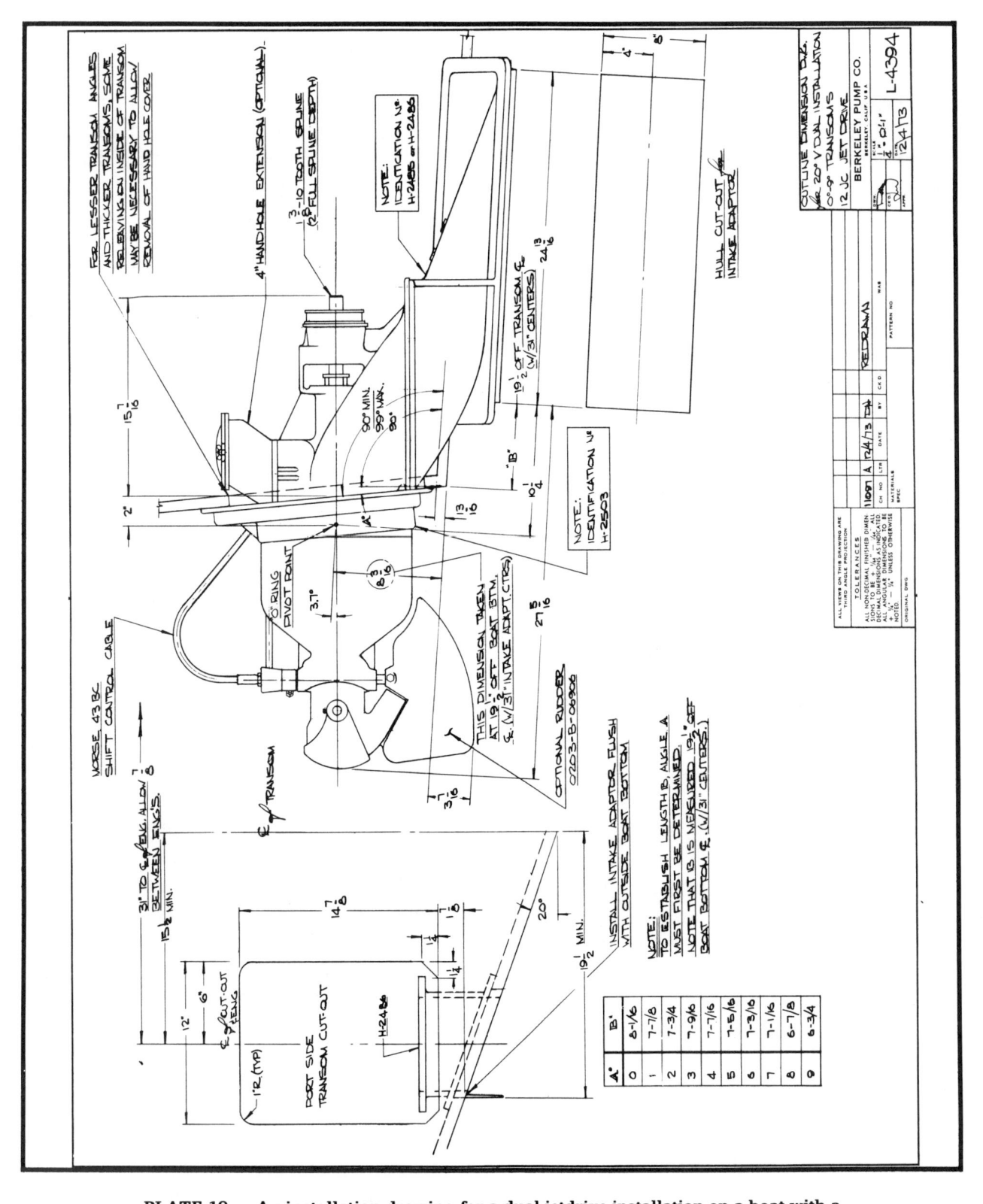

**PLATE 19 — An installation drawing for a dual jetdrive installation on a boat with a 20 degree bottom and transom angle between 0 and 9 degrees. (Courtesy of Berkeley Pump Co., Berkeley, Calif.)**

times available in stainless and bronze where salt water corrosion may be a problem. Impellers are usually aluminum or stainless steel, with the latter being recommended for saltwater use or where heavy-duty use is contemplated.

While each manufacturer's jet pump will vary somewhat in installation method, most are relatively simple to install. Basically, most jet pumps require a hole in the bottom of the boat somewhat forward of the transom for the intake, and another hole through the transom or stern for the nozzle or "bowl" unit. Generally, two configurations of jet pumps are common; the "bowl outboard" type (see Fig. 6-1) with the impeller housing basically at, or aft of, the transom, and the "bowl inboard" type with the impeller housing within the boat. The former type allows more room in the boat by locating the engine farther aft, however, some don't like the appearance of the unit protruding out the back of the boat. The latter type is less conspicuous, but does take up more room inside the boat. Otherwise, the units are similar in installation.

Depending on the boat, modifications may be required to the hull in order to install the jet pump. Because holes will be made in the hull, there must be adequate structure in way of these openings to maintain the structural integrity of the hull. The hole through the transom for the nozzle end of the jet pump usually does not decrease strength much since most transoms are either made from plywood or consist of a plywood core. If the plywood is not thick enough, additional plywood layers may be required around the opening. Along the bottom

of the boat where the intake will be located, sufficient thickness is necessary for the mounting bolts. On single engine boats with the motor at the centerline, there is often sufficient hull thickness in this area. If not, additional blocking sized as required is necessary. For example, on new construction with plywood or wood hulls, the keel member on the inside of the hull can be widened in this area (see Plate 17) to provide sufficient thickness and strength at the intake opening.

Usually the jet pump, together with the intake and outlet portions, forms a single component which makes a strong knee-type brace from the transom to the keel or hull bottom to take the thrust reaction of the jet, and consequently additional strength or bracing to the transom is not necessary. However, this may vary with the unit, and additional transom bracing could be required. In no case should the installation of the jet unit weaken the structure of the hull. Since the jet pump unit is bolted through the transom as well as the bottom of the hull, any structural strength lost by cutting openings in the hull is usually restored after installation as long as there is sufficient bolting thickness and reinforcement at the openings.

The jet unit is usually connected to the inboard motor by a torque tube such as is used on a vee drive system, or a close-coupled universal joint. The installation does not require critical alignment, as universal joints are used in either case. In some cases, power units are available complete with the jet and inboard engine as shown by Fig. 6-4. These units are close-coupled with universal joints like that shown in Fig. 6-1 so that the engine can be located as far aft in the boat as possible. However, with the torque tube, depending on the length of the tube, the engine could be located farther forward if need be for best balance, even though this is seldom done in practice. The point is, there is considerable latitude with jet units in engine mounting unlike other power transmission systems, thereby allowing the builder to shift the engine as required to fit the engine around structural obstructions such as frames and floor timbers.

Cables of the sheathed push-pull type are used on the jet unit for steering control and for actuating forward,

The chart at the right demonstrates jet boat performance compiled by the Berkeley Pump Co., Berkeley, Calif., in tests with their 12 J jet pump assembly. As this company states in the notes below, such charts are not predictable as to all boats because of the many variables. The chart does indicate the relative performance of a series of boats, however, and demonstrates the importance of the pounds per horsepower factor.

NOTES:

a. This chart is intended only as a guide. It does NOT imply any guarantee of performance. Predictions involving boat lengths, boat weights, boat speeds or engine shaft horsepower beyond the testing of Berkeley Pump Companies test experience will NOT be reliable.

b. This chart summarizes a number of boat tests by the measurement of speed and power/weight ratio. The boats tested were light, fast planing hulls between 15' and 19' long. Their operating weights ranged from 1500 to 4000 lbs. Engine output varied between 85 SHP and 250 SHP.

c. Weight of the boat means the total including passengers, equipment, fuel, etc.

d. The shaft horsepower available from an engine approximated 75 to 90% of the manufacturer's advertised rating.

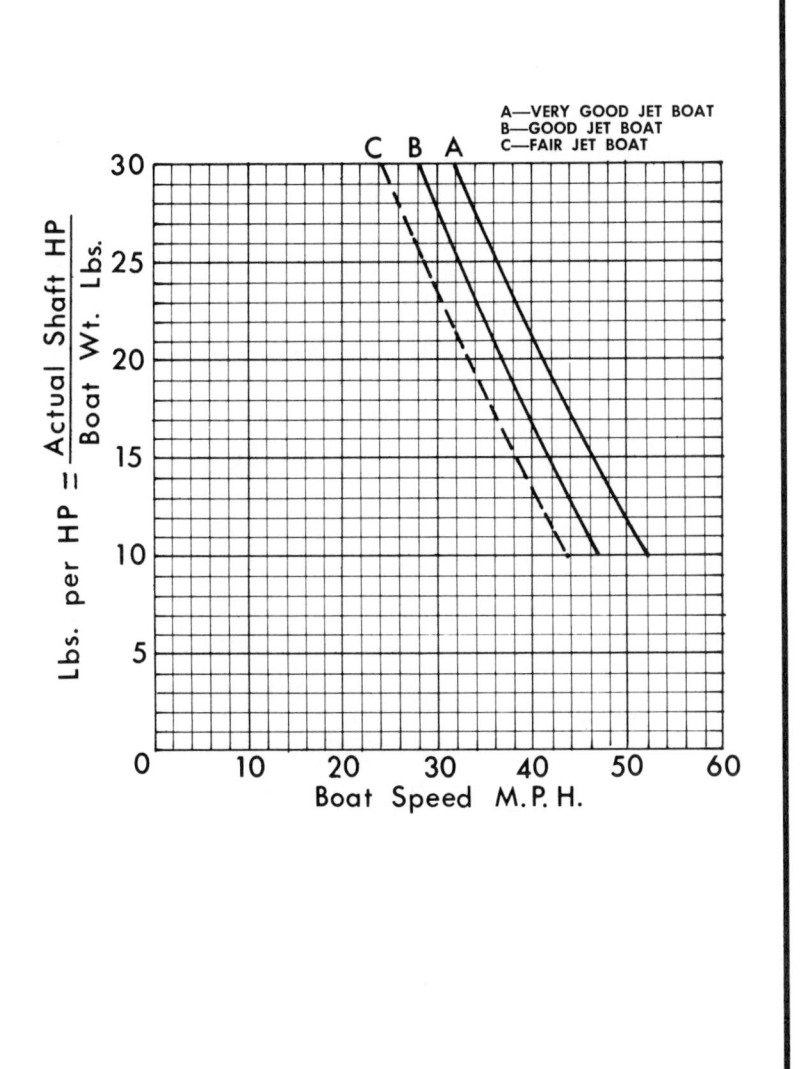

PLATE 20 — Jet boat performance chart. (Courtesy of Berkeley Pump Co., Berkeley, Calif.)

neutral, and reverse operation. Virtually any steering system that will adapt to the cable can be used, with the rack-and-pinion and single push-pull cable types being common for this use. (see Chapter 16). The shifting lever is mounted adjacent to the helmsman and can be the typical single lever type that actuates the throttle as well, or can be separate from the throttle. Most jet manufacturers have control components available especially intended and suited for use with their units.

For the smaller trailerable boat, the jet drive installation is popular and durable. However, for boats which will remain in saltwater and in the larger sizes, several points should be observed. Most jet pumps are cast from aluminum. Although they are treated and protected as much as possible, both in design and manufacture, corrosion can be a problem. Even in trailerable-type boats, it is recommended that the jet unit be washed or flushed out after each use in salt water. Metallic anti-fouling bottom paints can accelerate this corrosion and should therefore never be applied or make

contact with the aluminum parts of the jet pump. All metal parts should be isolated from contact with the jet unit as well. This would be especially critical in metal hulled boats. No electrical connections should be made with the jet unit and it should never be used as a ground return for lights or electrical accessories. While special units are available of corrosion-resistant metals, their cost and weight are quite high.

In jet boats with stern mounted motors, the hull must be suitably shaped to carry the load. This is the same type of situation as with stern-drive systems described in Chapter 5 which should be consulted for more information. With most stern mounted jet engine systems, however, balance of the hull in a fore-and-aft direction is not quite as critical since most jets are somewhat lighter in weight than most outdrive units, and the longitudinal center of gravity of both the jet pump unit and the engine will usually be slightly farther forward than the stern-drive/engine combination.

FIG. 6-5 thru FIG. 6-16 — These photos show a typical jet drive installation in a vee bottom boat. Photos courtesy of Berkeley Pump Co., Berkeley, California.

FIG. 6-5 — The centerline of the hull is marked on the outside of the transom and hull bottom.

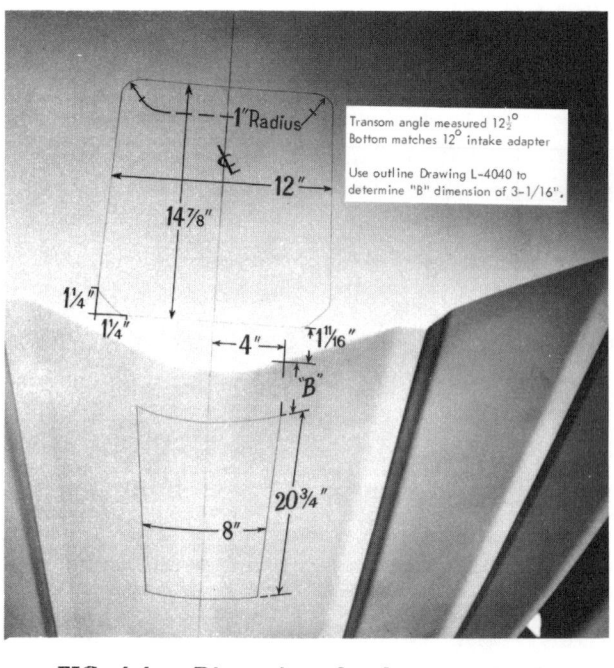

FIG. 6-6 — Dimensions for the pump intake and outlet cut-outs are marked to the hull.

FIG. 6-7 — In lieu of noted dimensions, some jet manufacturers may provide a fixture for locating the jet pump.

FIG. 6-8 — The locating fixture is positioned to the hull with the marking template against the transom, angled to suit.

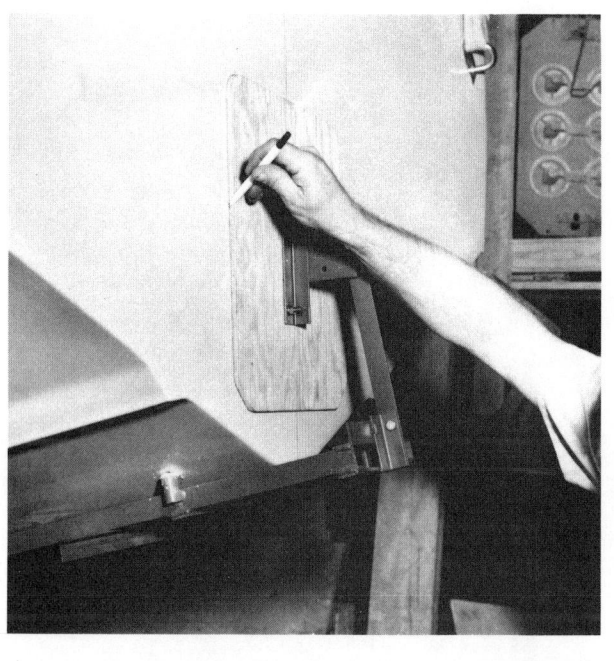

FIG. 6-9 — A mark is made around the marking template of the locating fixture for the pump outlet.

FIG. 6-10 — Holes are drilled through the bottom of the boat through guides in the locating fixture.

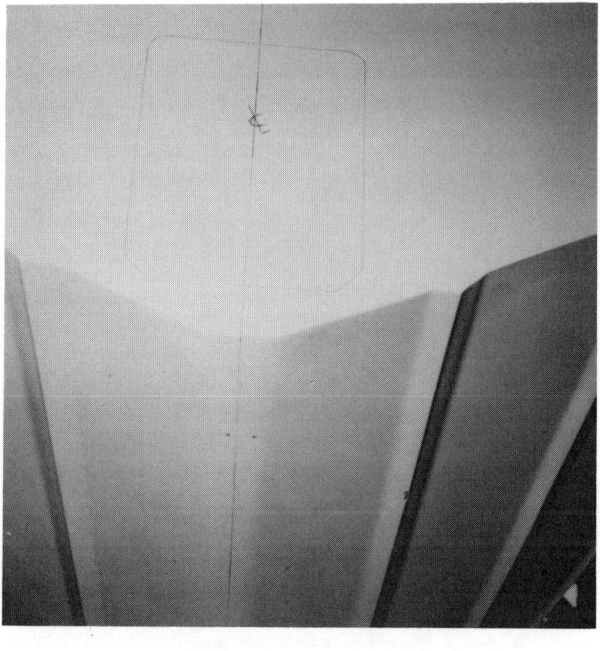

FIG. 6-11 — After removing the locating fixture, a mark will remain for the outlet opening and four holes on the bottom for the intake cut-out.

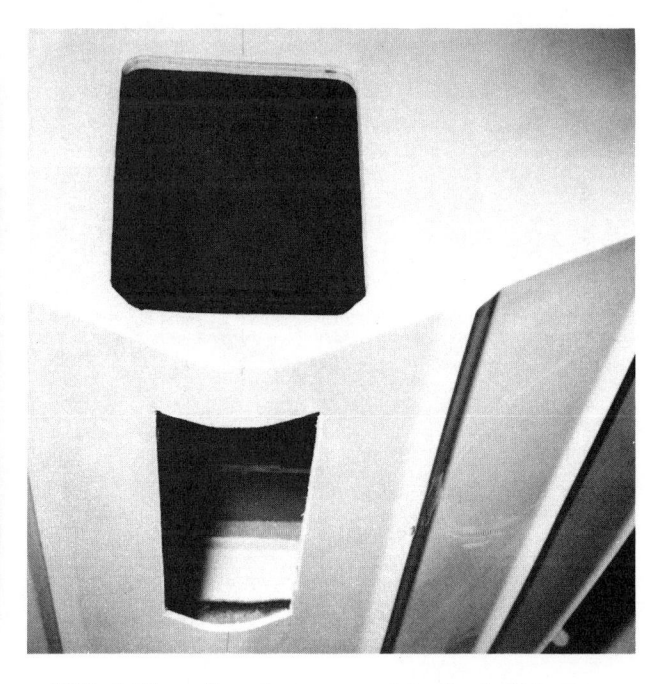

FIG. 6-12 — Openings are cut in the hull bottom and transom for the jet pump intake and outlet using a saber saw. Note the plywood transom core and the extra thickness of the hull along the center.

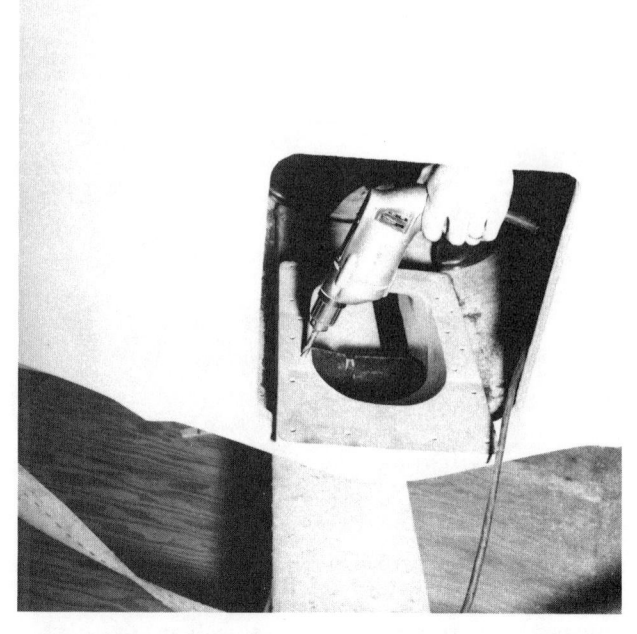

FIG. 6-13 — After aligning and fitting the intake unit, holes are drilled through the hull for mounting the unit.

FIG. 6-14 — The unit is bedded in sealant and bolted in place ready for connection to the motor and fitting of the transom housing.

FIG. 6-15 — The rod passing through the transom plate with this jet unit connects to a tiller arm which is used to turn the nozzle in either direction for steering.

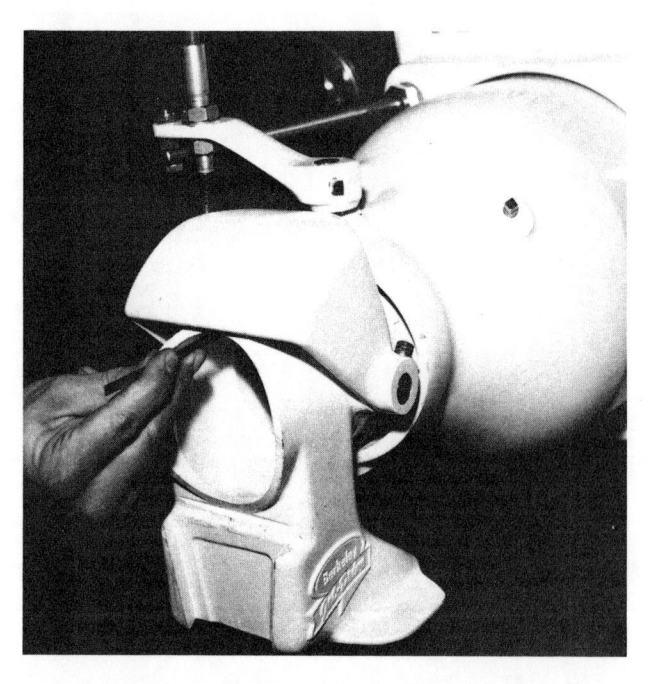

FIG. 6-16 — This view of the nozzle shows the reversing gate in the raised position. The push-pull cable coming down through the tiller arm is used to actuate reverse by lowering the gate and diverting the flow of water down and forward instead of through the nozzle opening.

# CHAPTER 7 — MOTOR COUPLING METHODS

The method of coupling the motor or transmission to a propeller shaft in the conventional straight shaft or vee drive installation can be accomplished in several different ways. These include flange couplings, split sleeve couplings, chain couplings, universal joint couplings, and flexible couplings. Because jet drives, stern drives, and other transmission systems often have couplings included as a part of the unit, these units will not be discussed.

## FLANGE COUPLINGS

By far the most common coupling is the flange type (see Fig. 7-1). The flange coupling consists of two nearly identical parts, with one piece joined

**FIG. 7-1 — A conventional flange coupling on the end of a marine transmission.**

to the propeller shaft and the other to the transmission or the motor. A standard key and keyway are used to lock the pieces to the shafts. The flanged portions mate together and are bolted after alignment thereby making a rigid coupling. Because the mating faces of the flanges are carefully machined, accurate alignment of the engine or transmission to the propeller is possible.

Several precautions should be taken when installing flange couplings. In most instances the coupling fits very tightly to the shaft. Placing the flange coupling in a pan of hot water will expand the hole for the shaft sufficiently to allow the flange coupling to slip onto the shaft easily. A hardened set screw is used to keep the shaft in the coupling. This screw should be counterbored into the shaft slightly, and tightened in place securely. Note that the entire forward thrust of the propeller shaft will work against this coupling. With an improperly fastened set screw, the shaft and propeller could come out of the boat with the motor operating in reverse. A wire lead through a hole in the head of the set screw and around the coupling can be used to prevent loosening during operation.

## SPLIT SLEEVE COUPLINGS

As noted previously, the split sleeve

coupling is used on independently mounted vee drive units having stub shafts instead of flange couplings. Split sleeve couplings, however, are not used with other installations, since there is no way to allow precise alignment between the propeller shaft and the motor. The split sleeve coupling (see Fig. 7-2) also uses a standard key in a keyway together with four locking screws to hold the shafts together. Sometimes, a split sleeve coupling is used to join two shorter shafts together in order to make a single length.

## CHAIN COUPLINGS

Although not common, a chain coupling is sometimes used. This type of coupling (see Fig. 7-3) is intended to absorb minor misalignments such as are sometimes a problem on boats where racking of the hull and consequent shaft misalignment is common. In affect, a chain coupling is a flexible coupling such as described later, but

of a special type. This coupling, however, has the disadvantage of requiring a thrust bearing between it and the propeller since it cannot accept this force.

## UNIVERSAL JOINTS

Because of the desire to mount the engine level or nearly so, many wish to use a universal joint between the propeller shaft and the engine to take up the angularity difference. Several objections to this method arise. The universal joint cannot operate practically while taking thrust, and this means that a thrust bearing must be placed between the universal joint and the propeller shaft thrust. As noted previously, universal joints are intended to take up misalignment in one direction only. For this reason it is necessary to use two universals to take up misalignment in all directions, something that is rather difficult to do. Another factor is that shaft speeds are

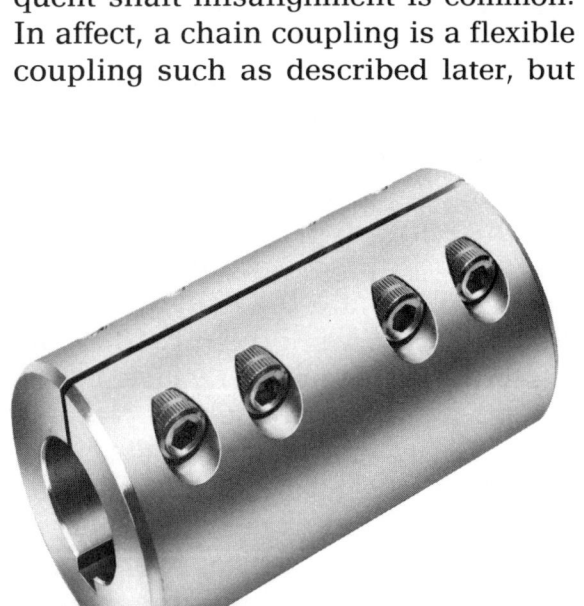

FIG. 7-2 — A typical split sleeve coupling. (Courtesy of Glenwood Marine Equipment)

FIG. 7-3 — A chain coupling allows for some minor misalignment, however, a separate thrust bearing is required between it and the propeller. (Courtesy of Glenwood Marine Equipment.)

limited and reliability can be questionable. In some instances, the double universal joint can be used as has been discussed. However, for standard installations, they are seldom practical.

## FLEXIBLE COUPLINGS

Several types of so-called flexible couplings are available since most are of a proprietary or patented type of product. Geared-type flexible couplings are available, however, these require lubrication that is built into the coupling. Most other types consist of some sort of isolation design using various rubber-type inserts so that lubrication is not required. With this feature, vibration and noise from the propeller and shaft, or from the engine to the propeller shaft, are significantly reduced. One type of flexible coupling is shown in Fig. 7-4 and Fig. 7-5.

The novice may think that by using a flexible coupling instead of the rigid type, he can be a little more careless in the motor alignment process. However, this is not really the case. The engine should still be properly aligned, but perhaps not quite as closely as with rigid types. The main reason for using flexible couplings is that they reduce noise and vibration. Another reason is that most flexible couplings can absorb both the thrust and torsional loads of the propeller shaft, thereby protecting the transmission thrust bearings and seals from excessive stress and wear due to shaft misalignment. On motor installations using a shaft tube with stern tube bearing, the use of a flexible coupling can reduce wear on the stern tube bearing as well.

While most flexible couplings can handle some degree of parallel and

FIG. 7-4 — A flexible coupling such as this reduces noise and vibration, allows for slight misalignment, and permits mounting the engine on flexible mounts. (Courtesy of Federal Marine Motors, St. Petersburg, Fla.)

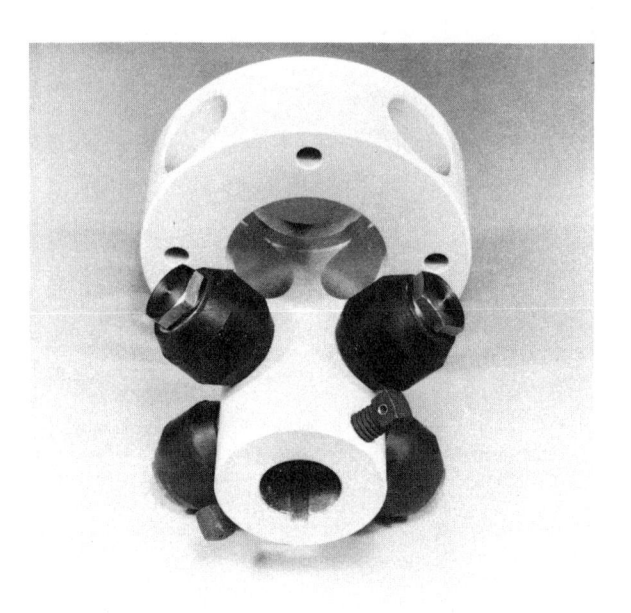

FIG. 7-5 — A disassembled view of the flexible coupling shown in FIG. 7-4. Note the keyway and set screws for the propeller shaft. (Courtesy of Federal Marine Motors, St. Petersburg, Fla.)

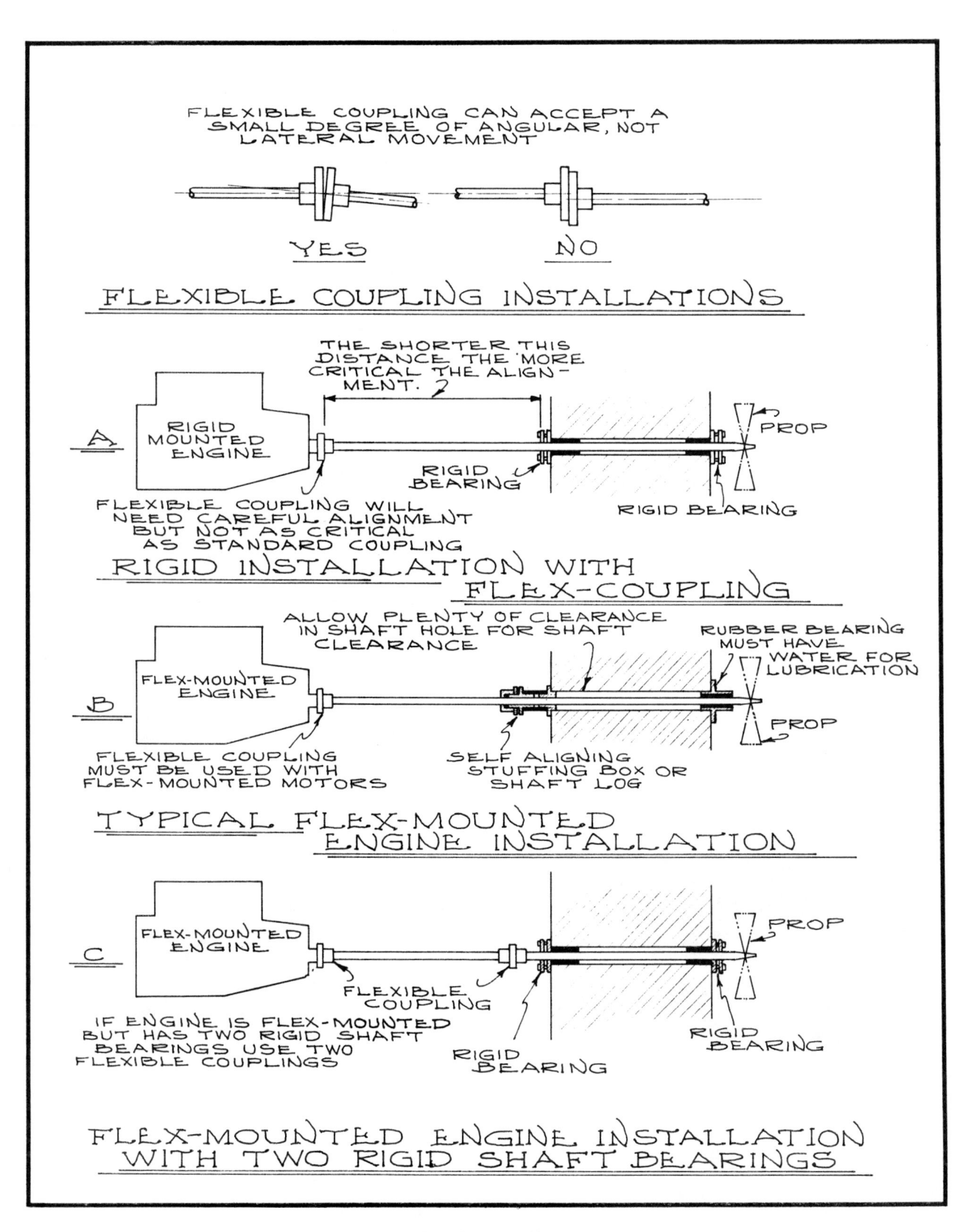

FLEXIBLE COUPLING CAN ACCEPT A
SMALL DEGREE OF ANGULAR, NOT
LATERAL MOVEMENT

YES        NO

FLEXIBLE COUPLING INSTALLATIONS

THE SHORTER THIS
DISTANCE THE MORE
CRITICAL THE ALIGN-
MENT.

A    RIGID
MOUNTED
ENGINE                                    PROP

RIGID
BEARING                    RIGID BEARING

FLEXIBLE COUPLING WILL
NEED CAREFUL ALIGNMENT
BUT NOT AS CRITICAL
AS STANDARD COUPLING

RIGID INSTALLATION WITH
FLEX-COUPLING

ALLOW PLENTY OF CLEARANCE
IN SHAFT HOLE FOR SHAFT
CLEARANCE                    RUBBER BEARING
                             MUST HAVE
                             WATER FOR
B    FLEX-MOUNTED            LUBRICATION
     ENGINE
                                          PROP

FLEXIBLE COUPLING
MUST BE USED WITH          SELF ALIGNING
FLEX-MOUNTED MOTORS        STUFFING BOX OR
                          SHAFT LOG

TYPICAL FLEX-MOUNTED
ENGINE INSTALLATION

C    FLEX-MOUNTED                         PROP
     ENGINE

              FLEXIBLE
              COUPLING

IF ENGINE IS FLEX-MOUNTED                 RIGID
BUT HAS TWO RIGID SHAFT                    BEARING
BEARINGS USE TWO            RIGID
FLEXIBLE COUPLINGS         BEARING

FLEX-MOUNTED ENGINE INSTALLATION
WITH TWO RIGID SHAFT BEARINGS

**PLATE 21 — Flexible coupling installations.**

angular misalignment due to minor hull distortion and engine movement, they are not designed to work as a universal joint. Only a small degree of angular misalignment should be allowed. For example, if the engine and propeller shaft are each rigidly mounted, the engine should still be carefully aligned even if a flexible coupling will be used (see Plate 21-A). However, the situation changes as soon as the engine is mounted on flexible mounts.

For flexibly mounted engines, a flexible coupling is a "must" since the motor must be allowed to "float free" (i.e. vibrate). However, a proper flex-mounted set-up needs another consideration. The propeller shaft should not be rigidly mounted in such a situation, as this will cause the rigid bearing to wear out since there will be no way to absorb any of the vibration transferred to this point along the shaft. To overcome this situation, a rubber water lubricated bearing should be installed at the end of the shaft, and a packing gland with rubber hose (such as is used with the conventional self-aligning shaft log or stuffing box described in Chapter 8) used where the shaft passes through the hull (see Plate 21-B). Then the movement along the shaft will be absorbed throughout the shaft. Of course, there must be plenty of clearance in the shaft bore or shaft tube to allow the shaft to "move"

If inner and outer rigid stern bearings (two rigid shaft supports) are used and the engine is mounted on flexible mounts, the problem can be overcome by using two flexible couplings joined between with a separate shaft section (see Plate 21-C). While it

FIG. 7-6 — While not actually a flexible coupling, this resilient disc drive fits between the flanges of the standard coupling thereby reducing noise and vibration. (Courtesy of Globe Rubber Works, Rockland, Mass.)

is desirable to align the engine carefully, such an installation can accept several degrees of misalignment. One of the advantages of a flexible coupling over time is that even though the engine may be very carefully aligned during the motor installation and/or construction of the boat, the hull will often "settle" (i.e. distort) after some period which could cause misalignment with consequent vibration and noise problems with rigid coupled installations.

Installation with most flexible shaft couplings is not difficult. The engine is aligned in the normal way using the standard flange-type couplings. Once the alignment is checked, the coupling is removed from the propeller shaft and replaced with the flexible coupling. Since there is no metal-to-metal contact between the engine and shaft with most flexible couplings, a grounding strap is often provided across the coupling for boats with bonded electrical systems (see Chapter 19).

# CHAPTER 8 — STRAIGHT SHAFT INSTALLATIONS

Several configurations are possible when using a straight propeller shaft installation, whether the engine is centrally mounted or if using a vee drive system. The variations result mainly because of differences in the basic design of the vessel. For example, a high speed planing hull has an entirely different hull and structural design than a deep keeled monohull sailboat. Then too, a boat built in wood will require different methods of shaft installation as well as different components than a boat built in steel. Most of the common straight shaft configurations are illustrated by Plate 22. Note that any of these configurations could conceivably be used with a centrally located engine or with a vee drive installation. The same principles apply in either instance.

In any straight shaft configuration several functions must be fulfilled, and hence there may be many components required. Perhaps because of the seemingly complex nature of the various straight line installations, the novice may be scared off from doing his own motor installation. However, like many other things, once an understanding of the system, together with its component parts is grasped, it will be seen that the straight shaft set-ups are rather basic. In the following, we will break down the basic system into the various component parts and show what they do and why they are re-quired. It should be emphasized that these straight shaft set-ups are considered the standard conventional means of transmitting power to move a boat, and have withstood the test of time. When proper components, correct installation procedures and suitable maintenance are used, these systems are highly reliable, efficient and trouble-free.

Since the basic need of the power transmission system is to transmit the engine's power to the propeller, and because this is done by means of the propeller shaft in the straight line set-up, it goes without saying that the shaft must pass through the hull at some point. Consequently, this means that there will be a hole in the boat which cannot leak any (or much) water since obviously the boat could sink. Because the propeller shaft will be spinning around at perhaps a considerable rate of speed together with perhaps a hefty propeller on one end, some means must be provided to support the shaft and keep it rigid. In many boats, there may be considerable structure in the area of the hull where the shaft passes through, and this area should be given special treatment for one reason or another as will be noted. These are the basic functions of the various components used in straight shaft installation, and each item will be described.

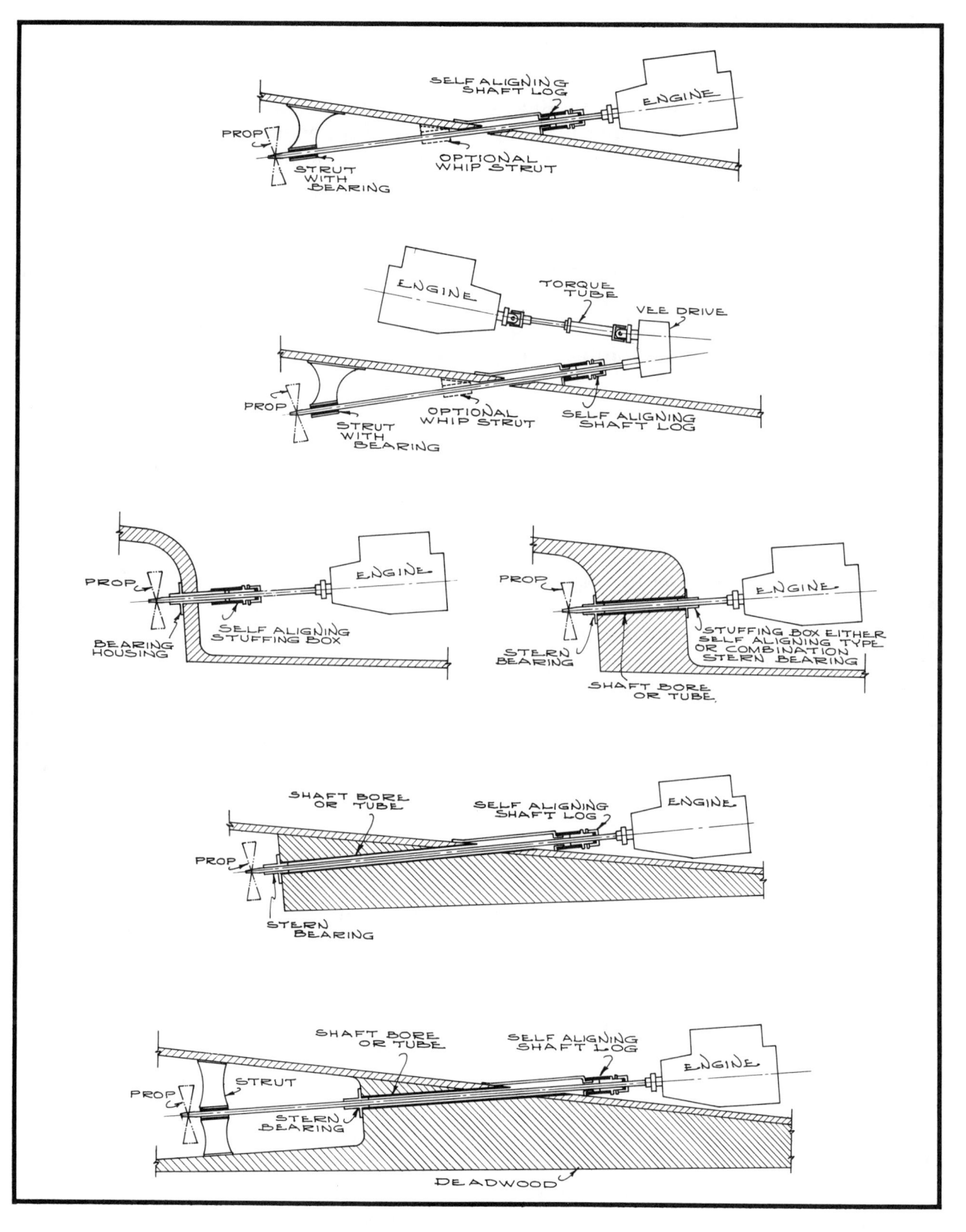

**PLATE 22 — Typical straight shaft configuration on inboard boats.**

95

## STRUTS & SHAFT SUPPORT

The strut is an underwater component connected to the outside of the boat which locates and supports the aft end of the propeller shaft. In addition to these functions, the strut contains a bearing to minimize friction and wear on the spinning propeller shaft. There are many different types and sizes of struts to suit many different hull types, but their function is the same. Some typical examples are given in Fig. 8-1.

Most struts are cast from metal, with bronze being common for salt water use. In some high speed sport or competition boats, steel struts are used for greater strength (see Fig. 8-2). In planing boats, the single leg fixed drop strut is commonly used (as in Fig. 8-3). An adjustable type strut in this configuration is sometimes used also (see Fig. 8-4). Although considerably easier to install because the strut can be adjusted to suit the shaft angle, they are more cumbersome thereby adding to drag. Because the adjustable type is not as strong as the fixed leg strut, they are not recommended for large propellers or high RPM's.

Where more strength is desired and speeds are more moderate, a vee-type strut may be used. Because this strut has two legs splayed out in a vee shape, they are considerably stronger than the single leg drop type. For boats having a deadwood skeg supporting a rudder aft, the double arm strut is frequently used. This type of strut fits to the underside of the hull and to the skeg below. Both fixed leg and adjustable leg versions are available with this type of strut.

In some types of boats an additional intermediate strut located forward along the shaft may be required. In some cases, the extra support is needed in order to provide the correct bearing spacing for proper shaft support. In other cases, such as in high speed competition craft, a smaller diameter shaft than would normally be used on similar sized conventional type boats, or an extremely high shaft speed, may require the use of an intermediate support to prevent shaft whipping. Hence, the terminology "whip strut" is frequently applied to these intermediate struts (see Fig. 8-5). These whip struts are generally located directly adjacent to the hull where the shaft passes through.

Since the strut operates under water, the bearing housed in the strut and the shaft within the bearing are water lubricated. Originally, struts had babbitt metal or lignum vitae wood for bearing material. However, these materials often lack durability especially under high speed conditions, and have been largely replaced by the patented "cutless" rubber and "Micarta" synthetic material types (see Fig. 8-6). These bearings have internal grooves or fluting running longitudinally along the bearing so that when underway, the momentum of the boat forces water through the bearing. A further advantage of the rubber-type bearing is that some vibration is eliminated. However, with this type of bearing, a somewhat larger housing is required which does increase drag to a slight extent, especially on smaller, faster boats. Bearings are held within the strut housing by either a press fit or a press fit together with at least two set screws for struts of larger sizes. The positioning of these set screws should be as shown

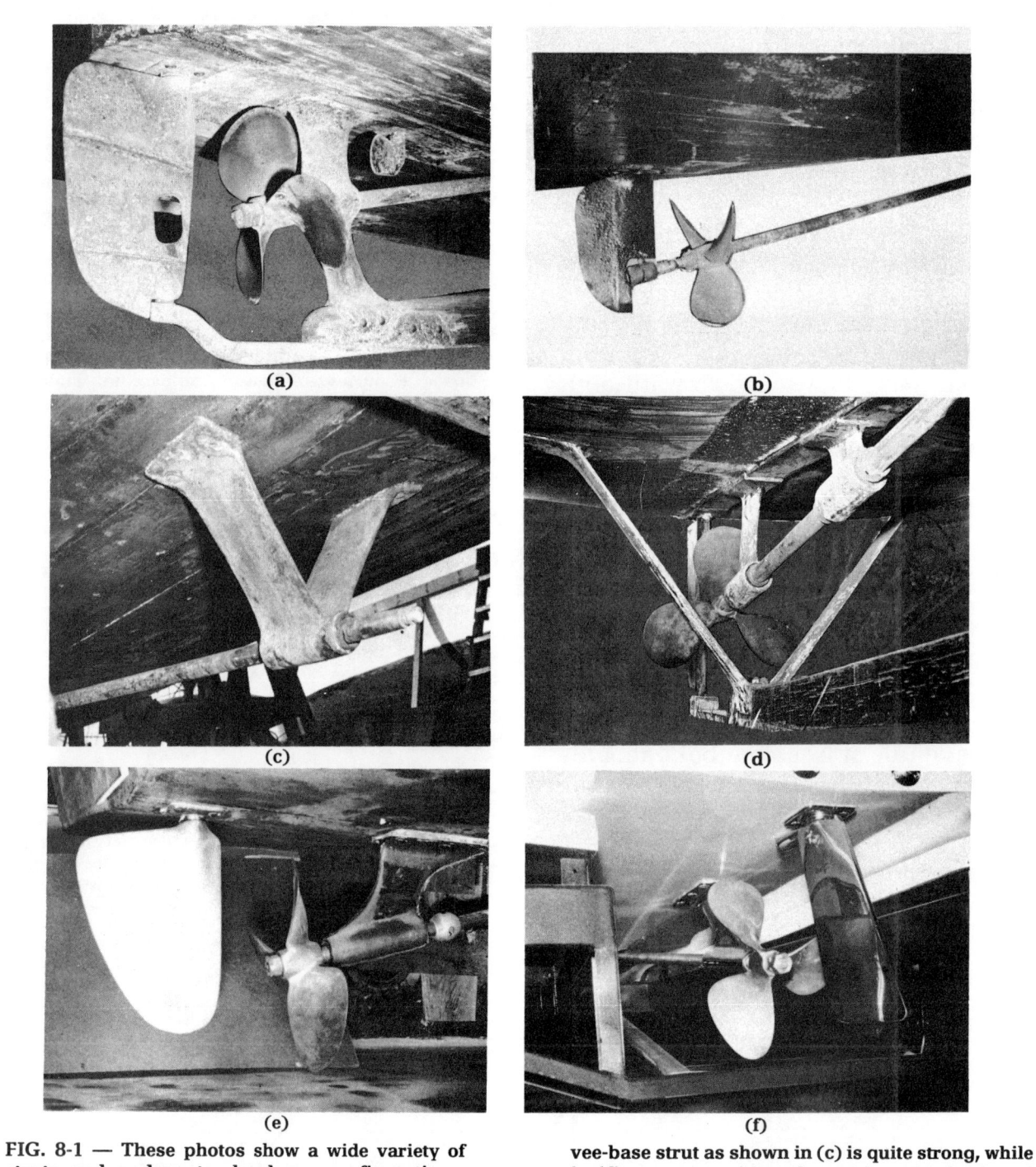

(a)

(b)

(c)

(d)

(e)

(f)

FIG. 8-1 — These photos show a wide variety of struts and underwater hardware configurations. The strut in (a) has an upper and lower base connecting from the hull to the aft end of a deadwood keel. Note the small auxiliary rudder forward of the strut as an aid in steering when backing, and the hole in the rudder for removing the shaft without first removing the rudder. In (b) the shaft is supported at the aft end by a special mount on the rudder so that a strut as such is not necessary. Such an installation is not common, however. A vee-base strut as shown in (c) is quite strong, while in (d), a vee strut is used to support the deadwood while the shaft is supported by a single leg drop strut plus a "whip" strut forward. Such an installation is best suited to slower boats due to the drag caused by the numerous underwater parts. In (e) and (f) are two typical planing boat installations using a single leg drop strut. Note the chromed wedge-type rudder in (f) indicating an emphasis on high speed performance.

by Plate 23.

The shape of the strut may vary considerably. The bearing, however, must be long enough to provide adequate support. As a rule, the shaft bearing should be at least 4 times as long as the shaft diameter. In other words, a 1″ shaft would use a 4″ long bearing, while a 2″ shaft would use an 8″ bearing, etc. Since the propeller should run in undisturbed water, especially on high speed boats, the single leg drop type strut is often raked forward and up to the base to be well ahead of the propeller. Streamlining of struts so that the leading and trailing edges come to a taper is important to minimize resistance and prevent cavitation. The base of the strut must be sufficiently large to distribute the stresses over an ample area of the hull. On metal boats, the struts are often welded to the hull. Otherwise, struts are usually bolted in place through the base. As a general rule at least four bolts should be used through every strut base, with

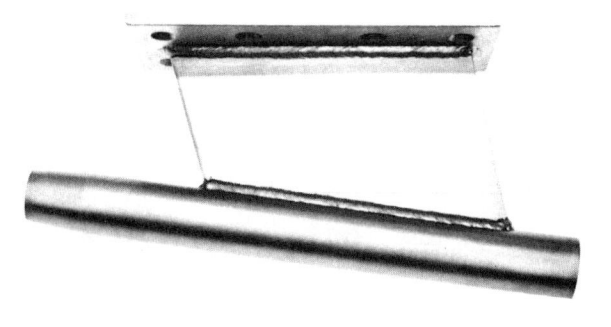

FIG. 8-2 — In high speed boats where an extremely strong strut is required welded steel is sometimes used. (Courtesy of Nicson Engineering, Santa Fe Springs, Calif.)

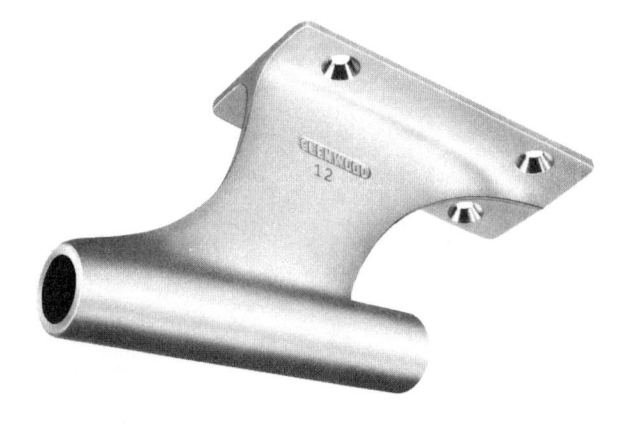

FIG. 8-3 — The typical single leg drop strut cast from bronze is available in a wide variety of angles and drop dimensions as well as a variety of bearing surfaces. (Courtesy of Glenwood Marine Equipment)

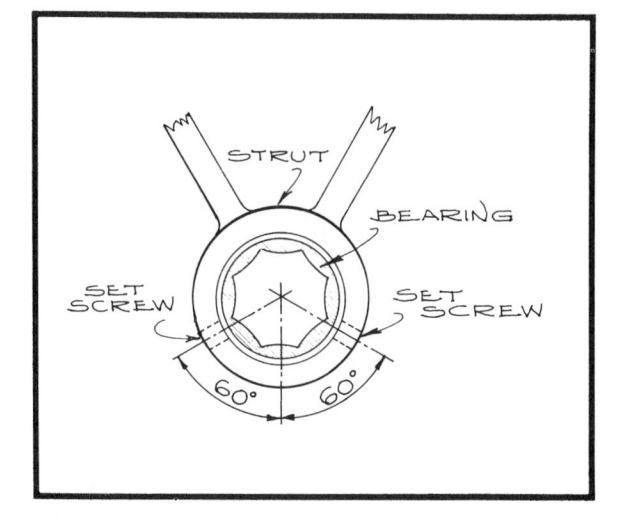

PLATE 23 — Two set screws should be used to secure the shaft bearing to the strut, or alternately depending on the strut, the bearing may be pressed in place without the use of set screws.

FIG. 8-4 — An adjustable strut can be varied in angle to suit the installation, although such a strut is inherently weaker and causes more drag.

no smaller than ⅜" diameter bolts. Larger struts require larger bolts. Bolts should be near each corner of the base, and whenever possible, six or more bolts are desirable. To minimize resistance, flat head machine bolts can be used, countersunk into the strut base.

## MAKING A STRUT PATTERN

Even though a wide variety of sizes and types of struts is available, there are cases where a stock strut will not be available, or the cost may be prohibitive. In cases such as this, a custom strut can be made. In order to cast such a strut, a pattern must first be made. A typical wooden strut pattern is shown by Plate 24 for sand casting a single arm strut that would be used for a 12" to 14" propeller. Progressively larger struts could be made by the same process increasing the various wall thicknesses and dimensions. Note, however, that for bigger struts, naval architects use certain proportions and formulas for determining the thickness and size proportions. If their professional services cannot be obtained, it would be preferable to take dimensions from a strut on a boat of similar size and type.

FIG. 8-6 — The typical rubber-type shaft bearing with longitudinal fluting for waterflow lubrication. (Courtesy of Lucian Q. Moffit, Inc.)

The various dimensions should be determined first, namely the size of the base, angle, drop distance to suit the particular installation, and the diameter of the bearing housing. The latter may be determined by checking the outer diameter of the particular bearing being used, and then adding ⅜" for wall thickness.

The fabrication of the strut pattern may be from any type of wood. Generally, a soft wood such as white pine is advisable. The strut housing may be turned on a wood lathe, rounding all corners generously. The arm of the strut may be dadoed into the housing portion. Note that the junction of the base with the arm, and the arm with the housing, are generously radiused or filleted. This can be accomplished by either purchasing fillet wax from a pattern or foundry supply house, or it can be done with plastic wood and sanded smooth.

FIG. 8-5 — A typical "whip" strut is used on some boats near where the shaft passes through the hull. (Courtesy of Glenwood Marine Equipment)

99

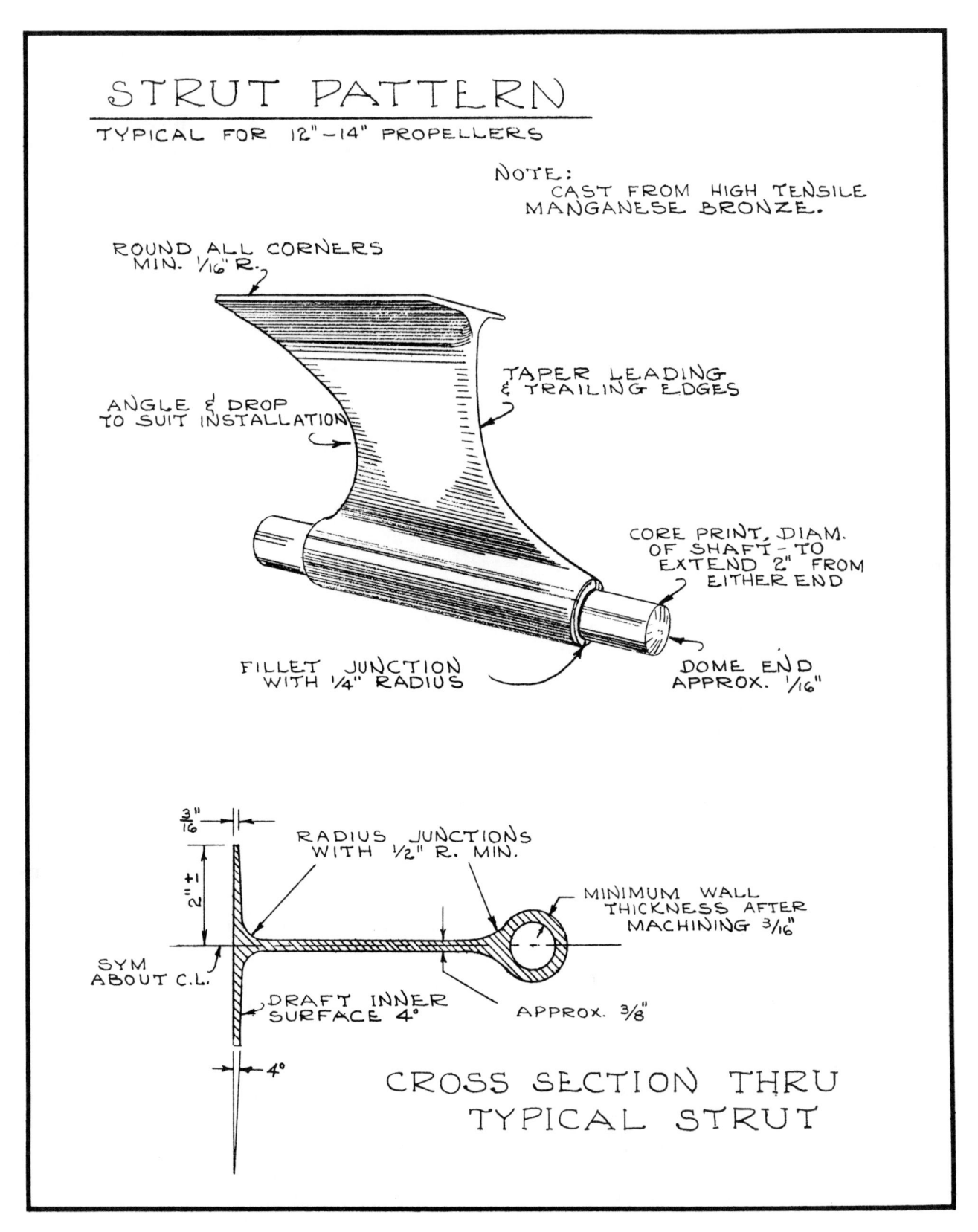

STRUT PATTERN

TYPICAL FOR 12"–14" PROPELLERS

NOTE:
CAST FROM HIGH TENSILE MANGANESE BRONZE.

ROUND ALL CORNERS MIN. 1/16" R.

TAPER LEADING & TRAILING EDGES

ANGLE & DROP TO SUIT INSTALLATION

CORE PRINT, DIAM. OF SHAFT - TO EXTEND 2" FROM EITHER END

FILLET JUNCTION WITH 1/4" RADIUS

DOME END APPROX. 1/16"

3/16"

2" +1

RADIUS JUNCTIONS WITH 1/2" R. MIN.

MINIMUM WALL THICKNESS AFTER MACHINING 3/16"

SYM ABOUT C.L.

DRAFT INNER SURFACE 4°

APPROX. 3/8"

4°

CROSS SECTION THRU TYPICAL STRUT

**PLATE 24 — How to make a pattern for a single leg drop type strut.**

The leading and trailing edges of the arm should be tapered and all corners should be rounded with a minimum 1/16″ radius. After assembly and sanding, the pattern should be coated with orange shellac or other suitable coating. Proper procedure calls for black core prints which are done by adding a little lamp black to the shellac for these core prints that extend approximately 2″ from either end of the bearing housing portion. It is best to contact the foundry who will make the casting to be sure that they have the stock core size required. As noted, the diameter, which will be the same as that of the shaft together with the bearing, will leave adequate clearance for machining. In some instances, this could be increased, depending on the amount of bearing to be used.

The strut should be cast from the best high-tensile manganese bronze available for most applications. Do not attempt to use red brass since it is considerably weaker. The cost to cast and machine such a strut will seldom be an economy measure. However, as noted, it may be necessary in some cases. On boats used exclusively in fresh water, or that will not remain in salt water for long periods, such as trailerable type boats, it is possible to weld a strut from steel. The nominal dimensions shown can be used for fabrication. Tubing can be used for the bearing housing, and the arm and base welded together. Such a strut could be hot dipped galvanized after fabrication, however, the bearing hole would have to be reamed out to a smooth surface. Without such treatment, however, steel struts will still be subject to rust regardless of the water where the boat is used, although chromed struts are often used on sport and competition boats.

It must be emphasized here that considerable forces are exerted on the typical strut. If a strut fails, the propeller could go through the boat's hull and perhaps cause the boat to sink, not to mention other incidental damage to various parts. Therefore, if available, a ready-made manufactured strut is recommended.

## STRUT INSTALLATION

A common strut installation consists of the typical single leg drop strut used on a planing type boat. Such an installation is illustrated by Fig. 8-7 and Fig. 8-8, and the basic principles can be extrapolated to other types of strut installations. If the boat has a vee bottom and the strut has a flat base, the portion of the hull which will mate with the base must be flattened, assuming a single screw installation with the shaft on the centerline of the hull. In a wood boat, the excess material can be faired off, or a shaped filler block can be added. In other cases, a vee based strut may be available to suit the vee in the bottom of the boat. In the case of twin screw boats with vee bottoms, shims or wedge blocks may be required for the flat base strut. With other than wood construction used for the hull, provisions for the strut base may have to be provided in the construction, or made to adapt to the hull material.

In wood boats, or where wood blocking has been used for the base, minor misalignments between the fixed angularity of the strut and the required shaft angle may be made by slightly recessing one end of the strut so that

101

FIG. 8-7 — The bottom must be flattened to accommodate the base of the strut if of the flat base type.

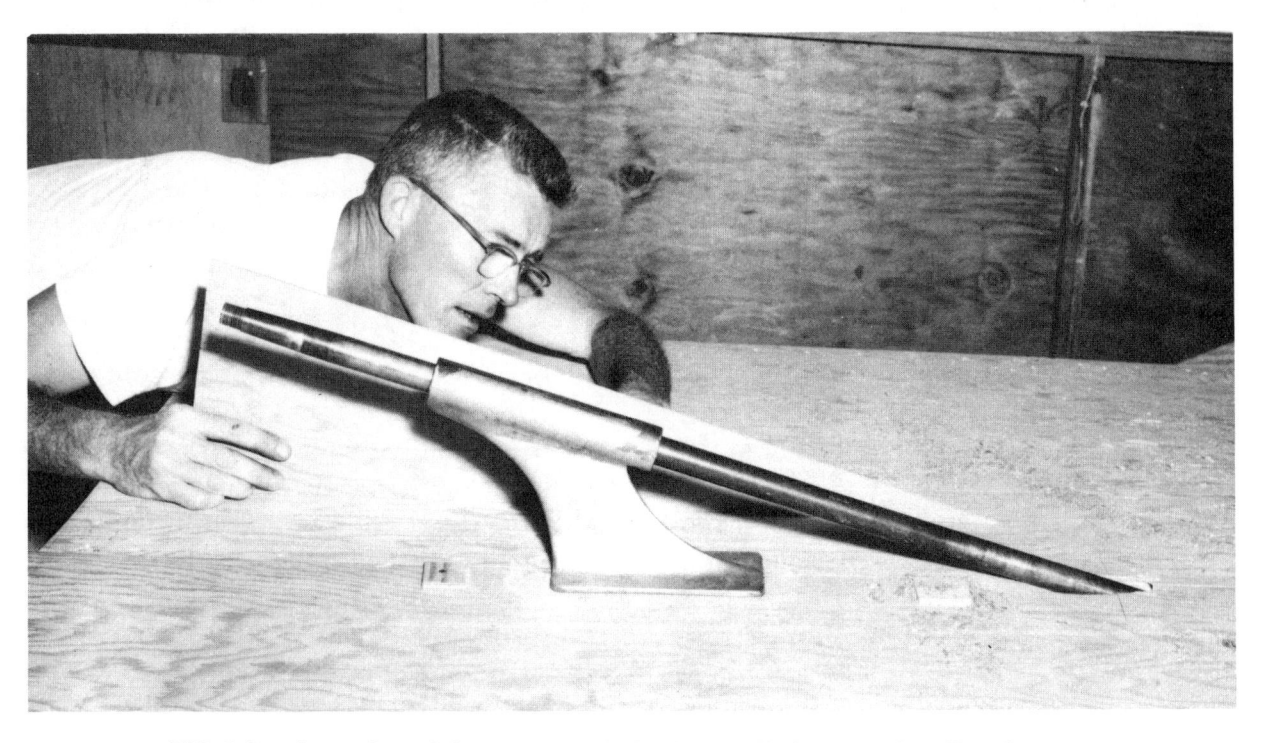

FIG. 8-8 — A template of the proper angle for the installation is used to align the strut. Minor differences in angles can be taken up by recessing one end of the strut base more or less. If the angle discrepancy is severe, a shim may be used. These are not as desirable where speed and efficiency is important as they tend to block the flow of water to the propeller.

the desired angle is obtained. In other words, while a strut may not be available to suit the precise angle or drop dimension required, one that is close to the same requirements can probably be adapted. It is also possible to shift the strut fore or aft to a minor degree which will help align the strut to the shaft angle and drop. Shimming can also be resorted to, but only to a very minor degree.

The strut must be carefully aligned so that the bearing housing is directly centered over the hull centerline or shaft centerline in the case of twin screw boats. A chalk line can be used to simplify this task. A template to the proper angle can be used to align the strut to the proper shaft angle. As noted, the number of bolts and bolt sizes will vary, but should be no less than four ⅜" bolts, one on each corner of the base for struts that will be bolted to the hull.

In general, all hulls regardless of the construction material, should have extra reinforcing or thickness provided on the inside of the hull where the strut base will be attached. In single screw installations, most hulls will have extra material or members along the centerline already. However, in twin screw installations, extra thickness in the form or solid blocking or equivalent members spread over a large area should be added unless there are structural members already available that will perform the same task.

Bolts are then driven through the strut flanges and backing areas to secure the strut. While flat head machine bolts are commonly used, sometimes the strut base can be punched with square holes so that carriage bolts can be used. Above all, the bolts should be

of the same type material as the strut to minimize corrosion. NEVER use, for example, galvanized steel bolts to secure a bronze strut, especially in salt water. On the inside of the hull, the strut bolts should be backed up with a large metal plate under the bolt nuts, or oversize washers, in order to provide well-distributed bearing.

On metal boats where the strut might be made from bronze, the bronze strut must be insulated by a non-conductive gasket or barrier from the metal hull material, and the bolts must be fitted with similar sleeves so that the dissimilar metals do not come in contact with each other. For steel boats, it is therefore often desirable to make the strut from steel so that the two materials are galvanically compatible.

## STERN BEARINGS

In some boats, the propeller shaft may be supported by a stern bearing where it passes through the hull. Depending on the design, the propeller may be located just abaft of the stern bearing, or a certain length of shaft may extend beyond the stern bearing and also be supported by a strut and bearing with the propeller aft of this. In either case, the type of stern bearing is similar as well as its installation.

The stern bearing is usually a casting of bronze secured to the hull where it passes through, and houses a shaft support bearing. Several types of bearings can be used in the housing, including the bronze and babbitt metal type, "Micarta", and rubber "cutless" types. For most pleasure boat use, the "Micarta" and rubber types are commonly used.

Most stern bearing housings are an

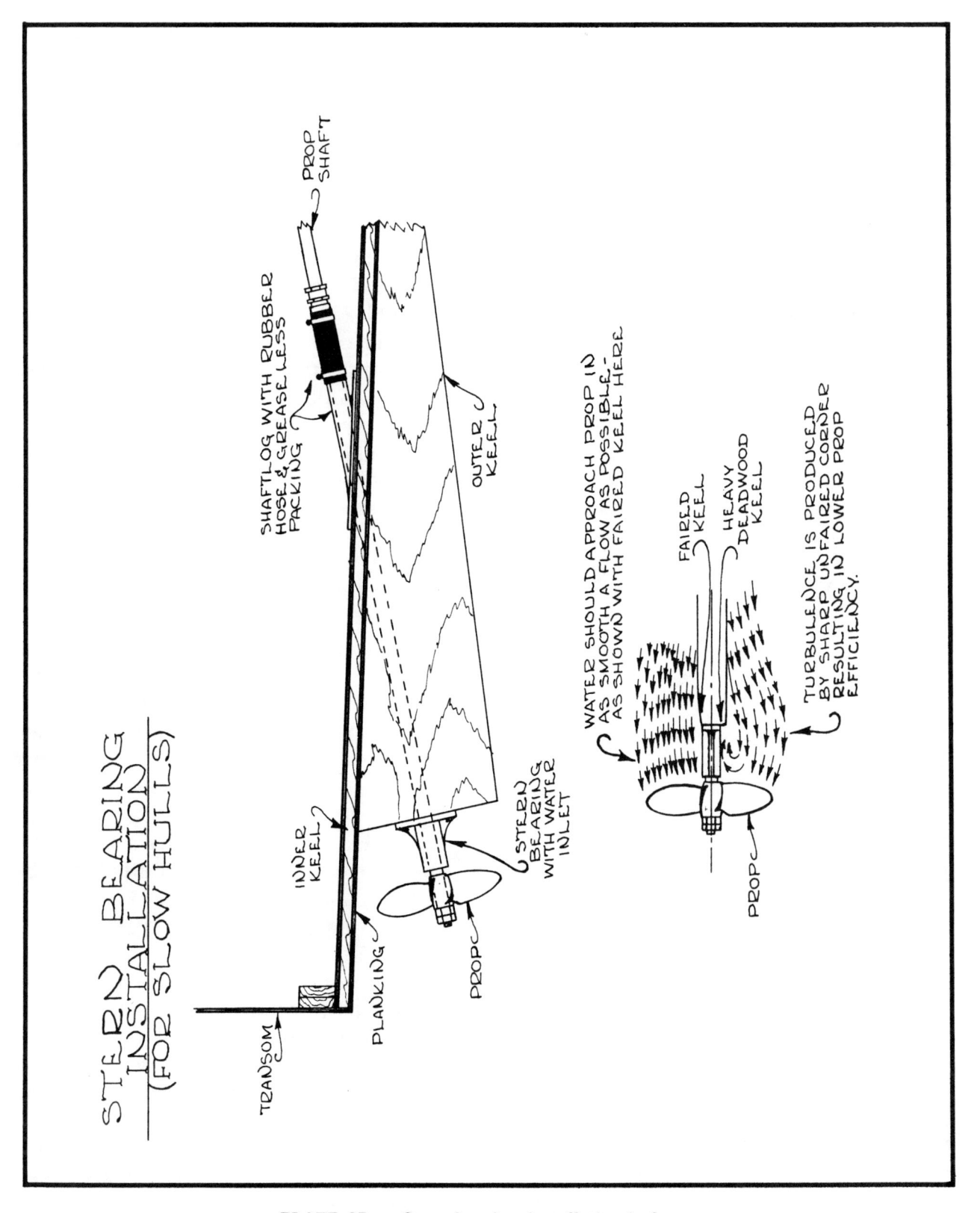

PLATE 25 — Stern bearing installation in boats
with outer keels or deadwoods not using a strut.

104

appendage that projects from the hull at least several inches (see Plate 25). The common type uses a water scoop inlet at the forward end so that water can be forced in to lubricate the bearing. In installation, the hull should be shaped or faired so that this water scoop will have a positive flow of water entering into it.

The bases of stern bearings may be of several types including both rectangular and oval shapes. The oval type may have just an upper and a lower fastening, while the rectangular base may have four or more fastening holes. Depending on the hull, the stern bearing may be through-bolted in place, fastened with lag screws, or secured with hanger bolts. In many cases, through-bolts cannot be used due to the long lengths of bolts that would be required. In this case, the hanger bolts offer the advantage that removal and replacement of the stern bearing housing is somewhat simpler since only the nuts are removed while the mounting studs remain in the hull. The stern bearing housing must be in alignment with the propeller shaft. Either the hull can be faired off as required, or shims can be added to achieve this accuracy if changing an existing installation. In metal and fiberglass hulls, the stern bearing housing may be built into the hull, or specialized types may be used instead, bonded in place to the hull.

## SHAFT LOGS & STUFFING BOXES

The propeller shaft passes through the boat via a hole that is somewhat larger than the shaft itself. Some means or device must be provided to keep water from entering this hole, and

yet still allow the propeller shaft to rotate. The shaft log and stuffing box perform this function (see Plate 26). In most modern boats, the shaft log is not really a "log", but a metal casting or machined part that fits over the propeller shaft hole on the inside of the boat. The stuffing box, which is similar to a water pump packing gland, fits around the shaft and clamps to the shaft log. While water is allowed to enter into the hole for the propeller shaft (which is called the shaft bore or shaft tube and will be discussed later), it is this stuffing box which has the all important job of sealing the shaft to keep water out of the boat. One type of stuffing box is shown by Fig. 8-9.

There are numerous types of shaft logs available to suit different hull types. However, the popular variety is the so-called "self-aligning" type (see Fig. 8-10). This type uses a rubber hose connection between the shaft log and the stuffing box thereby allowing minor discrepancies in alignment between the propeller shaft and the shaft log. Types are available for vertical mounting, or for a wide variety of angles. If a shaft log of a specific angle is not available, usually the shaft log can be wedged or shimmed to the required angle. A shaft log within a degree or two will usually suffice without any correction, since the self-aligning feature will take up this discrepancy. This self-aligning feature not only simplifies installation and alignment, but also reduces shaft vibration and noise because of the rubber hose.

## SHAFT LOG INSTALLATION

The installation of the shaft log must be done carefully so as not to bind on

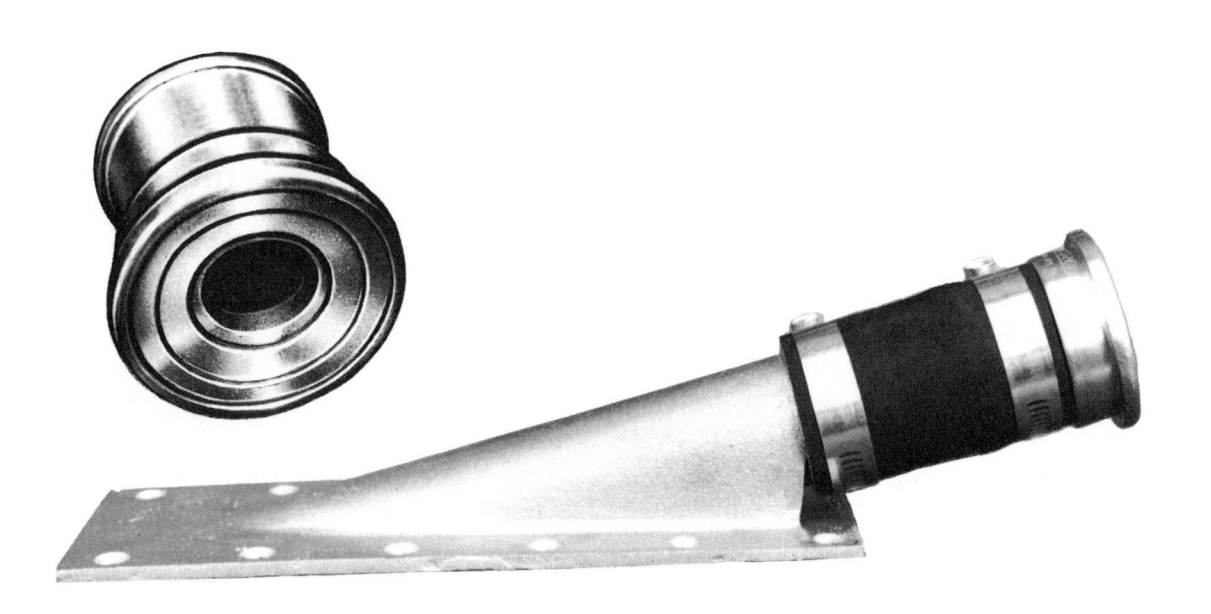

FIG. 8-9 — A seal-type stuffing box and shaft log. (Courtesy of Syntron Company)

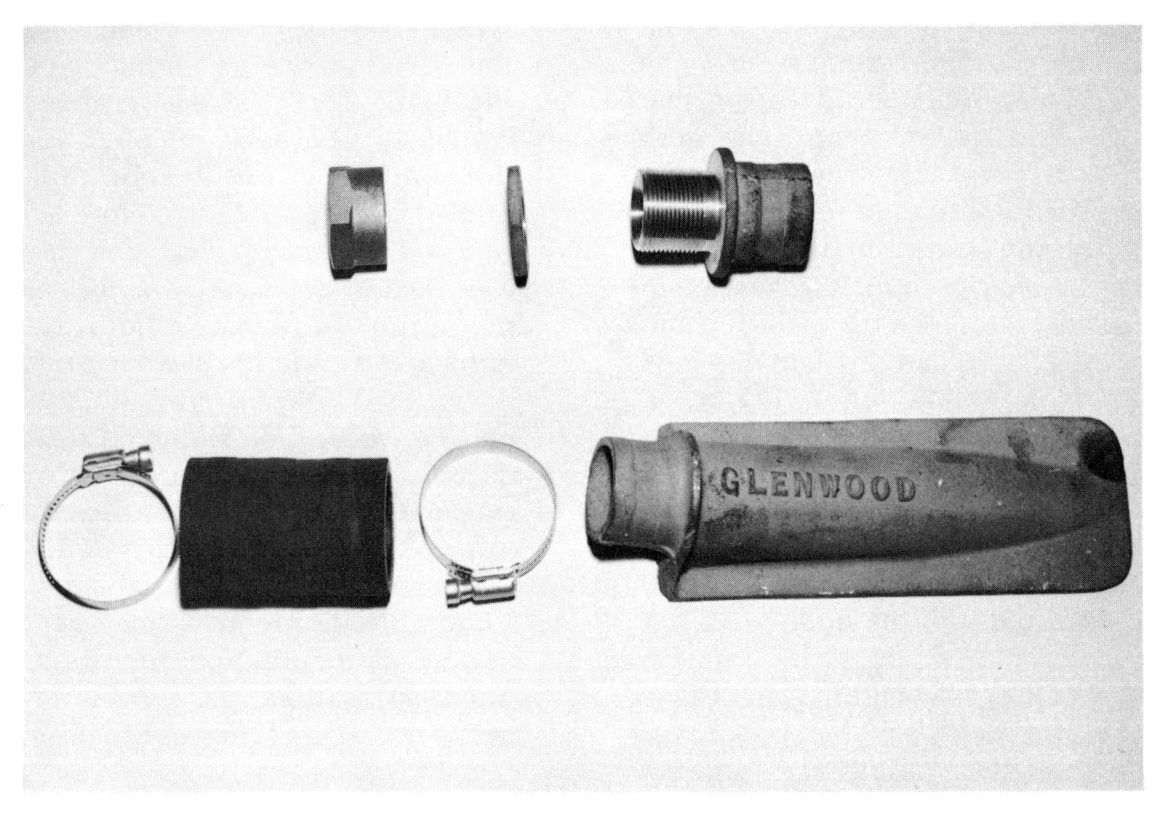

FIG. 8-10 — Components used in the typical self-aligning shaft log. The rubber hose between the shaft log and the stuffing box or packing gland allows for minor misalignment between the propeller shaft and the shaft log. (Courtesy of Glenwood Marine Equipment)

the propeller shaft. The propeller shaft should be inserted through the strut or stern bearing in such a way that it will continue through the shaft hole and project into the boat on the centerline or propeller shaft alignment line if for twin screws. (Making a shaft lay-out, boring the shaft hole, and the aligning procedures are discussed in future chapters). Align the shaft carefully so that it does not bind, and hold it into position with a series of wedges in the shaft hole. It can also be blocked into position on the inside of the hull. If the motor is in position and aligned, slip the shaft log and stuffing box together over the shaft, and place the shaft coupling in position to the motor or transmission. Loosen all clamps holding

the hose to the shaft log and stuffing box. Slide the log down the shaft to mate with the hull. Assuming the proper angularity of the shaft log has been selected, the fit should be simple. If not, the shaft log will require some shimming to compensate for the difference in angularity.

Mark the position of the shaft log to the hull and slide it up the shaft. Spread plenty of mastic or sealant over the mounting area on the hull to form a watertight gasket and fasten the shaft log in position. Depending on the type of shaft log and hull structure, screws, bolts, or hanger bolts can be used. If screws are used, they should be of as large a wire size and as long as possible, to provide deep, long threads for

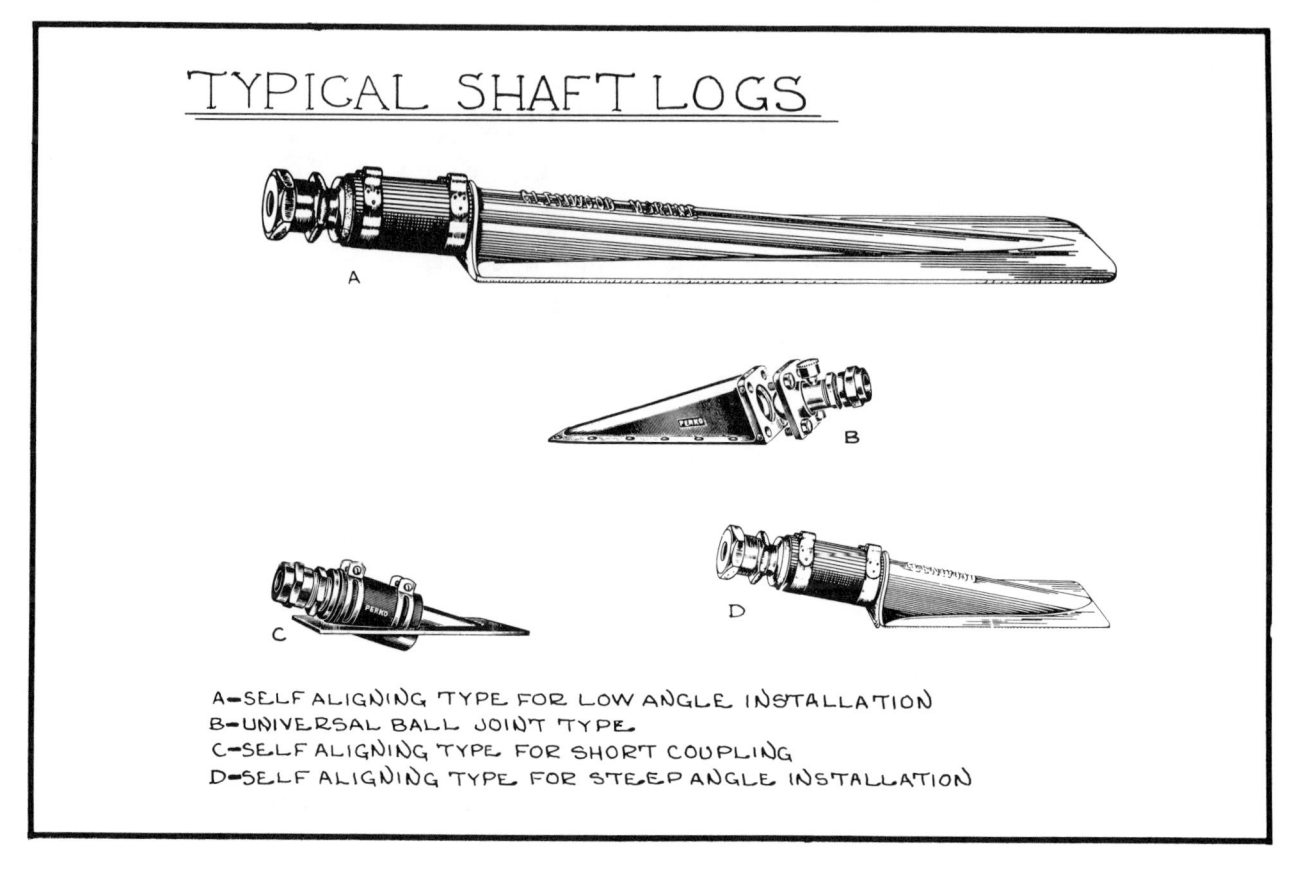

TYPICAL SHAFT LOGS

A—SELF ALIGNING TYPE FOR LOW ANGLE INSTALLATION
B—UNIVERSAL BALL JOINT TYPE
C—SELF ALIGNING TYPE FOR SHORT COUPLING
D—SELF ALIGNING TYPE FOR STEEP ANGLE INSTALLATION

**PLATE 26 — Various types of self-aligning shaft logs.**

better holding power. In all cases, fastenings should be closely spaced to form a watertight seal under the shaft log base, seldom more than about 2″ apart. After fastening, rotate the shaft to position the stuffing box. Then secure the clamps holding the hose to the shaft log.

In some cases, the position of the shaft and the resulting location required for the shaft log will cause interference with one or more structural members of the hull. In order to install the shaft log or the propeller shaft, a certain portion of the structure may be altered or removed. In wood boats, this is frequently an athwartship frame member or floor timber. Naturally such a member that is cut away would weaken the hull at this point. Hence, any portion that is removed or cut away must be reinforced to restore its original strength. One way that this can be done is shown by Plate 27. This consists basically of lapping the frame member in question with a large web or gusset which can be made from wood or metal fastened in place. In many cases, the designer has planned for such conditions, however, and has detailed these in the plans so that they can be included when building the boat. However, in cases where the details do not exist, such as when repowering, it must be emphasized that the structural integrity of the hull structure must be maintained.

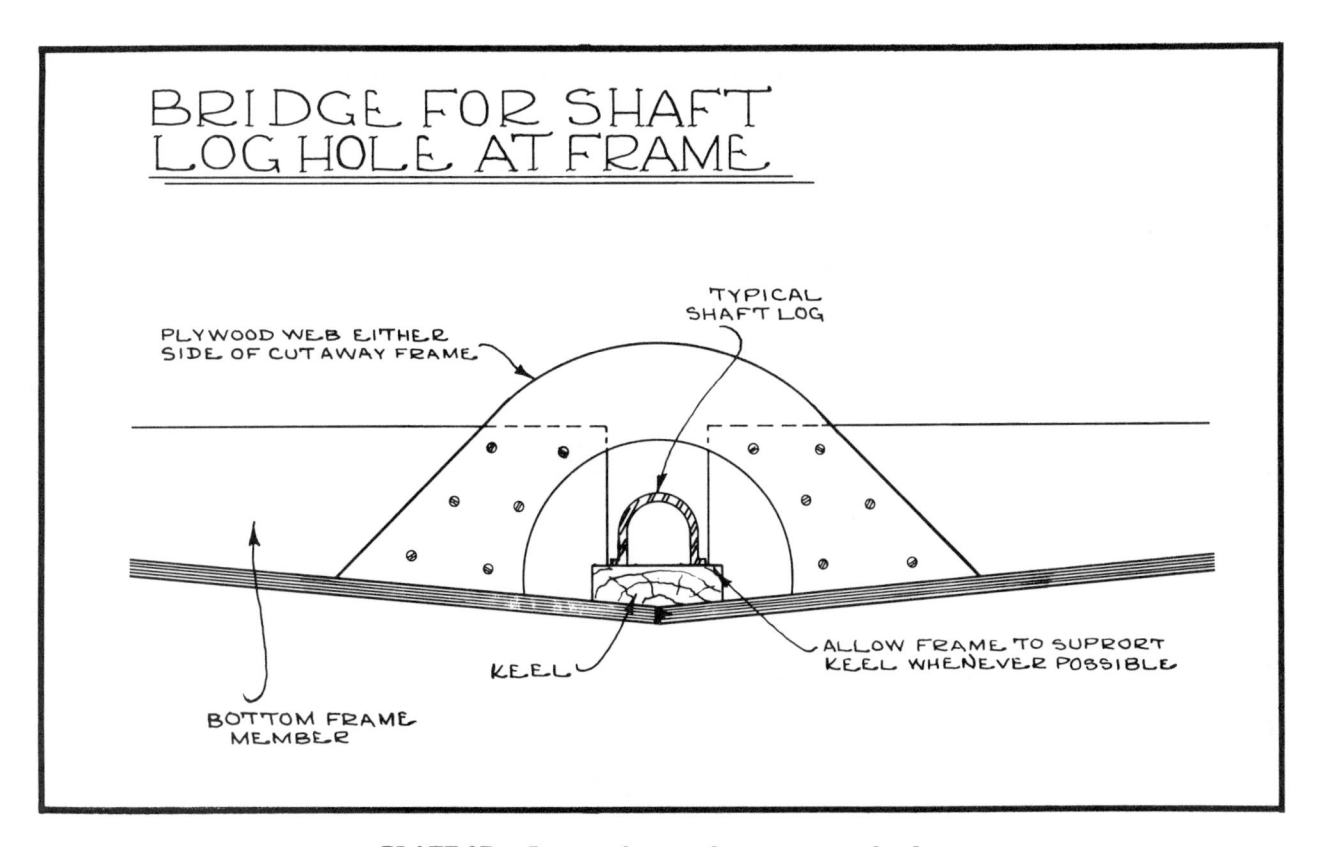

**PLATE 27 — In some boats a frame may need to be cut away for the shaft log. If this is done, a web can be used to restore the integrity of the cutaway frame.**

## STUFFING BOX APPLICATION

After the shaft log is in place, the stuffing box (which is sometimes called the packing box or gland) can be secured. There is more than one type of packing or sealing method available, hence there is more than one method of application. The common packing methods are the packing gland type and the patented seal types. Although a matter of personal preference, the packing gland type has an important advantage. In the event that the packing fails underway thereby allowing water to enter the boat, it is possible to replace the packing with more packing simply by stopping the boat, removing the packing nut, and retightening. Even if spare packing is not available, there is usually some "make-shift" material that can be used to form the packing, such as an old shoe string or small rope. Granted, such a packing would not be suitable for the long term normal operation of the boat, but it would allow the boat to limp back to port. With other types of seals which cannot be removed without pulling the propeller shaft free from the motor or coupling, a repair at sea would be much more difficult if not impractical.

With the packing gland seal, packing is quite often done incorrectly. The packing usually consists of a waxed flax or other impregnated braid that looks like a small piece of rope (although never use graphite impregnated packing that could corrode the shaft). Several rings of this packing are placed around the shaft with the joints staggered so as not to end together in one position. The packing nut is used to force the packing against the gland and should be tightened by hand only, or at best with very light pressure from pliers. The locking nut is run up against the packing nut. A check should be made after by turning the shaft several times. It should turn freely without binding.

When the hull is launched, the packing will undoubtedly leak slightly after the motor has been run awhile. Loosen the lock nut and tighten the gland again, being sure to run up the lock nut after. Going through this procedure several times may be required until the packing is seated. Many individuals use a wrench and tighten the nut so tightly that the packing is forced against the shaft. This can cause the shaft to become overheated and it may possibly freeze to the gland. If this occurs, the shaft may tear the rubber hose loose thereby causing a serious leak. Many skippers are willing to accept a slightly dripping stuffing box when under power which is assurance that the nut is not too tight. A little water seepage will also help keep the packing cool, and what small amount of water enters the bilge can usually be ignored.

With the seal type packing, all these procedures are not necessary since the sealing is automatically provided by the "O" ring seal. Seal type packings are available with single and double type seals, with or without water discharge outlets that can be used to cool the packing. In addition, a Zerk fitting is often provided for grease lubrication. With these a waterproof-type grease should be used as required. Most seal type packings use a Neoprene-type ring seal.

## INNER STERN BEARINGS

In some boats, especially those with deep hulls and extensive deadwood areas, an inner stern bearing much like an outer stern bearing is provided. With these units the stuffing box is often made integral, and frequently does not have the self-aligning feature. When this is the case, alignment of the assembly is much more critical to prevent shaft binding. Bronze or babbitt metal is commonly used for the bearings, and since most boats so equipped operate at slower speeds with consequent slower shaft speed, such installations are acceptable, if more difficult to align.

## OTHER BEARINGS

In most inboard installations in the sizes of boats covered by this text, the propeller shaft will be adequately supported with the components just described. However, sometimes the shaft will be of such a length that additional support is necessary. When this is the case, special bearings may be necessary. One common support bearing is the ordinary pillow block type (see Fig. 8-11). The pillow block is used inside the hull since it is not suitable to use in water. Installation is simple. After the shaft is aligned, blocking is fitted to the hull as required and the pillow block is rigidly fastened in place.

In other cases, the unsupported shaft may require a bearing that must be located in a quite inaccessible location, such as in the shaft bore or the deadwood. In such cases, custom adaptation may be required to suit. Various types of bearings may be possible. For example, if a supply of water can be provided, either directly from the sea or diverted from the engine's

exhaust system for example, then a water lubricated bearing can be used. Where the bearing will be isolated from the effects of water, an oil lubricated bearing might be used, provided with a grease fitting or other means of positive lubrication. Finally, there are bearings available made from lubricant impregnated hardwood, which are suitable for use in either dry or submerged conditions. This wood bearing encased in a copper alloy casing is self-lubricating and not affected by water.

## SHAFT HOLE LININGS

Depending on the type of boat, the hole through the hull for the propeller shaft will vary considerably in length (see Chapter 12). Since water will be allowed to enter this hole on most boats, it must be able to withstand its effects. This can be accomplished in several ways depending on the length of the hole, the type of hull construction and material used, and the desires of the owner.

In the wood boat, deterioration of the structure in this area can be caused by marine growths and worm damage in

FIG. 8-11 — A typical pillow block shaft bearing can be used to provide intermediate support of a shaft inside the boat. This type is self-aligning. (Courtesy of Glenwood Marine Equipment)

those waters so affected, and by rot. At the very least the area should be well coated with paint or wood preservative. A better method, especially with plywood boats or where the hole is not too long, is to cover the shaft hole with fiberglass. The fiberglass cloth or mat can be wrapped onto a wood dowel or broomstick and wetted out with resin. The broomstick is then inserted into the hole and the material unrolled against the surfaces. Several layers of material are recommended. When fiberglass is used it is also possible to bed the shaft log in fiberglass saturated with resin in lieu of sealant. Note that the fiberglass must be used only over a dry, clean, bare wood surface free from grease or oil.

In other cases the shaft hole is lined with a tube or sleeve, or in the case of metal and fiberglass boats, such a tube may be built-in integrally with the hull thereby forming the shaft hole. With wood boats reference is frequently given to the shaft bore being lined with a lead pipe or tubing. Because lead is quite maleable, it is easy to shape flanges on the ends which can be used to lap over and secure the tubing or pipe in place once cut to the proper length. However, lead tubing and pipe is quite difficult to locate. Hence other metals such as bronze, brass, and stainless steel are often substituted.

Another option is to use a tube made from fiberglass. Many such tubes are available ready-made, often using the filament wound principle. However, it is also easy to fabricate a fiberglass tube using a mandrel of the required size around which a thin padding of paper is wrapped plus a final layer of waxed paper to allow the fiberglass to be pulled free. Then the fiberglass

cloth and resin are applied in the required layers to form a tube of any required thickness and length. After curing, the tube is removed from the mandrel, cut to length, and inserted into the shaft hole. Fiberglass filler and scrap pieces of cloth or mat can be used to bond the ends of the tube in place. Such a tube is commonly used on fiberglass hulls also.

## FAIRING OF DEADWOODS & SKEGS

In many boats, there may be a deadwood or skeg located just ahead of the propeller, or some distance forward. The terms deadwood and skeg can have varied meanings and in some cases may be synonymous. For purposes of clarification the term deadwood refers to an outer keel or appendage extending from near the forward portion of the boat to very close to the stern, with the boat's propeller positioned near the aft end of the deadwood. The deadwood often provides the necessary structure to support a stern bearing for propeller shaft support as well as the lower rudder support in many boats. A skeg, on the other hand, refers to a smaller appendage that will end forward of the point where the propeller shaft passes through the bottom of the boat. The skeg in this instance is not used to support the shaft or rudder. It's function is primarily to provide directional stability in most cases. Because the deadwood or skeg may have considerable thickness, there will be some amount of drag or resistance as the boat moves through the water. In affect, the skeg or deadwood will disturb the flow of water which will want to fill in to its original state after the boat passes.

If the skeg or deadwood ends with a blunt trailing or after edge, the water flowing along the member underway will not be able to close in behind the skeg quickly enough. In trying to do so, turbulence or "eddies" will be created, effectively slowing the boat's progress to some extent. Instead of solid water getting to the propeller, the eddies will cause air, or air mixed with water, to enter the propeller's water supply. Obviously such a condition slows the boat and decreases its economy.

Therefore, all such appendages below the waterline must be faired or tapered in plan view so that a smooth and positive flow of water around and under the boat will be possible. Because certain members may not be practically faired to the ideal taper, however, certain compromises will have to be made. An example would be where a stern bearing is fastened to the hull. While ultimate fairing may not be possible right at the fitting, such fair-ing should be provided above and below. An example of this fairing is shown in Plate 25.

In high speed boats which have underwater skegs, not only is the fair-ing of the trailing edge important, but also the distance between the propeller and the end of the skeg. The faster the boat, the greater this distance should be, to the point where little if any skeg will exist at all. With high speed boats fortunately, directional stability and control tends to increase with boat speed, thereby making the need of a skeg less important. However, for normal pleasure boats operating at normal speeds, the distance from such a skeg to the propeller works out in practice to be about 4' apart. This distance may need to be decreased on smaller boats to approximately 30". Not only does this space or gap between the skeg and propeller help provide a flow of solid water to the propeller, but also prevents or minimizes propeller cavitation in turns.

# CHAPTER 9 — PROPELLERS

With the exception of jet drives, it is the propeller that transfers the power of the motor to the water and makes the boat go. Therefore, if the propeller is not selected properly, performance and perhaps economy could suffer. It is not possible to give information as to the size of propeller required for a particular boat. The calculation of a propeller involves so many variables and considerations that the average boat owner would be completely flabbergasted by them. Still, the understanding of the principle of the propeller, and how it operates, is important to a correct motor installation.

First of all, propellers are measured with two dimensions and a direction of rotation, plus the size and type of bore and the number of blades. For example, a typical propeller might be described as: 12″ x 10″ - R.H. - 1″ Std. taper - 3 blade. Translated, this would mean that the propeller has a 12″ diameter, a 10″ pitch, is of right-hand rotation, fits to a 1″ standard tapered shaft, and has three blades. Let's break this down into the various elements:

**DIAMETER:** This is simply the distance across the circle made by the outer tips of the revolving blades.

**PITCH:** The pitch is the theoretical distance that the propeller would move ahead in one revolution.

**ROTATION:** This is the direction a propeller rotates as it is seen from the back of the boat when looking forward.

It will turn either left (counterclockwise) or right (clockwise) handed. Diameter, pitch, and rotation are usually stamped on the propeller hub.

**SHAFT SIZE & TYPE:** This designates the bore size in the propeller hub which must correspond to the diameter of the propeller shaft. The type refers to the taper of the shaft end. In most instances the standard taper of the propeller is ¾″ to the foot (or 1/16″ to the inch) as will be discussed in Chapter 10.

**NUMBER OF BLADES:** The number of blades will vary depending on the usage of the propeller, varying from 2 to 5 blades, although 2 and 3 blade propellers are most common in pleasure boats. Various propeller types and blade configurations will be described later.

While the above terms commonly are used to describe a given propeller for identification purposes, there are many other important designations. For example, there are varying blade widths, areas, and thicknesses. Then, too, there are special types of propellers such as controllable pitch propellers, variable pitch propellers, "cupped" propellers, "cleaver" or "chopper" propellers, and the feathering and folding types most often used on sailboats.

Contrary to popular belief, a propeller does not "screw" or thread its way through the water. Perhaps this thought is most often brought up by the definition of "pitch". Actually, a propeller is a water pump without a housing. Its supply of water comes from all around the propeller. The propeller "pushes" or propels this water in a spiral form towards the stern due to the propeller's "shape" and rotation. The reaction of this force produces forward motion. Perhaps the best comparison is to a garden hose. While holding the hose there is a tendency for the hose to kick back as the water is turned on. The propeller in the boat operates in a similar manner.

Since the propeller can be considered as a water pump, it is essential that it be fed an ample supply of solid water; not water mixed with air. For this reason, the various appendages on a boat underwater, such as the strut and skeg, should be as small as possible and faired with tapered ends for a smooth flow of water. If the propeller is too close to the bottom of the boat, or too near or even beyond the transom of the boat, it may suck air instead of solid water, or "ventilate," causing what is popularly called "cavitation". In extreme cases of cavitation, the propeller may turn in more air than water, thereby reaching very high RPM's without imparting any forward thrust reaction. The result is that the boat will not move, or will proceed very slowly in relation to the power expended.

Racing powerboats, for example, turn small propellers at high speed. However, until these boats are fully planing, it is not unusual for them to "chew a hole" in the water due to cavitation. Repeated accelerations may be necessary to "dig in" and obtain speed enough to plane the hull. Air pockets under water in racing boats can be caused by the water flowing around

unfaired appendages which may not cause problems at lower speeds in conventional boats. However, at higher propeller RPM's and higher hull speeds, such pockets will extend over a longer portion of the slipstream and enter into the path of water being sucked by the propeller. When this occurs, the propeller begins to suck air with a consequent increase in RPM's and/or loss of speed. Hence, consideration should be given to the placement of all underwater fittings and appendages, and how they will affect the propeller's need for solid water with which to "pump".

Special types of propellers are often used in high speed racing craft which are especially designed to run closer to the surface of the water or otherwise operate in partial air conditions. These include the so-called "super cavitating" and "cleaver" or "chopper" types of propellers. A cleaver-type propeller is shown by Fig. 5-8 in Chapter 5. These types of propellers, however, are not used on the normal pleasure boat that must operate efficiently over a wide range of operating conditions.

Because the propeller is turning in water, it is not 100% efficient. Theoretically, if the propeller RPM is multiplied by the pitch in inches, and divided by 12 (the number of inches in a foot), the number of feet per minute that the boat is moving ahead will be obtained. To convert this to miles per hour, multiply by 60 (the number of minutes in an hour), and divide by 5,280 (the number of feet in a mile). As a formula, this is stated as:

$$\text{Theoretical Speed In Miles Per Hour} = \frac{\text{RPM X PITCH X 60}}{12 \times 5280}$$

Unfortunately, this gives only the theoretical speed and not the actual speed. Slippage may account for as much loss as 50% or as little as 10%, depending on many factors. Thus slippage is the difference between the THEORETICAL speed and the ACTUAL speed, and is expressed as a percentage. Normal slippage figures might be 20% for a runabout, 30% for a cruiser, 40% for a displacement cruiser, and perhaps 50% for a houseboat. While slippage percentages can be reduced by changing propeller size, this may not provide any actual performance benefits. Consequently slippage percentages do not always mean too much.

## BLADE CONFIGURATIONS

**TWO BLADE:** Two blade propellers are usually used for high speed use such as racing hydroplanes and other competitive type boats, and also powered sailboats where minimal blade area for reduced drag may be important, as will be discussed later in this chapter. Another specialty use for two-

blade propellers is the so-called "weedless" propeller available in smaller diameters for use in weed infested waters. For other installations, the two blade propeller tends to be rough and not as efficient as other types. A fixed two blade propeller is shown in Fig. 9-1.

**THREE BLADE:** The majority of inboard powered boats use three blade propellers, and are therefore considered "standard". For most boats the three blade propeller offers the best combination of efficiency, smoothness, and economy (see Fig. 9-3, 9-4, and 9-5).

**FOUR BLADE:** When there is insufficient room to handle a correct sized three blade propeller, a four blade will sometimes give enough blade area to compensate to a degree for diameter reduction. The four blade propeller (see Fig. 9-6) is becoming more common since they can reduce noise and vibration on many installations, especially on larger, slower and medium speed boats. Propeller tip speed should not exceed 10,500 ft. per minute. Depending on the use and the pro-

FIG. 9-1 — This fixed two blade propeller is a type commonly used on sailboats with auxiliary inboard powerplants. Other types of two blade propellers are also available. (Courtesy of Michigan Wheel Co., Grand Rapids, Mich.)

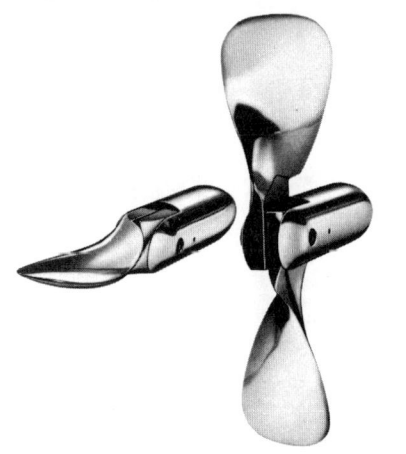

FIG. 9-2 — On some sailboats where minimum resistance is required, a folding two blade propeller is often used. Shaft rotation causes the blades to open out when under power. (Courtesy of Michigan Wheel Co., Grand Rapids, Mich.)

FIG. 9-3

FIG. 9-4

FIG. 9-5

FIG. 9-3 thru FIG. 9-5 — Three versions of three blade propellers. Each varies somewhat in blade design, shape, and area to suit specific conditions of use. (Courtesy of Michigan Wheel Co., Grand Rapids, Mich.)

peller, diameter and/or pitch may require a slight change when switching from a three blade propeller. Consult with the propeller manufacturer for adivce.

**FIVE BLADE:** This type of propeller was developed to eliminate vibration and stern rumble. They are mostly used on commercial craft and large slow-speed yachts since propeller tip speed should not exceed 8,000 ft. per minute. Reduce pitch by 1″ when changing from a three blade to a five blade type to keep RPM the same. A five blade propeller is shown in Fig. 9-7.

## BLADE DESIGN

The design or configuration of the propeller blades, as well as the area of the blades, plays a significant part on the intended use of the propeller. Some propellers, due to their tip design, may be limited in the speed (usually referred to as the peripheral tip speed in feet per minute) they can turn. If certain speeds are exceeded, then cavitation will usually occur. When changing from one type of propeller to another, the blade configuration should be carefully selected, and when in doubt, advice from a qualified propeller shop or propeller manufacturer should be obtained.

One of the most common questions regarding propellers is switching from a conventional propeller to one of the "cupped" type. Cupped-edged propellers are used on high speed boats where a top speed of at least 35 MPH can be obtained. Engine RPM should be 3,400 plus, and the boat should be capable of achieving at least several more miles per hour than when

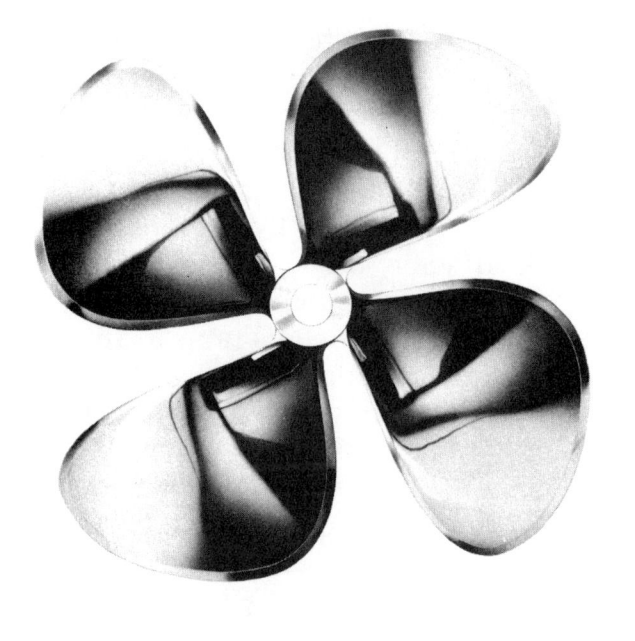

FIG. 9-6 — A four blade propeller is sometimes used in place of a three blade propeller for various reasons as noted in the text. (Courtesy of Michigan Wheel Co., Grand Rapids, Mich.)

FIG. 9-7 — The five blade propeller is used on larger, slower yachts and commercial craft where the elimination of noise and vibration is important. (Courtesy of Michigan Wheel Co., Grand Rapids, Mich.)

equipped with the conventional propeller. The cupped propeller should reduce slip and run smoother, while eliminating cavitation problems. Diameter will be the same as a conventional propeller, however, the pitch should be reduced by at least 1", and with propellers exceeding 14", the pitch should be reduced by 2". The pitch reduction permits maintaining the same engine RPM due to the additional "load" placed on the engine as the result of the "cupped" edge.

## PROPELLER MATERIALS

For most inboard boats, the most common and acceptable propeller material is bronze. Actually, in most cases bronze makes an ideal propeller material as it is ductile, strong, repairable, corrosion resistant, and in normal service if selected and used properly, should last as long as the engine. A standard bronze propeller can usually be re-pitched up or down in size up to 2" depending on the propeller. Thus if a propeller had a pitch of 15", it could be modified down to 13" or up to 17". Diameter can also be reduced slightly.

For high speed or competition use, propellers are made from forged alloy steels (often chrome plated) as well as stainless steel. Bronze often cannot be used in these applications because the propeller RPM is so high that the blades will deform. Some stainless steel propellers are also made on a "custom" basis for commercial craft where special conditions warrant their use.

Aluminum alloy (usually die cast) propellers are often provided as standard equipment on sterndrive units.

While low in cost, they are not nearly as corrosion resistant as bronze propellers. Depending on the type of material and the extent of damage, repair can be difficult or not possible. Often the costs of repair may exceed the cost of the propeller. Die cast propellers cannot be re-pitched.

## PROPELLER SELECTION & INSTALLATION

On the typical pleasure boat, always install a propeller of the largest possible diameter that will allow the proper clearances. A larger propeller will always give better speed, thrust, and acceleration than a smaller one except on specialized high speed racing craft. Large propellers should always be used on heavy boats, while smaller propellers are usually recommended where the most important factor is high speed alone. One of the facts of life with regards to propellers is that it is generaly not possible to get both top speed AND high power from the same fixed blade propeller; you must decide which is the most important characteristics and then select a propeller that will offer the best compromise. For example, if you have a ski boat, and towing several skiers behind is what the boat is used for most of the time, it would be a mistake to use a propeller specifically intended only for ultimate high speed use, as it may lack the necessary power at the low RPM end to pull the skiers out of the water.

Proper propeller clearance is important to both efficiency, and long life of the boat and propeller. While propeller clearances are noted in Chapter 11, they will be summarized here also. Propeller manufacturers advise having a clearance from the bottom of the boat of at least 10% of the propeller diameter for propellers of from 10″ to 18″ in diameter. This means, for example, that a 10″ propeller would have a 1″ clearance. While a 1″ clearance may work in some cases, practical experience shows that more clearance is desirable. For propellers above 18″ in diameter, clearance should be 15% of the propeller diameter, and not less than 2″ in any case.

What happens if there is not enough clearance? The propeller will probably cavitate and cause an annoying "rumble" and possibly damage the bottom of the boat. Cases exist where the bottom of boats with too little clearance from the propeller have completely eroded away from propeller cavitation! In addition to bottom clearance, there must be sufficient clearance ahead of the propeller in the aperture if the boat has this type of hull. The forward edges of all propeller apertures must be tapered or faired so that solid water will be available for the propeller. A similar situation exist on boats with skegs ahead of the propeller. On planing boats, the trailing edges of these skegs should also be tapered, and the distance between the propeller and the aft end of such skegs must be enough to prevent the propeller from sucking in air, especially on turns as has been emphasized previously. A gap between the aft end of the skeg (and lift strakes, too!) is often several feet or more, depending on the ultimate speed of the boat to prevent cavitation.

Does the boat use a right hand or a left hand propeller? Stand at the back of the boat and check the shaft rotation. If the shaft rotates clockwise, use a right-hand propeller; if it rotates counter-clockwise, use a left-hand propeller. Note that if you change the rotation of the engine (such as when repowering) you must also change the propeller to the proper rotation. Simply turning a propeller around will not change the rotation.

A common problem with single screw inboard powered boats is the so-called "torque reaction" sometimes (but not always) caused by the propeller. Many boats, especially those with deeper vees in the bottom, often will list to one side and steer harder to one side than the other. The first step in correcting this situation is to make sure that the helm is on the same side to which the propeller rotates. In other words, if the boat turns a right hand propeller, then the helmsman should

be sitting on the starboard side (see Plate 28). The helmsman can amount to a considerable percentage of the weight of the loaded boat, especially on smaller boats, so this will offset to some extent any torque reaction caused by the propeller.

However, other irregularities can cause or worsen the torque reaction problem. A warped or distorted bottom could very well be the source of the problem. In most high speed boats, the running lines of the hull should be straight and true when viewed in profile view (see Plate 30). Any curve upwards just forward of the transom (called a "rocker") or curve downwards (called a "hook"), especially on only one side of the centerline, could cause listing and steering problems,

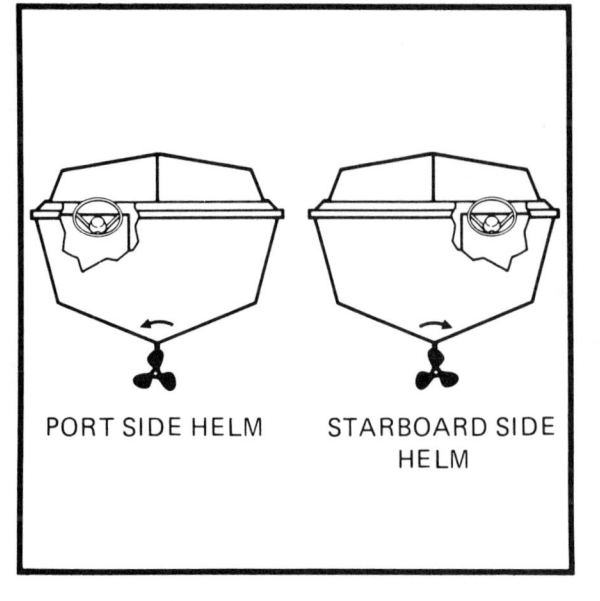

PLATE 28 — Due to the torque reaction of the propeller on many boats, it is recommended that the helmsman sit on the side of the boat to which the propeller rotates. For a right hand propeller, sit on the right or starboard side; for a left hand propeller, sit on the left or port side. (Courtesy of OMC, Waukegan, Ill.)

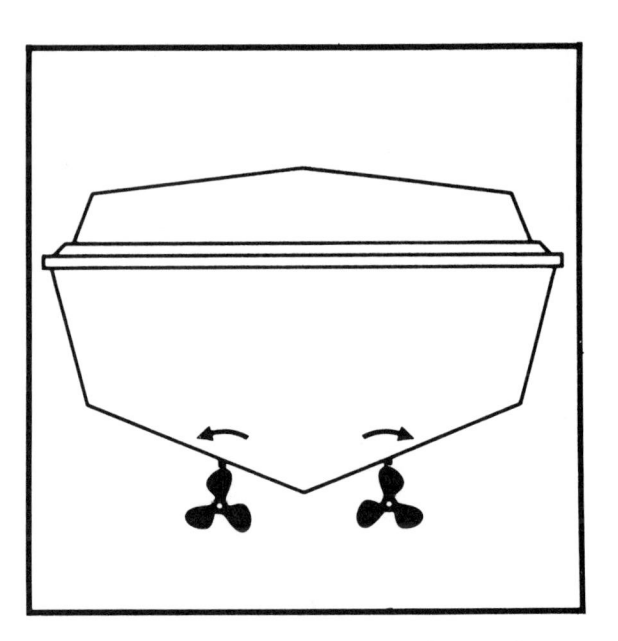

PLATE 29 — For twin screw boats, the propellers should ideally be counter-rotating, with the right hand propeller to starboard, and the left hand propeller to port. This prevents air from being sucked under the boat from the sides. (Courtesy of OMC, Waukegan, Ill.)

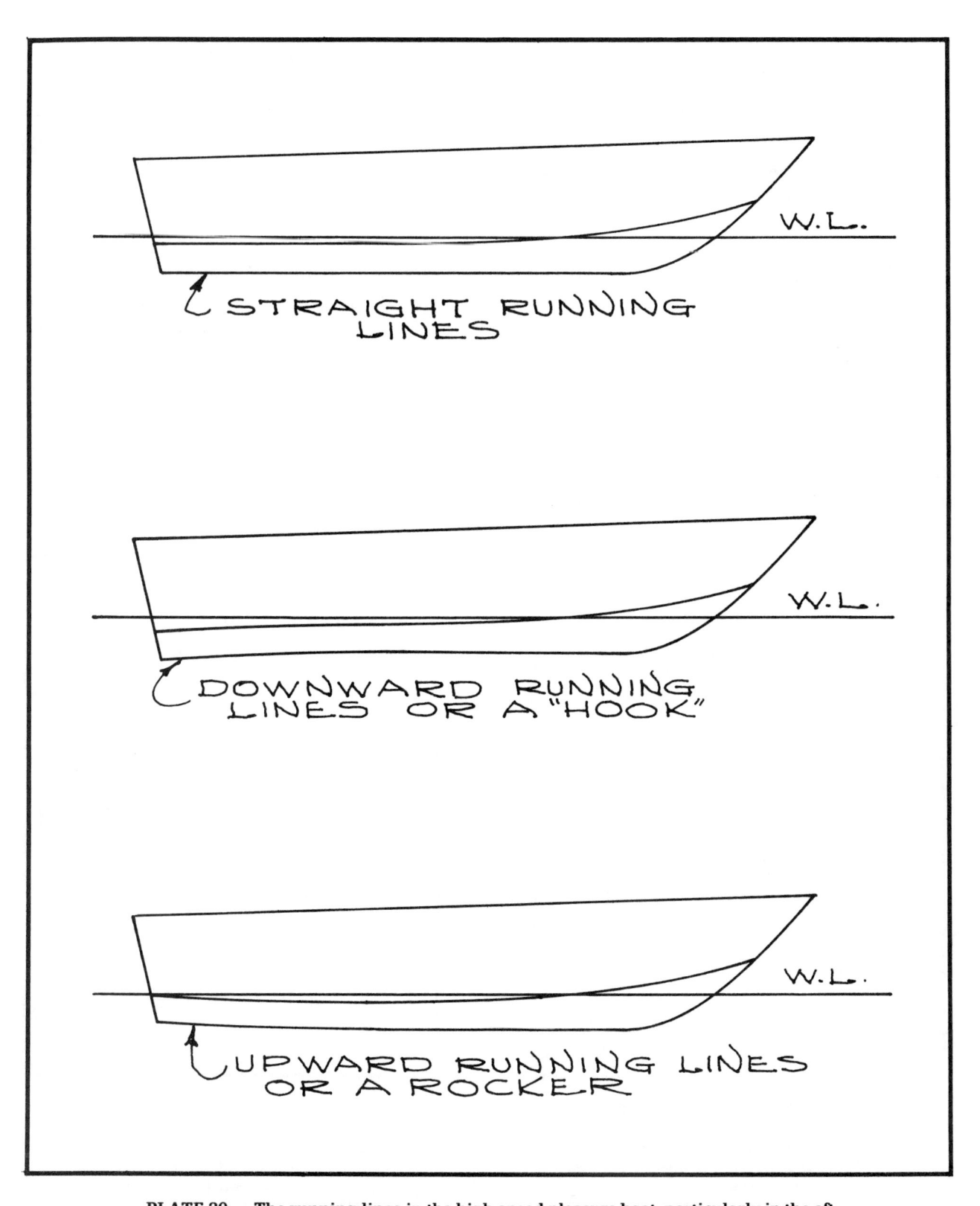

**PLATE 30 — The running lines in the high speed pleasure boat, particularly in the aft portion of the boat, should be straight. An upward curve or "rocker", or downward curve or "hook", can upset the performance of the boat.**

especially at higher speeds. A straight edge (one that is absolutely true!) can be used to check for this condition. If a hook or rocker exists it should be corrected, preferably in the hull itself. As an alternative, trim tabs of the adjustable type will help such problems (see Chapter 21). Other items that should be checked are the steering system and hook-ups, and the drive tilt and steering tab adjustments on sterndrive units, if so equipped.

In the case of twin screw boats it is always desirable to have opposite rotating propellers as an aid in maneuvering. However, non-opposite rotating engines are not uncommon. In powering a boat with twin engines, the rotation of the screws should be outboard from the centerline of the boat. In other words, the right hand propeller should rotate to starboard, and the left hand propeller should rotate to port (see Plate 29). This assures a positive flow of solid water to the propellers. If the propellers rotated in the other direction, there would be a tendency to suck in air from under the sides of the hull which could cause sluggish acceleration and perhaps make the boat squat, especially with high speed planing hulls.

To remove an old propeller, high heat should never be used. If a wheel or prop puller (see Fig. 9-8), and hammering with a soft hammer or mallet on the propeller and/or shaft end will not budge the propeller, then a gentle warming with a blow torch may help. However, don't use a welding torch since the quick, harsh heat may change the internal grain structure of the propeller metal which could result in a split hub that cannot be repaired.

The correct and incorrect way to

tighten the propeller nut is shown by Plate 31. Whether tightening or loosening, the wrench should always be on the same side of the propeller shaft as the wood block, always moving the wrench handle toward the block. This lessens the possibility of bending the shaft because the forces acting to bend the shaft tend to cancel each other. When putting the propeller on the shaft, always use a block of wood between the hammer and the propeller hub. Make sure that the end of the shaft (or the taper) and the propeller bore are quite clean and free of burrs. Also remove the key from the keyway and do the same to both. The key should be an easy slide fit in the keyway. If it is not, use a fine file or sandpaper and very slightly chamfer the edges until it fits right. Apply a very thin coating of light oil to the shaft taper and propeller bore, and then place the propeller onto the shaft taper

FIG. 9-8 — A propeller puller such as this is a useful tool for removing a propeller from the propeller shaft. (Courtesy of Glenwood Marine Equipment)

without the key to make sure it fits tight on the shaft. If the key is too long, shorten it on a grinder. Align the shaft and propeller keyways while the propeller is on the shaft, and insert the key. Don't force the key to the point where it upsets the propeller, however. Thread the nut on the shaft and tighten it, making sure that the nut is not pushing against the key. Then place the safety nut and use a cotter pin through the hole in the end of the shaft. Following these steps will insure that the propeller makes firm contact all around the shaft taper.

## SAILBOAT PROPELLERS

Propeller requirements and types may vary considerably for sailboats with inboard engines (called "auxiliaries") as opposed to powerboats. If the sailboat races under any particular measurement, handicap, or class rules, these are perhaps the most im-

portant consideration in selecting a propeller. Picking the wrong propeller could affect the boat's rating making it less competitive, irrespective of any actual performance changes. Otherwise, the sailboat owner must weigh the balance between sailing performance and powering efficiency. Because a propeller on a sailboat can create considerable drag, this can naturally detract from the sailing performance. On the other hand, the sea conditions which may normally be encountered in a given sailboat may require optimum powering efficiency. Hence, the selection of a propeller on the part of the owner must be a compromise.

Many possible configurations exist in selecting a propeller for a sailboat, which if carefully considered, will allow the sailboat owner to arrive at the best compromise between performance and efficiency. For example, two and three blade conventional fixed pro-

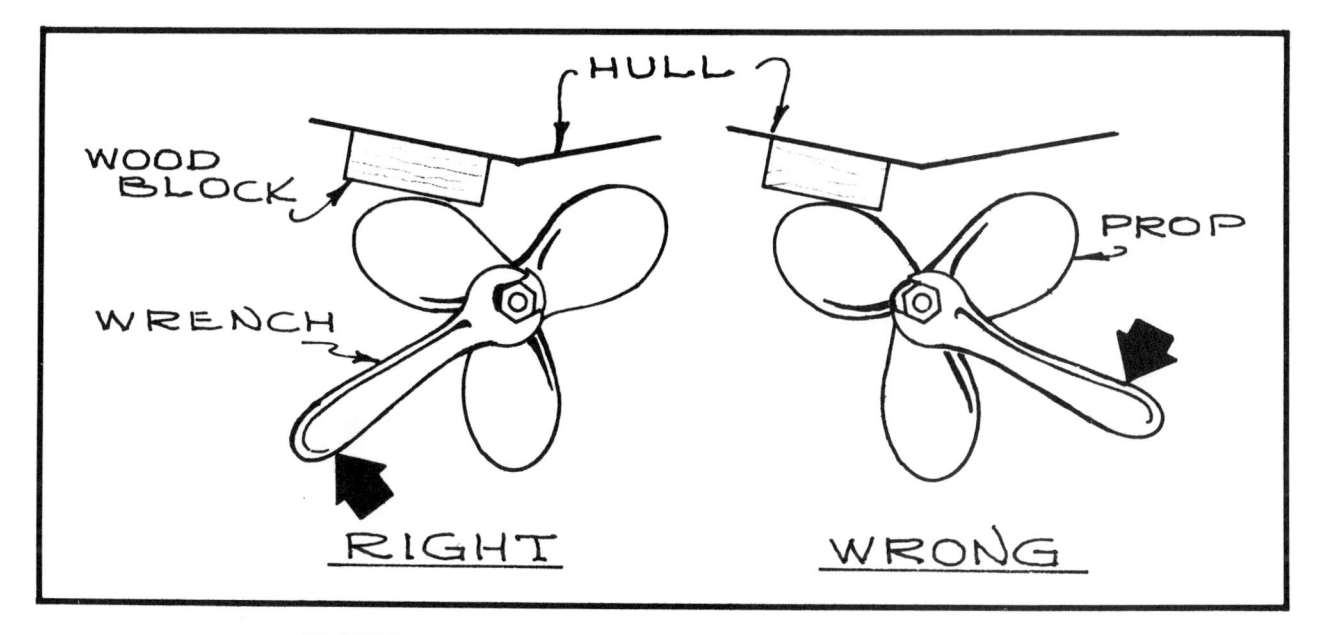

PLATE 31 — The right and wrong way to tighten a propeller nut.

122

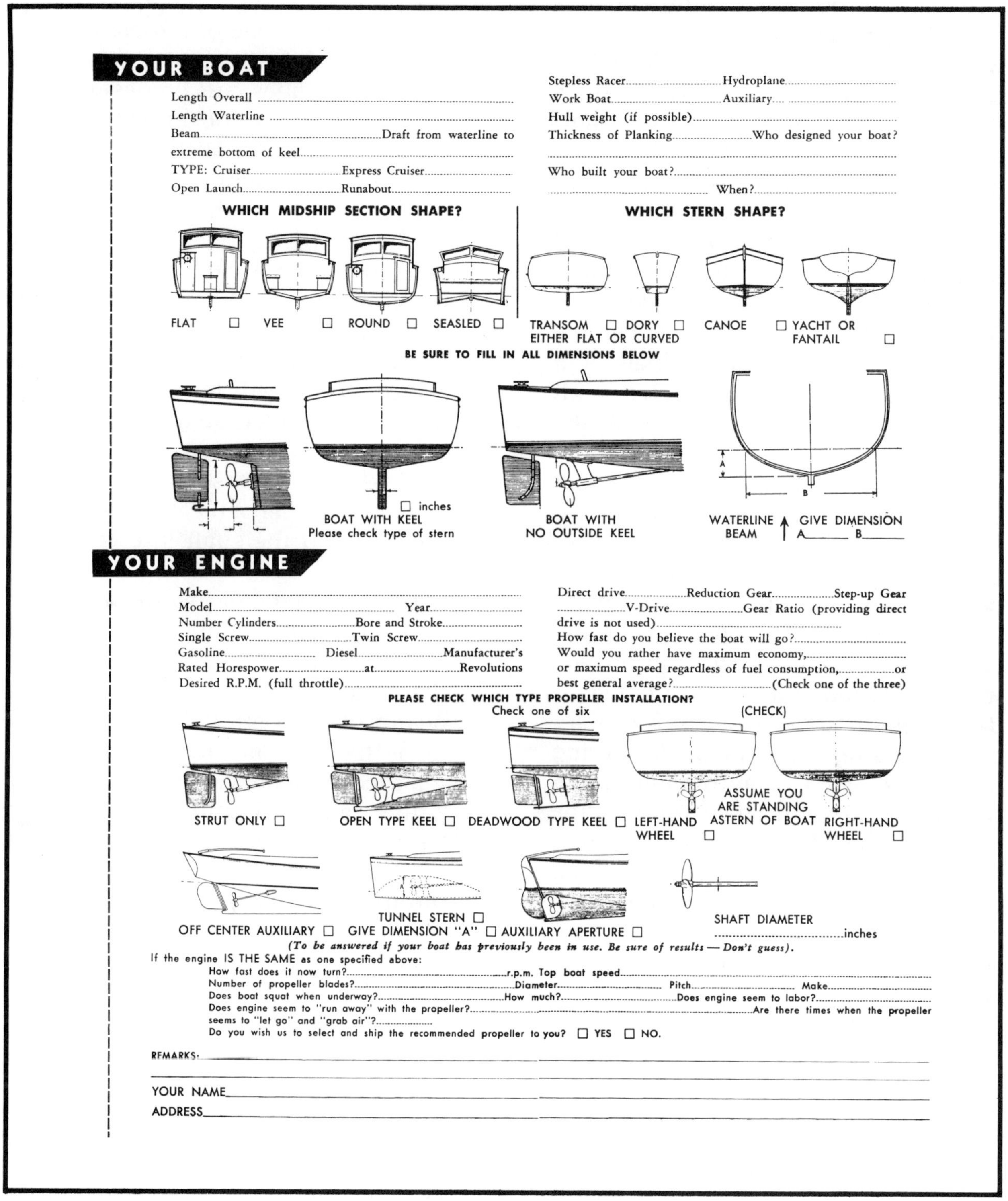

**YOUR BOAT**

Length Overall .........................................................
Length Waterline ......................................................
Beam......................................................Draft from waterline to
extreme bottom of keel...............................................
TYPE: Cruiser...................Express Cruiser........................
Open Launch...................Runabout................................

Stepless Racer.................. .............Hydroplane...............................
Work Boat.......................................Auxiliary....................................
Hull weight (if possible)...................................................
Thickness of Planking......................Who designed your boat?...........

Who built your boat?...............................................................
.......................................................When?...........................

**WHICH MIDSHIP SECTION SHAPE?**

FLAT  ☐    VEE  ☐    ROUND  ☐    SEASLED  ☐

**WHICH STERN SHAPE?**

TRANSOM ☐ DORY ☐    CANOE ☐ YACHT OR
EITHER FLAT OR CURVED              FANTAIL ☐

**BE SURE TO FILL IN ALL DIMENSIONS BELOW**

☐ inches
BOAT WITH KEEL
Please check type of stern

BOAT WITH
NO OUTSIDE KEEL

WATERLINE ▲ GIVE DIMENSION
BEAM      A _____ B

**YOUR ENGINE**

Make.......................................................................
Model......................................Year........................
Number Cylinders......................Bore and Stroke........................
Single Screw.....................Twin Screw...........................
Gasoline.............Diesel.............Manufacturer's
Rated Horsepower......................at....................Revolutions
Desired R.P.M. (full throttle)..........................................

Direct drive.................Reduction Gear.................Step-up Gear
...................V-Drive...................Gear Ratio (providing direct
drive is not used)...................................................
How fast do you believe the boat will go?..............................
Would you rather have maximum economy,................................
or maximum speed regardless of fuel consumption,.................or
best general average?..........................(Check one of the three)

**PLEASE CHECK WHICH TYPE PROPELLER INSTALLATION?**
Check one of six

(CHECK)

STRUT ONLY ☐    OPEN TYPE KEEL ☐ DEADWOOD TYPE KEEL ☐ LEFT-HAND WHEEL ☐

ASSUME YOU
ARE STANDING
ASTERN OF BOAT  RIGHT-HAND WHEEL ☐

OFF CENTER AUXILIARY ☐ GIVE DIMENSION "A" ☐ AUXILIARY APERTURE ☐

TUNNEL STERN ☐

SHAFT DIAMETER
..........................inches

*(To be answered if your boat has previously been in use. Be sure of results — Don't guess).*

If the engine IS THE SAME as one specified above:
How fast does it now turn?.....................................r.p.m. Top boat speed...........................
Number of propeller blades?.........................Diameter.................Pitch................Make...............
Does boat squat when underway?.........................How much?.................Does engine seem to labor?................
Does engine seem to "run away" with the propeller?...............................Are there times when the propeller
seems to "let go" and "grab air"?...................
Do you wish us to select and ship the recommended propeller to you? ☐ YES ☐ NO.

REMARKS:....................................................................

YOUR NAME..................................................................
ADDRESS....................................................................

FIG. 9-9 — **Propeller manufacturers have a wealth of experience and data regarding the proper size and type of propeller to use for a given installation. This questionnaire is typical of that which is available from the manufacturer so that they can make the best possible recommendation to suit your boat and motor.** (Courtesy of Michigan Propeller Co., Grand Rapids, Mich.)

pellers can be used, with either a locked propeller shaft under sail, or with the propeller being allowed to rotate while sailing as a way to reduce drag. In the latter case, the shaft should be disengaged from the transmission, or the transmission must be of a type intended for free rotation (see Chapter 4 and Plate 12). Fixed exposed propellers not located in an aperture, or behind the deadwood or skeg, are frequently left free to rotate. On the other hand, fixed 2-blade propellers in an aperture or behind a skeg or deadwood may be better off locked in the upright position. In this case, the shaft must be clearly marked inside the boat so that the operator knows when the blades are vertical. In most cases, however, there will be less drag in a sailboat if the propeller is left to rotate.

Several specialty propellers and devices are available to sailboat owners which offer much less drag than standard fixed blade propellers. These include folding propellers, feathering propellers, and controllable pitch propellers. There is some argument as to which type offers the least amount of drag, however, the folding type is often used on racing sailboats where low drag is important. The folding propeller has two blades which collapse when not in use, fairing into the water flow parallel with the propeller shaft. When the engine is operated and placed in gear, the blades spin open by centrifugal force.

Feathering propellers come in either two or three blade designs. The blades of feathering propellers pivot or "feather" to the optimum position parallel with the stream movement of the water over the blades when not under power. When under power, the blades assume

the proper angle or "pitch" for powering efficiency. One of the claimed advantages of feathering propellers is that their blades can be designed for better powering efficiency, than folding types, and yet still have minimal drag under sail alone.

With either folding or feathering type propellers their weight must be considered. Either type of propeller has much more mass than a fixed bladed propeller of the same diameter, perhaps weighing twice as much. Consequently, there will be a greater strain on the propeller shaft when under power. Therefore, a larger shaft should be used, or conversely, a smaller diameter propeller of the folding or feathering type if the shaft size cannot be increased.

The third type of low drag installation is the controllable pitch propeller. These are not too common, however, there are systems available. The beauty of the controllable pitch propeller is the fact that no reverse gear is required. Since the blades of the propeller can be infinitely varied from "full forward" to "full reverse" there is no lag between, nor any change in throttle necessary. Furthermore, by placing the blades at "neutral" (which would correspond with a feathering propeller not under power) there is minimal drag.

Just how important is the drag created by the propeller on a sailboat? That all depends on the intended use of the boat. But here are some examples. In general, the resistance for a locked fixed bladed propeller is about double that of one allowed to rotate freely, and may be even three times as much at higher speeds. Under sail, a fixed two blade propeller will give from

124

5 to 10% more speed than a three blade propeller. And the folding propeller may offer a 10 to 20% speed gain over a fixed two blade propeller.

All this emphasis on propeller drag sounds critical, and indeed it may be so under competitive conditions. But in the practical world where most boats operate, there may be other considerations. First, one must consider the speed limitation of most conventional monohulled sailboats. Since these are displacement boats, their hull speeds cannot exceed certain limits, or more precisely, a speed/length ratio of about 1.34 under power. In practice, however, most sailboats operate at even lower speed/length ratios of around 1.0. This means that a boat with a waterline length of 36' will have a hull speed of not much over 6 knots (the square root of 36' being 6). What this boils down to is that large variations in hull speed do not occur with variations in propeller types with perhaps a spread of ½ knot being the actual variation in performance.

Another consideration in sailboat propeller selection is the actual hull configuration. For example, boats with long keels having propeller apertures in the deadwood are often fitted with two blade propellers. However, under power such propellers may tend to vibrate to an annoying degree as the two blades alternate between the blocked area behind the deadwood to the free water on either side. This problem can be corrected by using a three blade propeller, albeit with more drag. Three blade propellers, on the other hand, usually give better powering efficiency and fuel economy, so they may be a better choice where considerable operation under power will be done.

In choosing between two and three blade propellers, one should consider that, because of the smaller blade area of the typical two-blade sailboat-type propeller, the diameter should be increased by 6 to 10% more than the comparable three-blade propeller for similar efficiency. With some boats, the clearances by the rudder should be checked to make sure that the rudder will not interfere with the propeller when the rudder is hard over.

Notwithstanding the effects of various racing rules on propeller selection, the engine power and reduction gear ratio are the most important factors in determining the size of the propeller. Most motor manufacturers give the optimum propeller size suitable for their engines with various reduction gears. Of course, the propeller aperture may limit the size of propeller that is possible also. In figuring the size of propeller, it is prudent to hold the maximum possible engine RPM to about 200 RPM less than the maximum rated engine speed. If propeller size information is not provided by the motor manufacturer, then the best idea is to contact one of the propeller manufacturers for their recommendations (see Fig. 9-9), or write to the designer or builder of the boat for advice, being sure to include figures for the reduction gear, and continuous shaft horsepower at the rated RPM.

# CHAPTER 10 — PROPELLER SHAFTS

On a propeller driven boat of the straight shaft or vee drive configuration it is the propeller shaft that transmits the power of the engine to the propeller. To do the job smoothly and quietly, the propeller shaft must be straight and true. A bent shaft not only causes noise, but vibrations that could ruin shaft bearings, couplings, and create other problems down the transmission line. A propeller shaft must be strong enough to take the "twist" or torque of the motor and transfer it to the propeller. While many boat owners consider only the torsional strength of the propeller shaft, some thought must be given to bending and impact strength on boats where the shaft is exposed. In today's littered waters, shaft damage from colliding with submerged or floating objects is all too common.

The size or diameter required for a propeller shaft depends on many variables, including the horsepower delivered through the shaft (called the "shaft horsepower", or SHP), the RPM of the propeller shaft, the propeller diameter, as well as the strength of the material to be used for the shaft. In the absence of any information other than propeller diameter, the propeller size as a general rule should not exceed about 14 times the diameter of the propeller shaft. This means that a 14" diameter propeller, for example, would use a 1" propeller shaft. A practical

guide of shaft sizes for varying propellers may be obtained from the following chart. Note that no consideration has been given to the various materials that can be used for the shaft.

## PROPELLER SHAFT SIZES

| DIAMETER OF PROPELLER | SHAFT DIAMETER |
|---|---|
| 10" | ¾" to 7/8" |
| 12" | 7/8" to 1" |
| 14" | 1" to 1⅛" |
| 16" | 1⅛" to 1¼" |
| 18" | 1¼" to 1⅜" |
| 20" | 1⅜" to 1½" |

Another element to consider in shaft size is the support of the shaft along its length. A common installation in boats is for the shaft to be supported at the propeller and at the engine coupling with no more than one shaft diameter overhanging beyond the stern bearing (plus thread and taper). In this installation, which is considered as two rigid supports, a considerable length of shaft (sometimes exceeding 6') can be supported without an intermediate bearing. However, the placement of bearings depends on the shaft diameter, shaft speed, and strength of the material used for the shaft. While there are formulas and graphs that can be used to determine bearing spacing, a practical rule of thumb often advocated states that there should be bearings spaced not closer than about 20 times the shaft diameter, and no more than about 40 times the shaft diameter apart. In other words, a 1" shaft should have an intermediate bearing if the distance between the engine flange and the strut or stern bearing is more than 40". This figure in practice, however, is frequently exceeded. In any case, if shaft whip occurs, an additional bearing should be installed.

## PROPELLER SHAFT MATERIALS

What is the "best" shaft material? This too depends on many variables, the first of which depends on if the boat will be used exclusively in fresh water, or whether it will be operated in salt or brackish waters. If the boat will be used in fresh water only, then corrosion problems may need little consideration, and consequently the propeller shaft will probably be cheaper. In salt water, however, various corrosion problems can occur making the selection of a suitable shaft material more critical.

Some of the more common shafting materials will be described in the following. This listing is an attempt to provide practical information for the laymen and is not meant to be all-inclusive. An attempt has been made to list the materials with their common names and terminologies so as to not confuse the non-technical person. Basically, shaft materials are usually either of copper bearing materials or various stainless steels.

The common copper bearing metals used for propeller shafting are Naval brass (sometimes called "Naval bronze"), various bronzes, and Monel alloys. Naval brass contains about 60% copper, whereas bronze must contain 90% or more copper, and is therefore superior. Monel is a trade name for alloys containing about one third copper and about two thirds nickle. The 400 Monel and K-500 Monel are common propeller shaft types. The K-500 type is one of the strongest and most corrosion resistant of shaft materials, and consequently one of the most expensive. The 400 type is less costly and also not quite as strong, but offers good value. A common shaft material often specified is Tobin bronze (another trade name), but it is not as strong as the Monel materials, and not as suitable for exposed conditions.

Exposed steel shafting is not too commonly used, primarily because it will rust even in fresh water, and corrode severely in most marine applications. However, various stainless steels are commonly used. The various grades and types of stainless steel tend to confuse the ordinary person, and the authors apologize that there are only number designations to identify the suitable types.

The stainless steels often used for propeller shafts include Types 303, 304, 316, and 630. All stainless steel shafting is strong, especially the 630 type (which is also known as "17-4

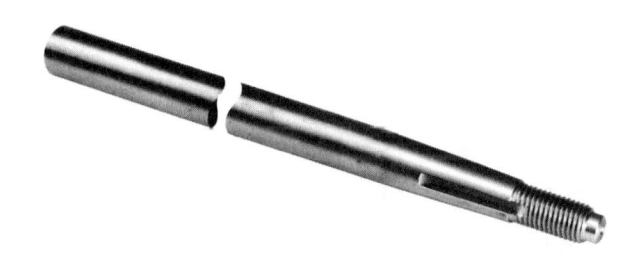

FIG. 10-1 — The typical propeller shaft machined on the aft end for the propeller with a locking keyway, threads for the nuts, and a hole for the cotter key. (Courtesy of Glenwood Marine Equipment)

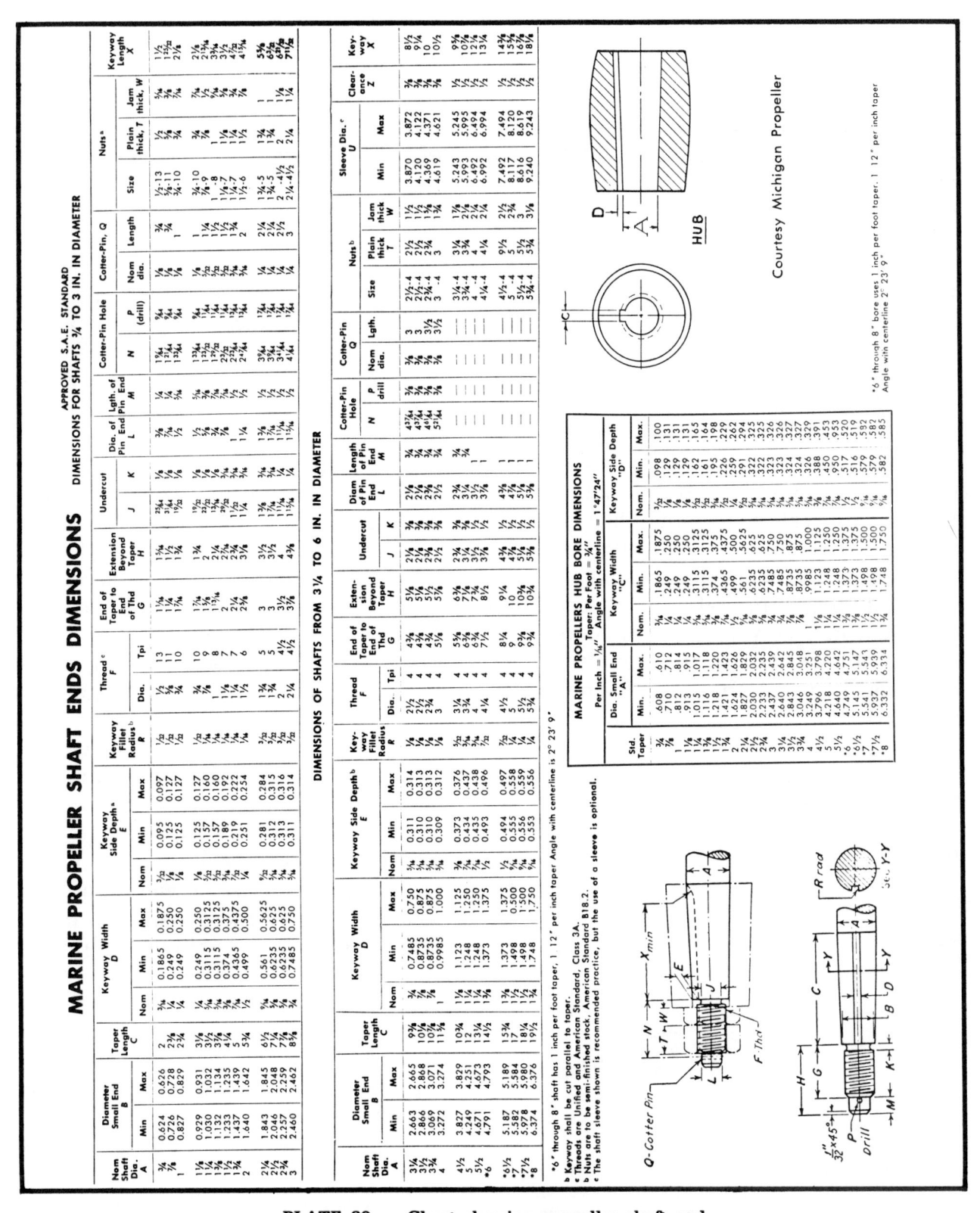

PLATE 32 — Chart showing propeller shaft end
dimensions and tolerances. (Courtesy of Michigan
Propeller Co., Grand Rapids, Mich.)

PH"). Stainless steel shafting in salt water is more-or-less subject to pitting which leads to crevice corrosion. Types 303 and 304 are probably worse in this respect, with type 316 being less susceptible, and therefore better suited to salt water use. The 630 type is probably neck-and-neck with K-500 Monel at this stage in technology for the winner in the "best shaft material" race. It costs more than the other stainless types, is stronger, and is less subject to corrosion.

Stainless steel shafting has certain installation and usage requirements that should be adhered to for long shaft life. Sacrificial galvanic anodes should be located adjacent to or on the propeller shafts in salt or brackish waters. If anode collars are used on the shafts, these may throw the shafts out of balance. Anodes of this type are also more subject to erosion than if located off the shaft. Take care to locate such anode collars so that they will not restrict the water flow to the propeller. In boats with a long shaft tube that will trap water next to the propeller shaft of stainless steel, there should be a means for providing a positive flow of water circulation in order to avoid the corrosive effects of stagnant water when in contact with stainless steel. All electrical equipment and all underwater equipment should be properly grounded to a negative ground underwater plate (see Chapter 19).

With shafting, the use of graphite packings or grease must be avoided to prevent pitting and subsequent galvanic corrosion. The shaft nuts, key, and cotter pin are preferably of the same or similar materials as the shafting. Most propeller shafts will be fitted with a standard taper at the end to suit the propeller. This taper together with the keyway is shown by Plate 32. The standard taper is ¾" to the foot, or 1/16" per inch. Because the propeller will be going in both directions (forward and reverse), a lock nut must be used, most often consisting of a nut with a jam nut plus cotter key. Some people try to get by with just a jam nut, or nut plus a cotter key. However, these same people often suffer the embarrassment of a lost propeller. While difficult to find, a coating of white lead is advised on the shaft under the propeller hub if of stainless steel or Monel to prevent corrosion between the shaft and the propeller, and to keep them from binding together which can make removal difficult.

# CHAPTER 11 — SHAFT ANGLES & LAYOUTS

The straight shaft inboard installation layout requires consideration of several variables. With the many variations possible in the size, power, and weight of the motor, this will also cause a variation in the size of propeller that can be used. This in turn can alter the strut angle and drop, and position of the hole in the boat for the shaft. As can be seen, a change in one element can lead to a change in another part of the procedure, with many variations possible in the same boat. To fix things in order to provide a starting point, it is therefore essential that the diameter of the propeller to be used be known, along with the specific motor, in order to determine the shaft angle and the shaft hole position.

The proper way to determine the accurate position of the various units that constitute the inboard motor installation is to make a full size layout, or a physical substitution or "mockup" of the entire propulsive system. This is the point where many individuals will throw up their hands in despair and shout, "I ain't no blankety-blank engineer or draftsman. How in blue blazes do you expect me to understand this kind of nonsense? The heck with this business; I'll do it my way!" This type of person then goes out and punches a hole in the bottom of the boat at some point where he thinks that it "looks right", and hopes that the motor will fit close to the point where the designer intended it to be. The chances are that he will be WRONG and the boat may turn out to perform in any manner except the RIGHT one. The layout does take time, BUT it is not complicated. If a person feels he can install an engine, he should be able to make a layout as well. So the advice is to stick to it and follow through the procedures a step at a time by following the text and illustrations provided.

In the examples shown by Plate 33, a standard planing type boat is used as an example. While there are other straight line shaft installations that are somewhat different, the principles are similar and can be extrapolated to various types of boats. In the illustration a few standard dimensions and clearances are given for an inboard installation. Note that the motor is directly located over the point indicated on the plans if building a new boat and if noted by the designer. In other cases no point will be given or available, and a "guesstimation" will be required. Usually with the motor located at the central location, a slight shift fore or aft will not have any severe consequences. However, if the point is known where the center of gravity of the motor should fall, then try to set the motor as close as possible to this point. The center of gravity of the motor may be indicated on an installation drawing provided by the motor manufacturer, or you can determine it for your motor by

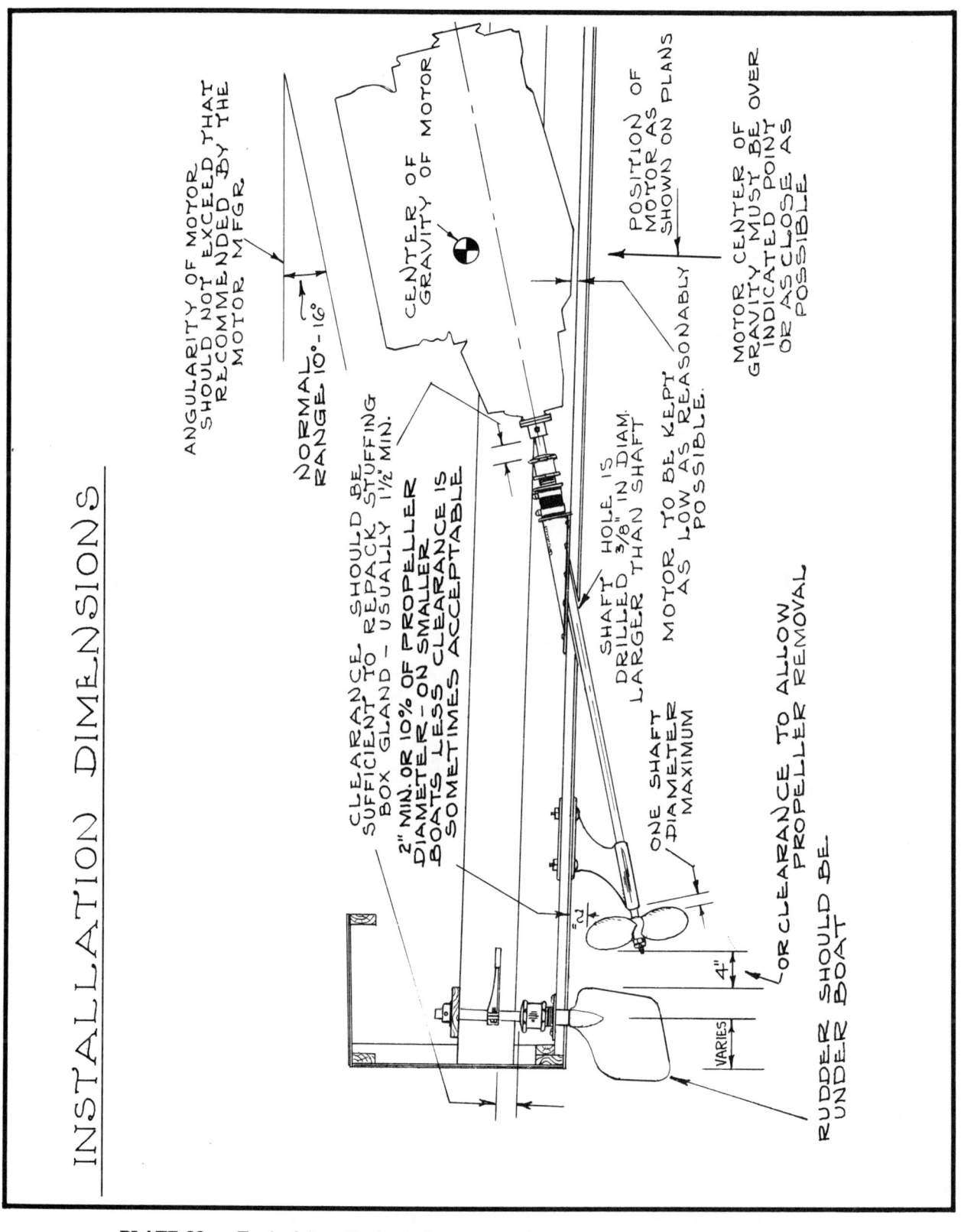

**PLATE 33 — Typical installation tolerances and considerations for a straight shaft centrally located inboard installation.**

131

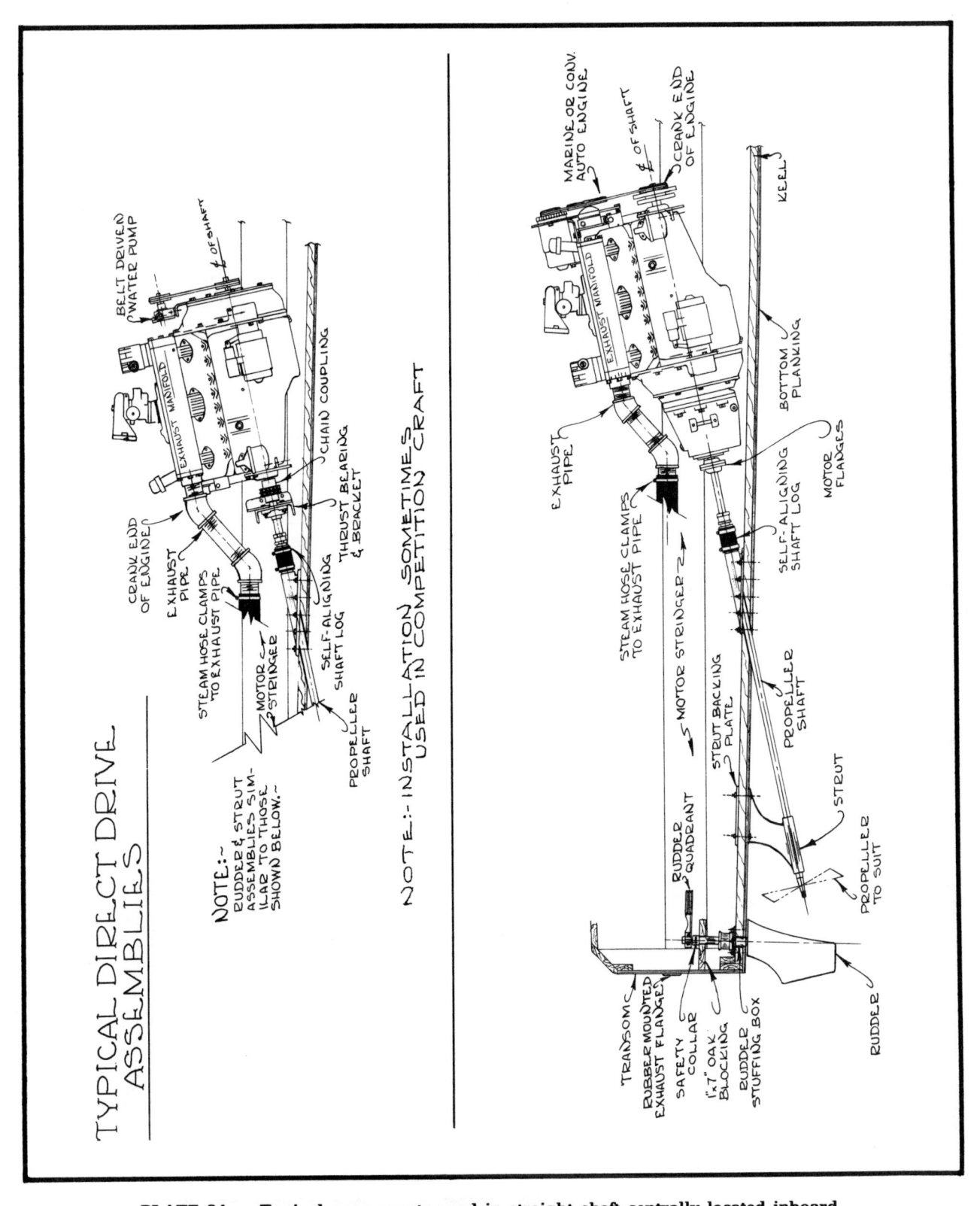

**PLATE 34 — Typical components used in straight shaft centrally located inboard installations. The "bob-tail" version is primarily used in competition craft where a transmission is not necessary.**

balancing it or lifting it with a chain hoist.

With most installations it will be desirable to get the engine as low in the boat as practicable in order to reduce the shaft angle. However practical limitations must be considered. The engine should not be subjected to excessive bilge water, and some clearance is desirable for access to certain motor components. Then too, a drip pan may be fitted under the engine and space must be provided for this. In some cases, the boat's structure may interfere with the motor installation as well. While entire structural members must not be cut away, some portions can sometimes be cut away and then reinforced to restore the member's original strength.

The position of the rudder can vary with certain designs, while in other cases, the designer provides quite specific size and location requirements for this component. With most boats solid water must be kept over the rudder which means that in most cases the rudder MUST be located under the boat. If placed too close to the transom, air may be sucked into the rudder causing poor steering and loss of control on turns. Sometimes the rudder can be located somewhat outboard from the transom, in which case a plate extended out from the transom over the rudder will cure this problem. It is also possible to set the rudder too far forward which will cause the shaft angle to increase. In general locate the rudder inboard as far as practical and at least so the aft edge of the blade is completely under the boat whenever possible.

The desirable distance between the propeller and rudder is at least 4" or as required to provide room to remove the propeller without first removing the rudder. Clearance between the bottom of the boat and the propeller should normally be at least 2" or 10% of the propeller diameter (see Chapter 9) whichever is least. While it is possible to "cheat" on these clearances somewhat, especially on small boats or other cases where cramped conditions apply, it is best to strive for the minimum tolerances noted for general practice. Then again, on very high speed competition type boats, the distance from the rudder to the propeller is often increased.

If you have a full size layout of the boat, or are building a boat from lofted lines, the layout for the engine installation can be readily made as illustrated by Plate 35. Failing this, it may be possible to make a full size layout from the designer's offsets, frame dimensions, or from full size patterns. The only areas of the hull that are important are the frames from the transom or stern forward, in way of the motor area, and the line of the keel or where the propeller shafts will intersect with the hull on twin screw boats. The outline templates representing the engine, propeller, and rudder may be cut from paper, cardboard, or wood. Motor dimensions can usually be obtained from scaled drawings available from the engine manufacturer or firm providing the conversion parts (see Plate 36). In some cases, full size drawings of motors are obtainable. If no dimensions or drawings are available, make a rough template taking dimensions directly from the motor, or sketch a rough outline in profile view. The engine crankshaft centerline is desirable for reference purposes and

133

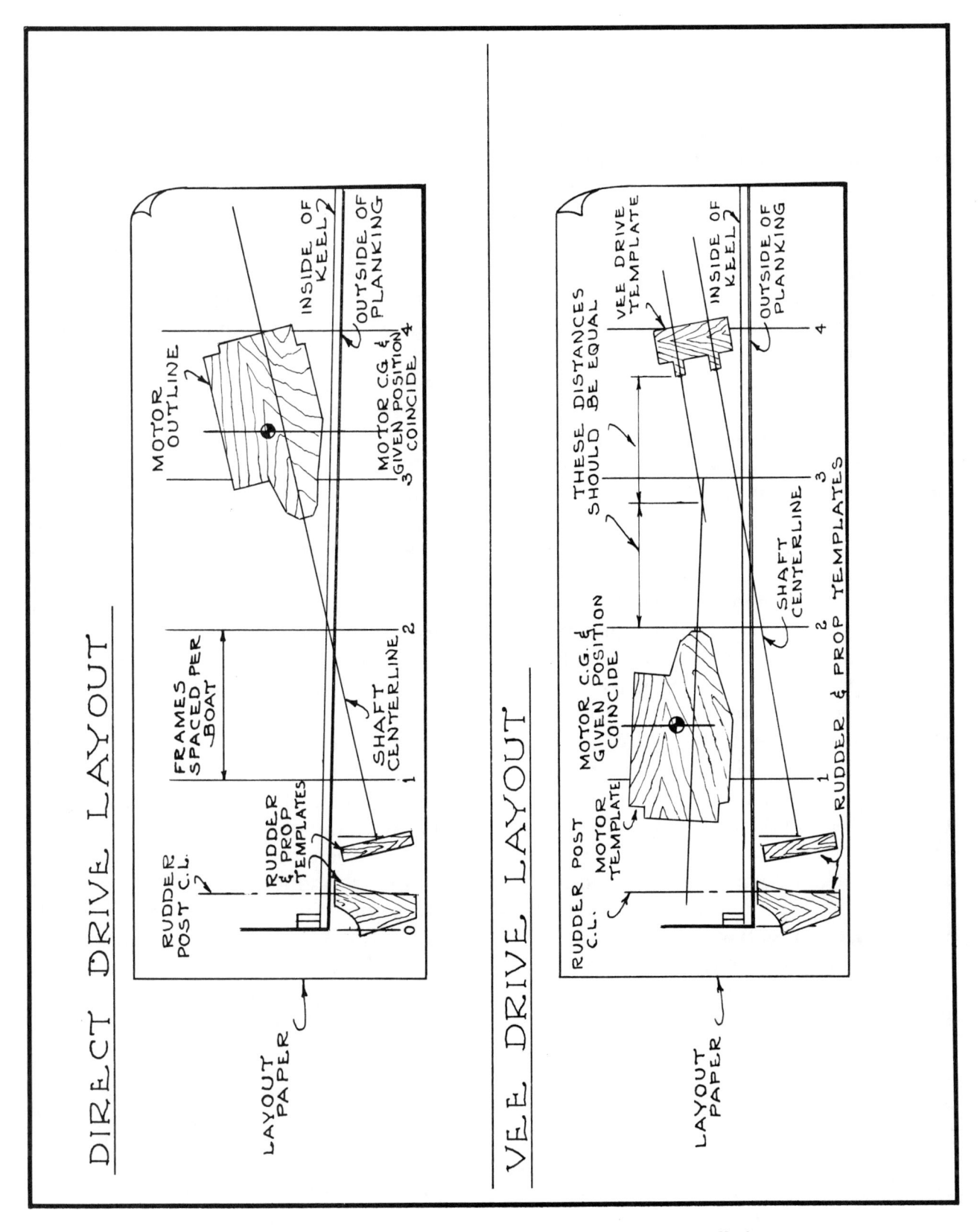

**PLATE 35 — Shaft layouts for both in-line and vee drive installations.**

should be rather accurately pin-pointed. The portion above this reference is desirable for checking heights and clearances, but may not be necessary in all cases. If the center of gravity (C.G.) of the motor is known or given, and necessary in the installation, mark this to the template. In lieu of rudder and propeller templates, the actual rudder or propeller can be used. If not available, templates for these can be made from dimensions furnished by the supplier's catalog. The width of the propeller can be estimated by dividing the pitch by the number of blades. For example, a propeller with a 12″ pitch and three blades would have a width of 4″. This is only an approximation, and if possible, the width or hub thickness of the propeller should be checked, or the supplier should have the information.

As shown by Plate 35 typical installation drawings are shown for both centrally located and vee drive straight shaft systems. Note that the point where the shaft passes through the boat may be readily found both on the inside and outside of the boat, assuming that the thickness of the hull at this point is fairly closely known. The shaft angle can be found by using a protractor, or figured from the chart in Plate 37.

In the case of the vee drive installation note the "jockeying" that can be done to the shaft angle in relation to the angle of the motor and the position or height of the vee drive above the inside of the hull or keel. The shaft angle should be as low as possible, and the angularity of the universals of the torque tube at a minimum. Shifting of the variables will determine the best possible position for the vee drive, and

best suitable shaft angle. When the shafts of the vee drive have an angle between them, the problem is similar, but the angularity on the universals can be decreased more (see Chapter 4 on vee drives).

If the builder is opposed to making drawings, as many people are, there are other methods of determining the pertinent points in an installation. From a practical standpoint, the same could be accomplished during the construction of a boat prior to applying the planking. It is then physically possible to fit templated parts of the installation in the required position in the boat, noting the shaft angle and also the point that the shaft will project through the hull. In other words, the installation requirements are taken directly from the work, or "mocked-up" in place.

If the hull has been built or already exists, and full size drawings are not available, another simple method for determining the shaft angularity and shaft hole position can be used as shown by Plate 38. A length of lumber (say a 1″ x 4″) is laid on the upright boat along the center of the boat (for single screw boats), or where the shaft centerline will be located (for twin screw boats), from just abaft the transom forward to a spot well beyond the determined or estimated engine location. Temporarily prop this board ("A") in place so that it is roughly parallel to the keel or horizontal line. Nail another board ("B") at right angles or 90 degrees to board "A" at the approximate point where the forward end of the motor will be. Fasten a second board ("C") so that it passes outside of the stern or transom, and follows the transom or stern angle, projecting several

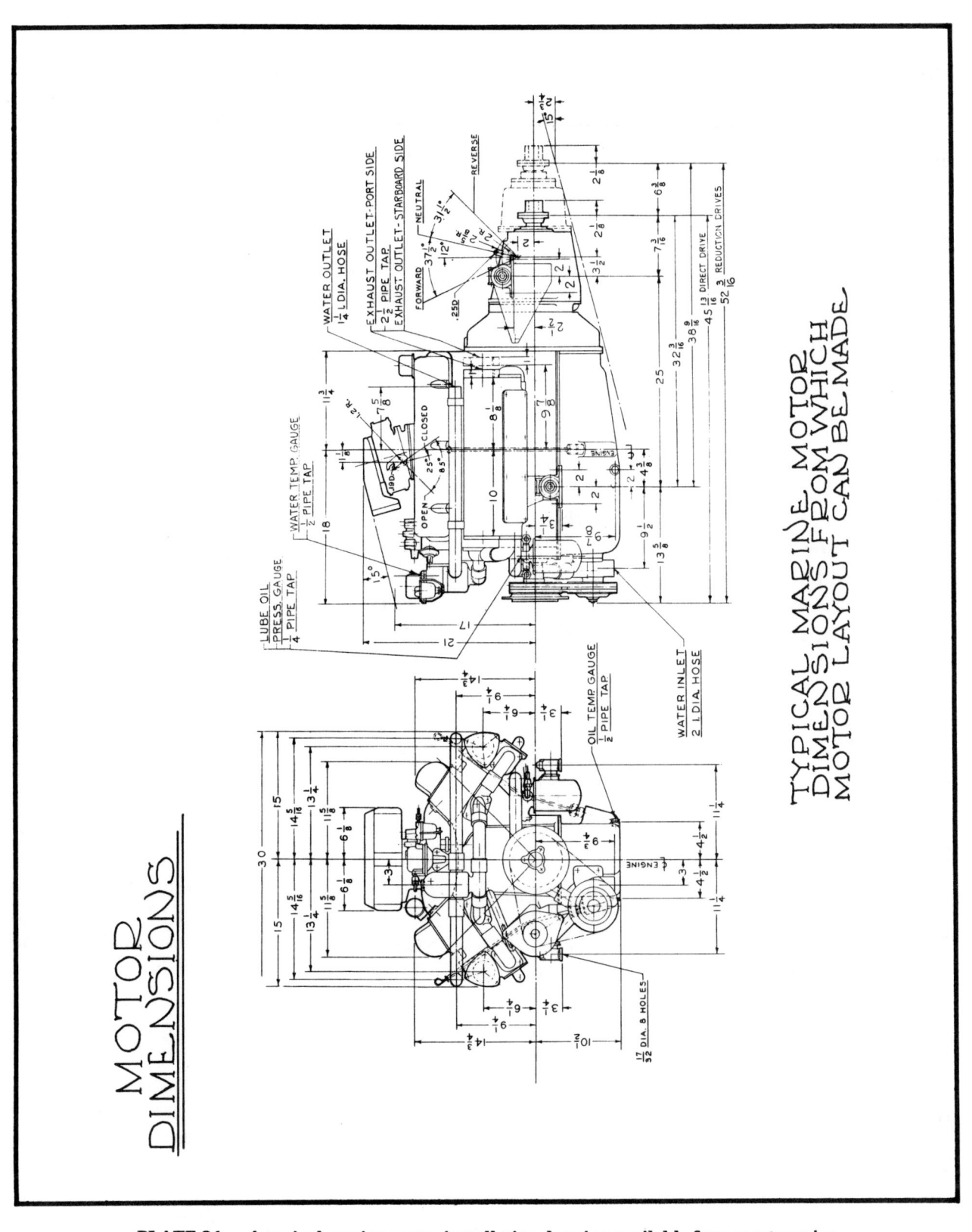

**PLATE 36 — A typical marine motor installation drawing available from most marine engine manufacturers can be used to make the motor and shaft layout.**

feet below the bottom of the boat by at least 6″ more than ½ the propeller diameter. Other boards ("D", "E", "F", etc.) are fastened to board "A" to hit the hull or keel in order to project the contour at several points. These boards can be spaced a foot or so apart along the length of board "A", and at right angles to it so that they just touch the bottom of the boat. This "jig", which is actually a full size "pattern" of the boat, can be removed and laid flat on the floor.

Again referring to the installation dimensions shown by Plate 33, the jig can be used to locate the relative positions of the various parts and the shaft angle. When the line of the shaft has been accurately determined by using a taut string, the points should be marked on the uprights "D", "E", "F", etc. Place the jig back in to the boat and find the shaft hole center by laying a straight-edge along the marks. The angularity of the shaft may also be determined by the angle formed between the bottom of the boat and the shaft centerline.

What is the proper shaft angle to use? As seen from the foregoing, the shaft angle more or less determines itself in most cases. In some instances it is possible to alter the shaft angle by shifting the variables. However, a shaft angle between 10 and 14 degrees is common, with 12 degrees sometimes considered as "standard". In many cases, however, a 16 degree shaft angle

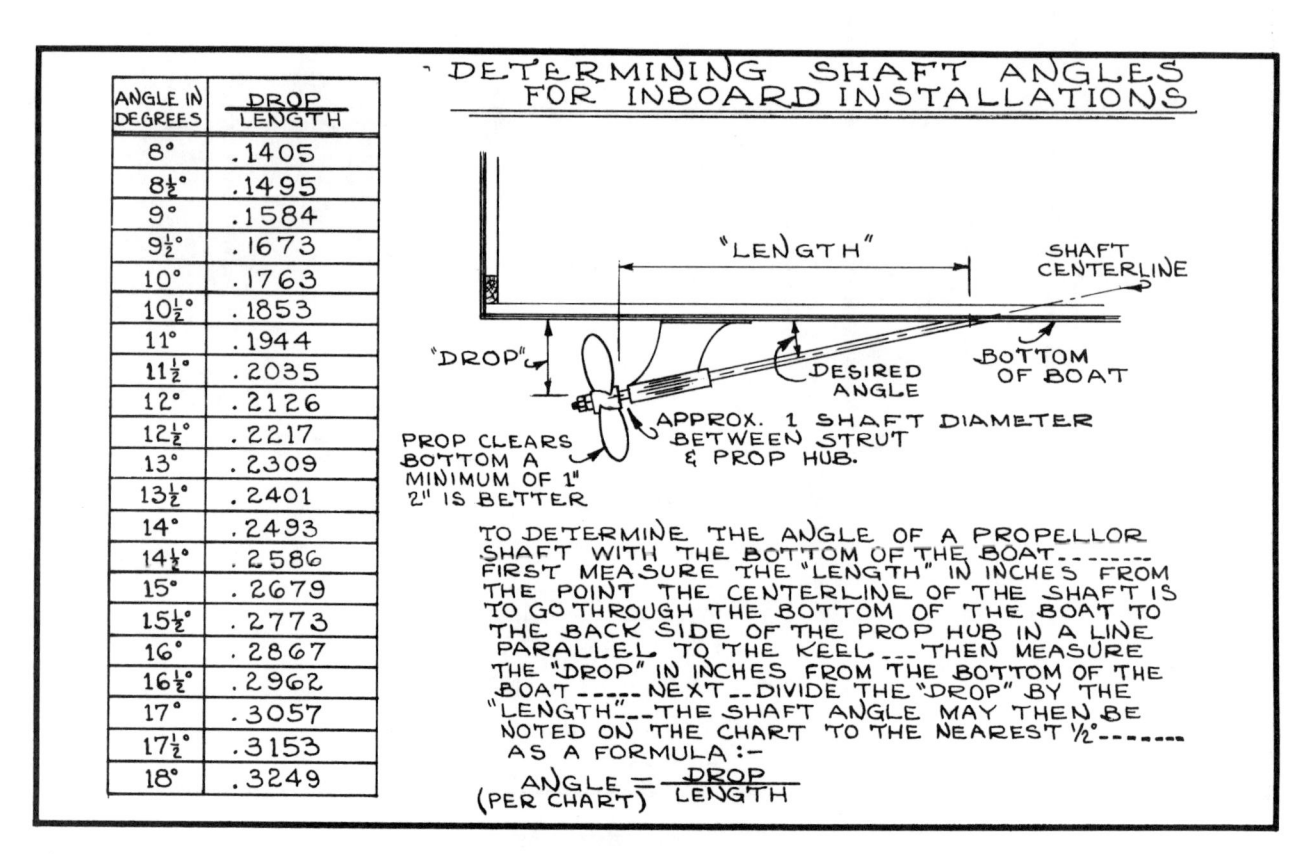

| ANGLE IN DEGREES | DROP LENGTH |
|---|---|
| 8° | .1405 |
| 8½° | .1495 |
| 9° | .1584 |
| 9½° | .1673 |
| 10° | .1763 |
| 10½° | .1853 |
| 11° | .1944 |
| 11½° | .2035 |
| 12° | .2126 |
| 12½° | .2217 |
| 13° | .2309 |
| 13½° | .2401 |
| 14° | .2493 |
| 14½° | .2586 |
| 15° | .2679 |
| 15½° | .2773 |
| 16° | .2867 |
| 16½° | .2962 |
| 17° | .3057 |
| 17½° | .3153 |
| 18° | .3249 |

DETERMINING SHAFT ANGLES FOR INBOARD INSTALLATIONS

TO DETERMINE THE ANGLE OF A PROPELLOR SHAFT WITH THE BOTTOM OF THE BOAT........ FIRST MEASURE THE "LENGTH" IN INCHES FROM THE POINT THE CENTERLINE OF THE SHAFT IS TO GO THROUGH THE BOTTOM OF THE BOAT TO THE BACK SIDE OF THE PROP HUB IN A LINE PARALLEL TO THE KEEL...THEN MEASURE THE "DROP" IN INCHES FROM THE BOTTOM OF THE BOAT......NEXT...DIVIDE THE "DROP" BY THE "LENGTH"...THE SHAFT ANGLE MAY THEN BE NOTED ON THE CHART TO THE NEAREST ½°....... AS A FORMULA :-

$$\text{ANGLE (PER CHART)} = \frac{\text{DROP}}{\text{LENGTH}}$$

**PLATE 37 — A method to determine the shaft angle for a straight shaft installation.**

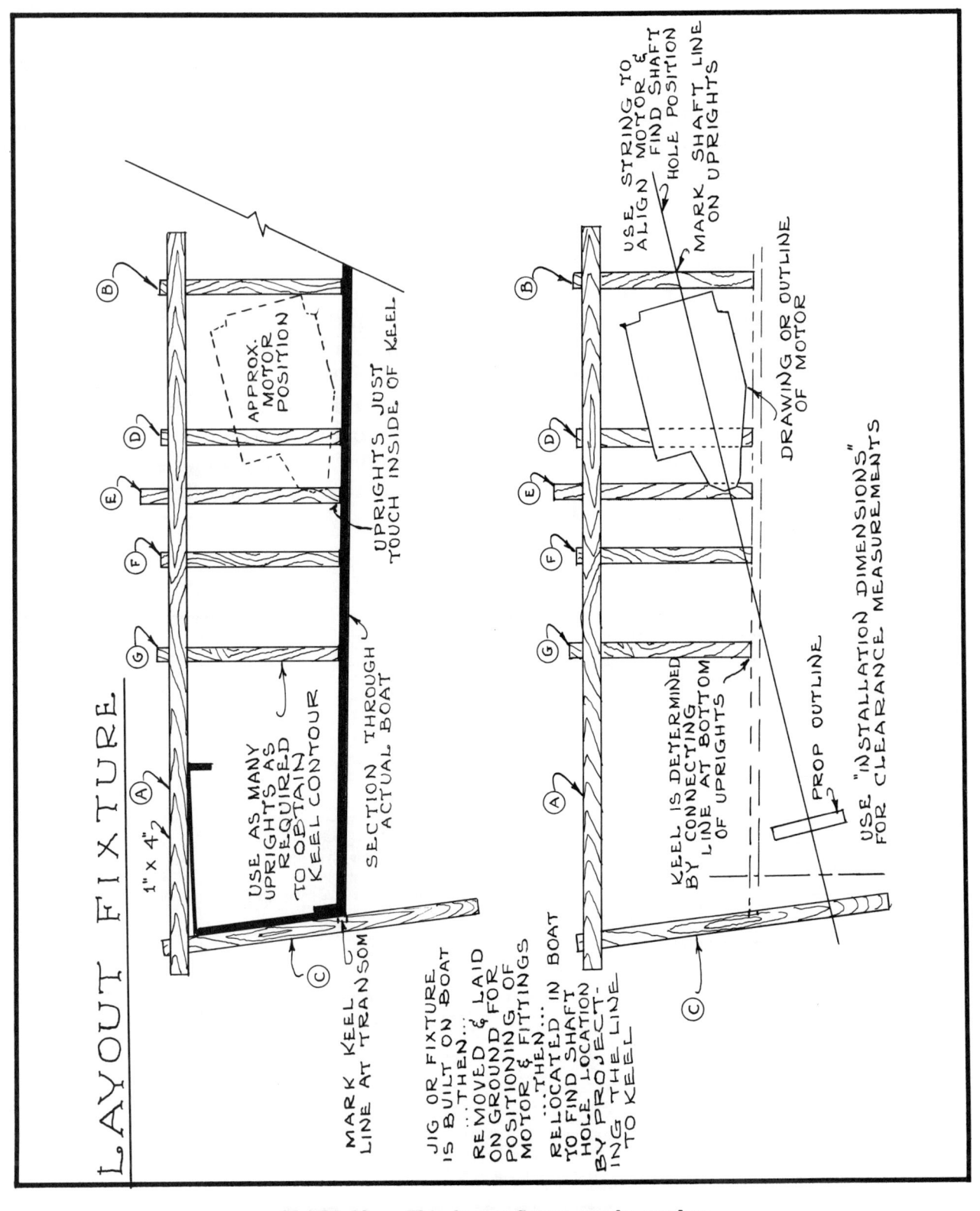

**PLATE 38 — This layout fixture can be used to make the shaft and motor layout in an existing boat.**

138

is used, especially in shorter boats. While shaft angles steeper than this are permissible (assuming that the engine can handle this inclination), sacrifices will be made to efficiency at the propeller. Therefore, it is best to avoid a shaft angle which exceeds 16 degrees. Also one must consider the operating condition of the boat. For example, a motor manufacturer may allow their motor to operate at shaft angles up to 16 degrees. However, the key word here is "operate". Depending on the boat and conditions of use, operating conditions could increase the angle of the motor, such as could occur when encountering rough seas, or if the boat trims down or "squats" by the transom while underway. Obviously, these factors could effectively increase the "operating" shaft angle and perhaps impair the lubrication capabilities of the engines. So whenever possible, the lower shaft angles are desirable.

In very fast boats, especially those used in competition, such as the vee drive type, or those with the motor forward of the driver, shaft angles will often be at much less than 12 degrees.

Theoretically, the thrust of the propeller resolves itself into two forces; one giving the lift, and the other imparting the forward motion. If the angle is at a minimum, there will be a greater force forward than if the angle were steeper. However, for normal boats at normal operating speeds under normal conditions, shaft angles between 10 and 16 degrees have shown through years of experience that there is little practical variation in speed and efficiency in this range of shaft angles.

Concerning the location of an engine in a vee drive installation, usually there is some leeway in a fore and aft direction of the motor location. Quite often, however, this apparent leeway diminishes once all the components and their dimensions are considered. Unless stipulated otherwise by the designer or boat manufacturer, it is usually acceptable to locate the engine as far aft as practical in the hull if extra clearances are necessary to make the installation. These circumstances are quite common in the typical vee drive runabout or ski boat intended for stern mounted motors.

# CHAPTER 12 — MAKING THE SHAFT HOLE

In wood boats and many of those built in fiberglass, the propeller shaft hole must be drilled or bored. In boats built of other materials, such as metal hulls, other provisions are usually built into the hull for the propeller shaft hole or tube, and no other explanation is necessary. Drilling or boring the shaft hole seems to worry the average amateur builder who has never done the job, and perhaps causes more anxiety than any other portion of the inboard installation. However, the task is relatively simple once the point is determined where the shaft hole is to be located. With this being done by one of the methods described in the preceding chapter, several methods and tools can be used for drilling the hole. Most of the methods described will be practical whether the hull is right side up or upsidedown. In general, the shaft can be drilled from either the outside or the inside. The equipment which is best to use, of course, will vary somewhat depending on just how long the hole needs to be and what tools are available to do the job. Obviously, certain modifications or variations may be required to suit certain boats and situations.

The method illustrated by Figs. 12-1 thru 12-4 is one that is considered easy with ordinary tools on a typical planing type or similar hull. Variations on this method could utilize a thin twist drill with a long shank, or shank with welded extension. Connected to a power drill, this long shank drill bit will rapidly drill a lead hole that will subsequently make the tracking of a standard auger or expansive bit a rather simple task. The template shown can be used as an angular guide for accuracy. Where the shaft hole will be of considerable length, it will be more difficult to assure that the bore is straight and true. The typical auger bit is normally not long enough, and often a longer type called a "ship's auger" will be used. However, the typical auger or ship's auger has a lead screw tip at the center of the bit which can cause the bit to track off center unless carefully guided or held in a jig. To avoid this, a special type of auger without the screw tip or cutting lips called a "barefoot auger" can be used, although this type of tool is hard to find. For long holes, extensions can be welded onto just about any type of auger. Because long shaft bores are frequently done through the deadwood or keel appendage, many builders obviate the need for making a long bore by building up the deadwood or keel appendage by laminations which allow the hole to be bored progressively a layer at a time.

Some use a block of wood fastened firmly over the point where the hole will need to be drilled in the hull. It is possible to pre-drill a hole in the block and cut the angle (if required) to match

140

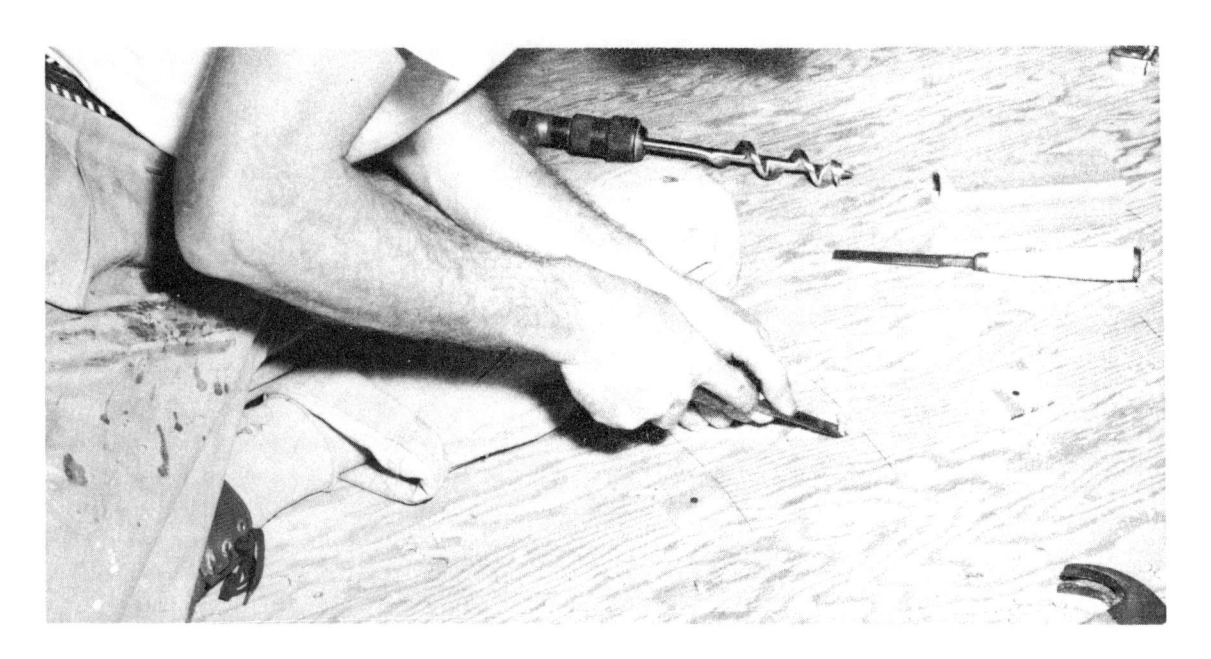

FIG. 12-1 — A cleft is made with a chisel at the point where the centerline of the shaft will start through the planking. The depth of the notch should be equal to the radius of the hole to be drilled. With a gouge, cut an arc to allow the auger to be inserted.

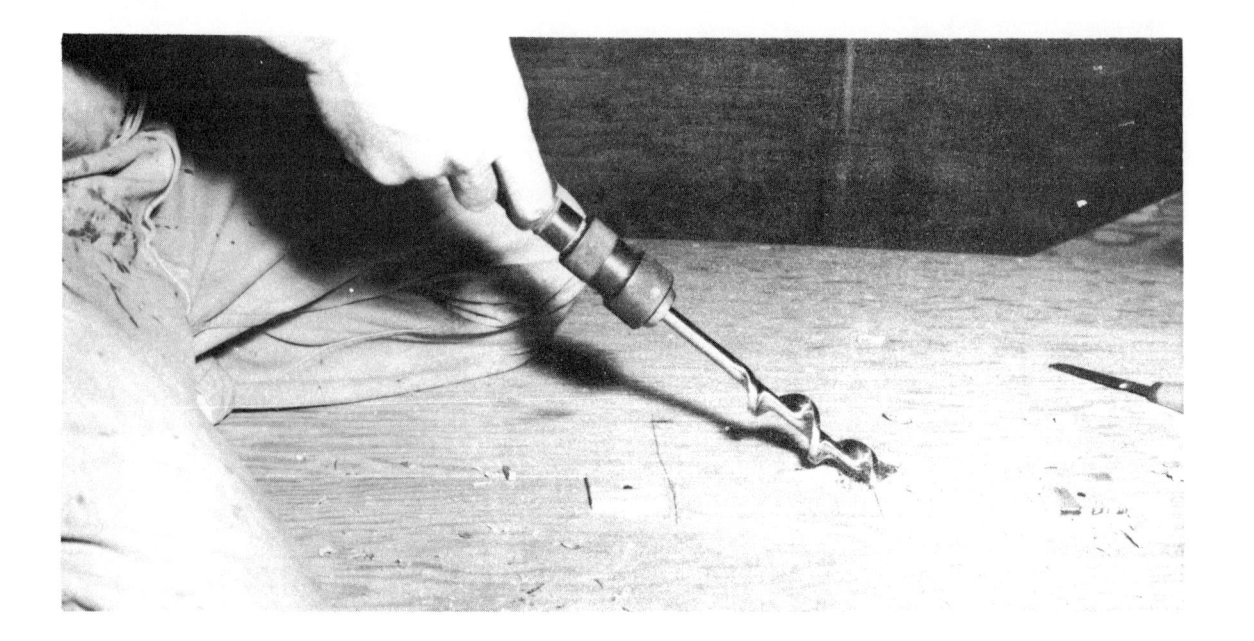

FIG. 12-2 — The hole to be drilled is generally large enough to allow at least ⅜″ overall diameter clearance. With a 1″ shaft, for example, a 1⅜″ shaft hole should be bored. Some prefer not to use an auger as the point tends to track with the grain. The same would hold true for an expansive bit. A ship's auger or a "barefoot" auger are better, especially if the hole is long, or a drill with a welded-on extension can be used. The hole is bored by starting the drill in the cleft point after removing all fastenings that may be in way of the shaft hole.

141

FIG. 12-3 — By gradually bringing the drill down, the hole may be bored. Note that the template taken from the line indicating the shaft angle with the bottom of the boat is used as a guide to determine the angularity. One person drilling and another checking the angle will assure correct alignment and direction of the operation.

FIG. 12-4 — When the shaft angle or the hole is long, an electrician's extension for the drill can be used. If a block of wood is fastened to the inside of the boat, the hole will be cleanly drilled without splintering out on the inside.

FIG. 12-5 — A boring tool for drilling a shaft hole. The tubular hole saw threads onto the boring bar. Note in the blow-up the saw teeth filed onto the end.

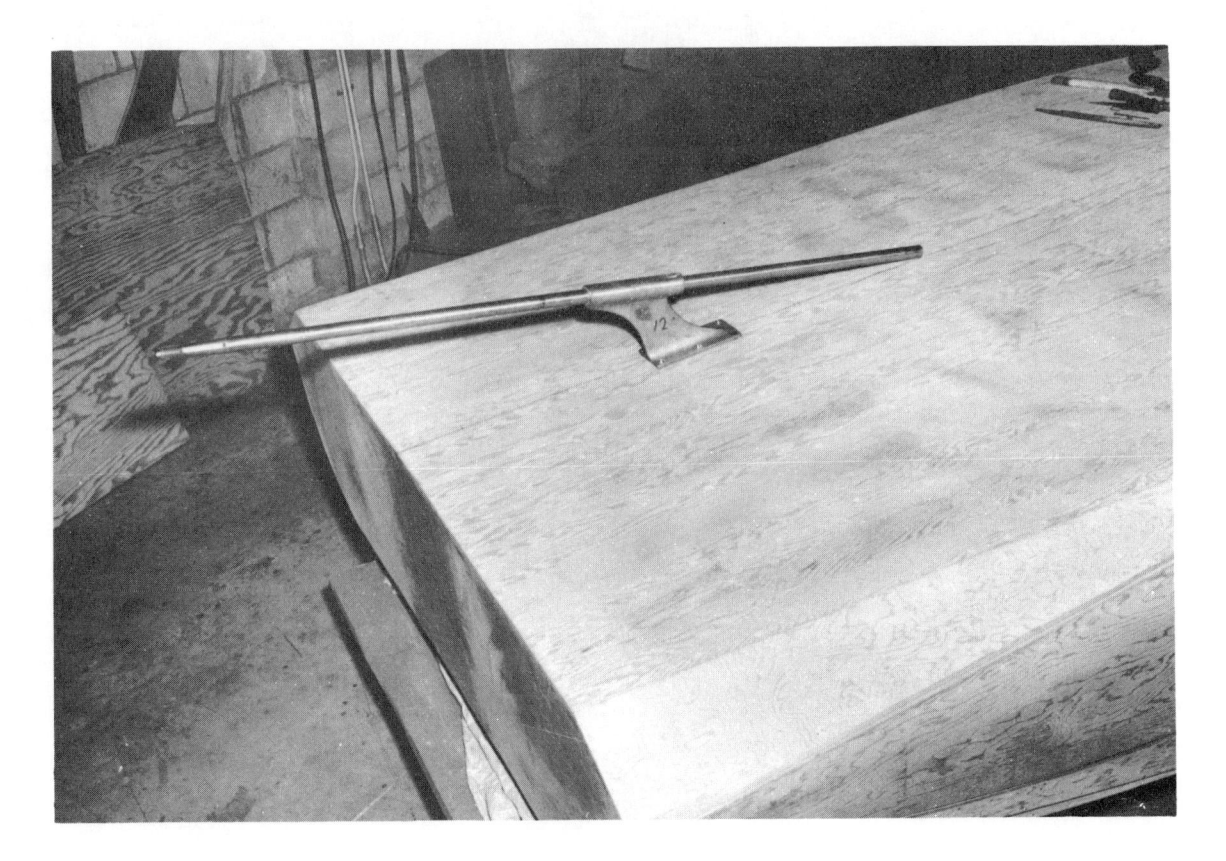

FIG. 12-6 — The strut is bolted into position in the manner described in Chapter 8. The boring tool shaft is then slipped through the strut.

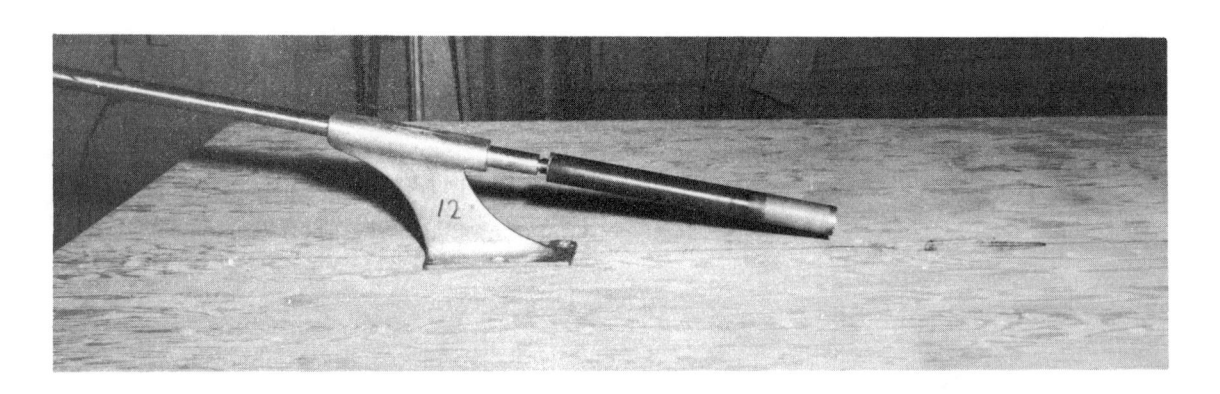

FIG. 12-7 — The boring tool shaft is threaded into the boring bit. Note that this shaft is the same size as the propeller shaft in order to fit into the strut firmly.

FIG. 12-8 — An electric drill is used to drive the boring tool. Starting the boring tool bit will require some pressure downward from a block of wood held by a helper to prevent the drill from creeping out of position. Alternately, a block of wood pre-drilled at the required angle as shown in PLATE 39 could be used.

FIG. 12-9 — The hole is drilled through clearly and rapidly. Shaft drilling can be accomplished in a matter of minutes with this tool.

the angularity required for the shaft hole (see Plate 39). The hole is used as a guide in the block to drill the shaft hole with a standard auger or expansive bit. Regardless of the method, the side opposite the one where the drilling is being done should have a block secured firmly in position so that the drill will make a clean splinter-free hole when breaking through.

Certain precautions should be made before boring the hole. By closely following the illustrations and captions, the task can probably be performed with a minimum of errors. Careful checking should be made throughout the operation to assure that the bore is going true. If a helper is available, careful sighting can be made in both directions. Any kind of a suitable guide or "jig" will help make the bore straight and true. Care should be taken to assure that no fastenings will interfere with the bit. If possible, any fastenings or bolts which are obviously in the way should be withdrawn and/or relocated. If the hole is not perfectly straight and true but is large enough, it may have little consequence on the installation as long as the shaft clears. An old trick of shipwrights is to ream out an untrue shaft bore with a red hot iron on wood hulls to "correct" an untrue shaft bore. However, always keep a fire extinguisher handy if using such a procedure.

There is another easy way of drilling shaft holes, much used by the professional builder. This method uses a special made tool (see Fig. 12-5) that consists of a hole saw or hollow boring bit on one end of a shaft of the diameter required for the hole. The hole saw can be made by using a length of seamless tubing with teeth filed on one

end. The length of the tube can be a foot or two depending on the length of the hole. The other end has a threaded portion welded at the tip to accommodate the boring shaft. The tube will need to be heat-treated after filing the teeth to harden them. As the teeth make the cut, the tube will fill with the excess material from the cut. Since the tube and the boring shaft are threaded together, the boring bar and tube can be withdrawn from the hole in making long cuts and the two pieces separated to clean out the tube before boring farther. With this tool, just about any length of hole can be made.

In use, the strut is located first and bolted in position. The boring bar, which is the same diameter as the shaft to be used, is inserted in the strut bearing to serve as a guide in drilling the hole. Usually, in starting the hole in the bottom of the boat, the hole saw will tend to creep forward. Holding a block with downward pressure on the hole saw will tend to cut a cleft similar to that shown in Fig. 12-1 in order to give the drill a chance to start to bite. The boring bar is powered by an electric drill and will do a quick job (see Figs. 12-6 thru 12-9).

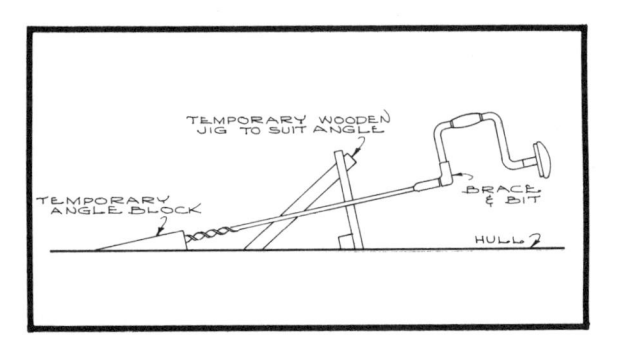

**PLATE 39 — This brace jig can be used as a guide in boring the shaft hole in a wood boat.**

# CHAPTER 13 — MOUNTING & ALIGNING THE MOTOR

If building a new boat, it is best to install and mount the engine prior to closing in the hull with the deck, cabin, or cockpit structure. This statement applies also to the installation of tanks, exhaust systems, and any other components that will be easier to install without the various structural units causing interference. The typical inboard motor installation, together with all the ancillary systems, takes quite a bit of planning and "head scratching" if the installation is to progress in an orderly sequence, so plan ahead!

The typical inboard straight shaft or vee drive installation uses motor stringers to take the load of the motor and distribute it to the hull. In most boats, the motor stringers are usually a part of the structure and are already installed. If a boat is to be repowered and a change is required in the motor stringers, the previous installation can be used as a guide. If building a new boat, the motor stringers are usually detailed on the plans. Materials used to make the motor stringers will vary depending on the hull construction material and other factors. Wood is used for motor stringers on most wood and plywood boats, while wood may also be used in fiberglass boats, either in the same way as they are used in wood boats, or bonded and fiberglassed into the hull. In some cases, special foam and fiberglass motor

stringers, or a molded-in "grid", may be provided for mounting the motors in a fiberglass hull. With metal boats, the motor stringers (or "foundation" as it is often called in the case of metal boats) are usually of the same material as the hull, and designed as an integral structure. In all boats, the motor stringers must be rigidly and strongly installed. Rolling, pitching, slamming, thrust, and torque forces can cause tremendous loads to be exerted onto these members as well as onto the hull structure itself. Steel plates or angles are often used on top of wood and fiberglass stringers for additional strength.

The spacing of the motor stringers must match that required for the motor used. If the motor will be mounted directly to the motor stringers, they must have the same center-to-center spacing as the motor mounts. If the motor will be mounted to motor beds which will, in turn, be mounted to the motor stringers, the motor stringers must be spaced far enough apart to allow clearance for the motor mounts to fit between them. In some cases, it may be necessary to cut away a portion of a motor stringer to allow clearance for some part of the engine. However, this should always be kept to a minimum and any motor stringer that has been cut away must be reinforced in that area. This is done in the case of wood stringers by bonding a layer of plywood to one or both sides of a solid

FIG. 13-1 — The engine coupling flanges must be aligned carefully. A feeler gage is shown being used to match the coupling alignment within .003".

FIG. 13-2 — After the motor is aligned in position, the motor beds that fit between the motor stringers are bolted in place.

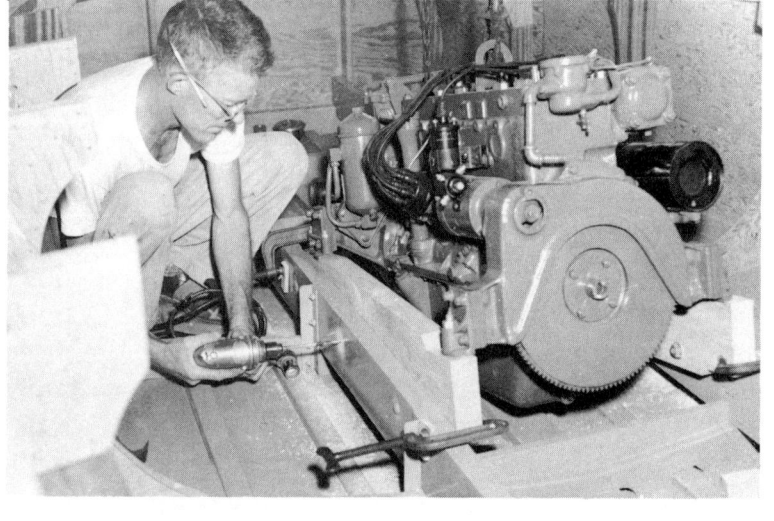

FIG. 13-3 — The completed installation. Note the metal angles at the junction of the motor stringers to the frames to spread the stresses out over the boat's structure.

wood stringer, or by the use of metal plates. In other cases, a frame or portion of it may be cut away as well, and it must be reinforced in a similar manner. If the frame must be cut away severely, a new frame or two may be required adjacent to the area.

If the motor stringers must be placed in the hull, a taut string or wire can be lead through the shaft hole to locate the engine centerline. This can be used as a reference for locating the tops of the motor stringers and/or motor beds, depending on the installation method. A drawing available from the motor manufacturer, or the actual engine, should be verified as to the location and position of the motor mounts. In some cases, the mounts will be in a straight line on either side of the engine, while in other cases, they may be staggered with the front mount usually somewhat lower than the rear mount to suit the angle at which the engine will be mounted. If the engine will mount to the top of the motor stringers, the motor stringers should be positioned from 1/16" to ½" or more below the level of the motor mounts to allow clearance for the mounts, shims, or wedges, which may be used for alignment.

Using the motor bed to motor stringer installation has an important advantage that makes it quick and easy, both in installing and aligning the engine. The motor, mounted on the motor beds, is dropped into the correct location and temporarily held in position with clamps holding the motor beds to the motor stringers. Loosening the clamps allows the motor to be shifted as required to achieve accurate alignment with the motor coupling. It may also be necessary to align the motor crossways, and this is usually done by

slotting the motor mounting holes slightly, or using bolts slightly smaller than in the motor mounts. When everything is in alignment, bolts are driven through the motor beds and motor stringers in perfect alignment. Carriage bolts are commonly used, however, other bolts may be used as long as the heads are accessible. In any installation of this type, at least four ⅜" bolts per member should be used, or bolts should be not less than 6" apart well staggered. An installation of this type is shown in Figs. 13-1 thru 13-3. In some boats used for competition or heavy duty use, metal backing plates are often used under the bolts and nuts against the motor stringers. This practice prevents the fastenings from recessing into the wood and also distributes the stresses over a larger area.

The method just described is simple, but there are many possibilities. It is possible to simply drop the engine into position without the beds, align the motor as closely as possible by blocking to the bottom of the hull or hanging it from a chain hoist. With the motor in this position, beds or brackets are slipped in and assembled. Upon release of the strain on the hoist or blocking, the motor will be somewhat out of alignment. This is overcome by slipping washers or shim stock under the various motor mount points to align the motor correctly. While a rather tedious and somewhat archaic process, the procedures are often used by boat manufacturers, especially in vee drive installations where alignment is not as critical (see Fig. 13-4). However, in straight line installations, the procedures can be tedious, since every-time one point is tightened down, the alignment is thrown out. It is simply a

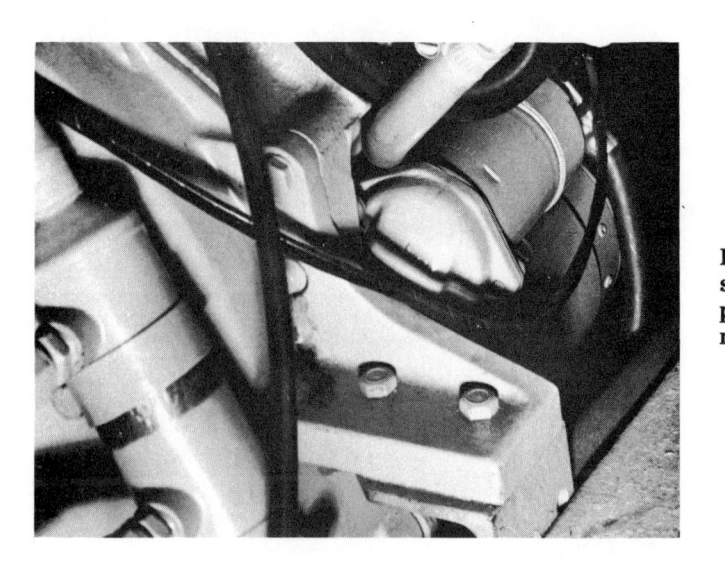

FIG. 13-4 — Angle clip mounts such as this are sometimes used on the vee drive type boat since precision alignment is more difficult than the motor bed type of installation.

FIG. 13-5 — A flexible type engine mount. (Courtesy of Globe Rubber Works, Rockland, Mass.)

FIG. 13-6 — These adjustable flexible rubber mounts help eliminate vibration and noise. When flexible mounts are used, a flexible coupling must be used to couple the motor to the propeller shaft in the in-line installation.

matter of trial-and-error until each point is brought into correct alignment. This procedure has been largely outmoded by the use of adjustable as well as flexible motor mounts. These types of mounts make fine adjustment at each mount possible and speed the alignment process. If flexible couplings are used, the use of flexible mounts is necessary as well. Some examples are shown by Fig. 13-5 and Fig. 13-6.

Regardless of the mounting method, the motor should be carefully aligned in position. The shaft should be blocked into position either at the shaft hole or at the shaft log position. With the self-aligning shaft log, there will no doubt be considerable spring in the shaft from the stern bearing or strut. The position of the shaft should be adjusted in such a way that it will turn freely and not bind at the bearing, checking carefully to assure that it is

FIG. 13-7 — This motor mount for a vee drive installation on an automobile conversion is an integral mount, cam cover plate, and pump drive, with the water pump mounted to it. The mount bolts to special angle clips which in turn bolt to the motor stringers. (Courtesy of Nicson Engineering, Santa Fe Springs, Calif.)

## OMC INBOARDS

Premature failure of all seals; gears and bearings; loss of RPM; vibration; or gear noise may be caused by a bent prop shaft or misalignment between the transmission output flange and shaft coupling.

### BEFORE ATTEMPTING FINAL ALIGNMENT. . . .

1. Check shaft coupler pilot diameter (2.499" to 2.501") and output flange pilot bore diameter (2.497" to 2.499"). There should be a light resistance between the coupler pilot and the output flange pilot bore during assembly. See Figure 1.
2. Check strut bearing to shaft clearance. Shaft diameters from ¾" to 1½" must have a total minimum clearance of .003" and a total maximum clearance of .007". See Figure 2.
3. Check the shaft coupler to propeller shaft fit. The coupler should be a light press fit and may be heated slightly to allow easier assembly. A coupler which is a few thousandths of an inch too large for a particular shaft will distort as the set screws are tightened. See Figure 3.
4. Check strut alignment. The shaft must be centered in the shaft log and the strut bearing. The packing gland and hose should be removed from the shaft log for this check. See Figure 4.
5. Check the propeller shaft, propeller shaft coupling, and transmission output flange for straightness. The fixture (Figure 5) is inexpensive and very reliable for checking the shaft and coupler. The maximum total runout for ¾" to 1½" shafts are as follows: Check at quarter points and center: See Figure 5.

| LENGTH | PERMISSIBLE VARIATION (Throw in one Complete Revolution) |
|---|---|
| Up to 3' | .005" |
| 3' to 4' | .0065" |
| 4' to 5' | .008" |
| 5' to 6' | .0095" |
| 6' to 7' | .011" |
| 7' to 8' | .0125" |
| 8' to 9' | .014" |
| 9' to 10' | .015" |

Permissible maximum total runout at coupler face is .002". See Figure 5.

### TROUBLESHOOTING

Check for straightness of these components in the boat in the following manner:
a. Remove the bolts from the couplers.
b. Using a .002" feeler gauge, check the air gap at 90 degree intervals between coupler and output flange. Maximum permissible air gap is .002". See Figure 6.
c. Rotate the shaft 360 degrees, stopping at 90 degree intervals, and recheck air gap. See Figure 7.
d. Note any change in position of air gap which will indicate a bent shaft or coupler.
e. To determine if the shaft is bent or the coupler defective, rotate the coupler 180 degrees on the shaft and note any change in position of air gap. See Figure 3. If the air gap position changes, the coupler is defective. If the air gap position does not change, the shaft is bent. See Figure 7.

It may be necessary to rework the shaft and coupler to obtain a light press fit. See checkpoint 3.

Holding the shaft and coupler in position, rotate the output flange 360 degrees, again noting any change of air gap position. The total permissible runout is .002". If the air gap position changes, the output flange may be defective.

Do not attempt to check runout of the output flange with a dial indicator! Only after checking the above items should the engine be adjusted to obtain final alignment. See Figure 8.

Final alignment is accomplished by changing the position of the engine using the micro-mount to obtain a maximum of .002" air gap between the output flange and shaft coupler faces in any position.

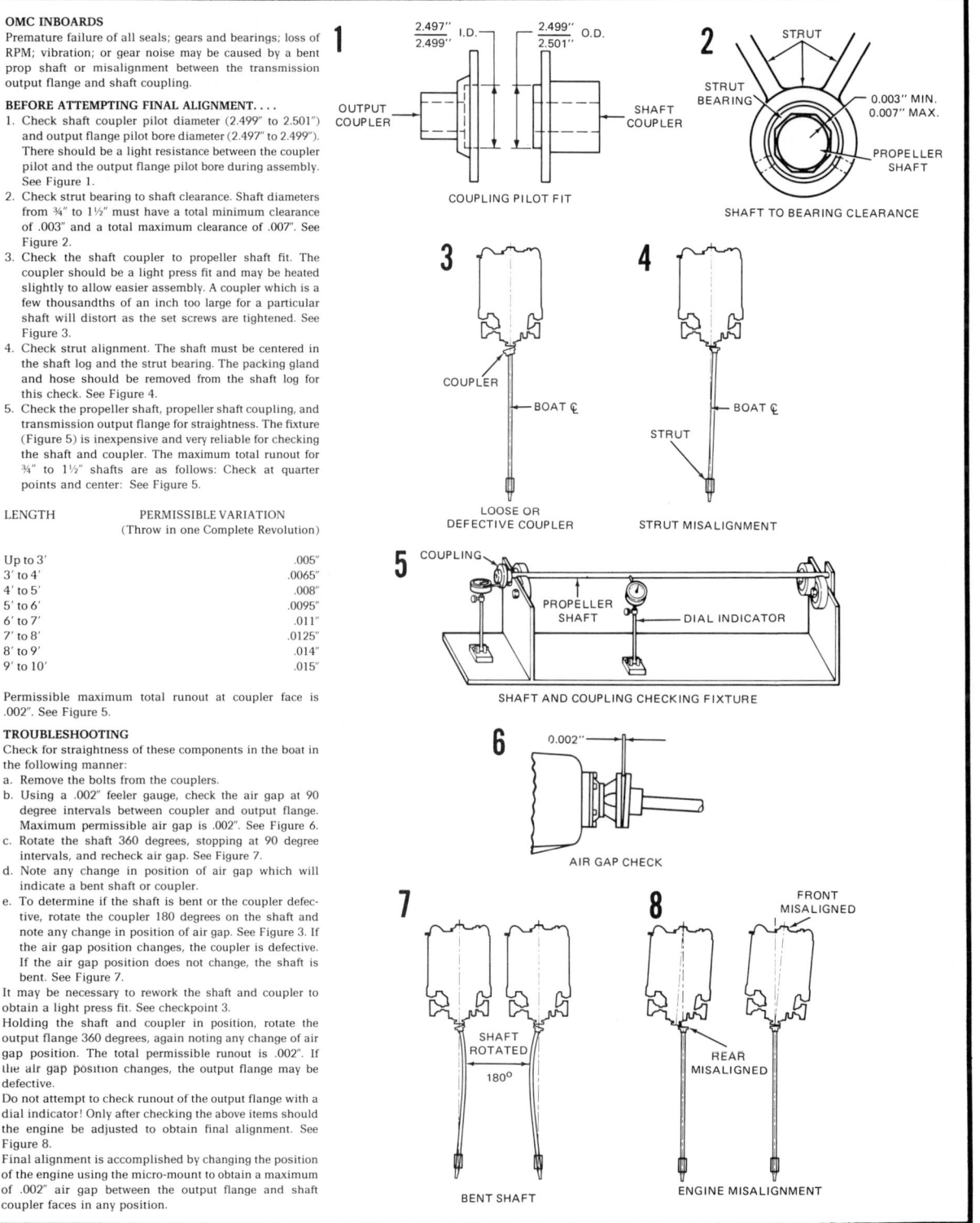

1. COUPLING PILOT FIT — 2.497"/2.499" I.D. — 2.499"/2.501" O.D. — OUTPUT COUPLER — SHAFT COUPLER

2. SHAFT TO BEARING CLEARANCE — STRUT — STRUT BEARING — 0.003" MIN. 0.007" MAX. — PROPELLER SHAFT

3. LOOSE OR DEFECTIVE COUPLER — COUPLER — BOAT ℄

4. STRUT MISALIGNMENT — BOAT ℄ — STRUT

5. SHAFT AND COUPLING CHECKING FIXTURE — COUPLING — PROPELLER SHAFT — DIAL INDICATOR

6. AIR GAP CHECK — 0.002"

7. BENT SHAFT — SHAFT ROTATED 180°

8. ENGINE MISALIGNMENT — FRONT MISALIGNED — REAR MISALIGNED

**PLATE 40 — The propeller shaft and engine alignment procedures recommended by one manufacturer of marine engines. While other engines may have certain variations, the basic procedures are similar with all straight shaft inboard installations. (Courtesy of OMC, Waukegan, Ill.)**

located on the centerline of the boat. A temporary brace can be used across the stringers to hold the shaft in place for alignment.

When the motor coupling is aligned to the shaft coupling, great care should be taken. Bring the motor into alignment to the shaft coupling flange. Don't force the shaft to line up with the motor. With the motor in neutral, the shaft should turn easily and smoothly without binding. If a spot binds, check the alignment again. In aligning the couplings, a .003″ or thinner feeler gage should be used. Check around the entire flange to assure correct alignment. If the alignment is not correct, shim, shift, or adjust the mount until it is. If a feeler gage is not available, use four strips of paper located around the flange equally spaced between the two flange faces. Any variation in alignment will be indicated by the looseness of one or more of the strips. Extra time spent in careful alignment will be worthwhile in terms of smoothness and added reliability. While somewhat tedious, the process is not really difficult. The alignment procedures are often specified by the motor manufacturer, an example of which is given by Plate 40.

Many types of boats are actually somewhat flexible and will change shape or "settle" somewhat after being launched. An additional check should be made of the alignment between the connecting flanges after the boat has been launched, and in the case of certain boats, at protracted intervals thereafter. In larger boats, it is advisable to leave the flanges loose and do the final adjusting when the boat is in the water. Additional checking should be made until no more change is noticed.

## ENGINE DRIP PANS

In many boats is it desirable to install an engine drip pan under the engine. Such a drip pan is more common in powerboats than in sailboats because a deep enough pan is often not possible in sailboats to overcome the effects of heeling which can cause any oil in the pan to overflow and enter the bilge, thereby negating the purpose of the pan in the first place. Drip pans can be made out of a variety of metals such as copper or galvanized steel, or can be molded to suit from fiberglass. A drain cock is often placed in the drip pan at the low point so that the contents can be drained into a container or pumped out. Insulation should be provided under the drip pan since the vibration of the engine can cause drumming between it and the hull structure. If a drip pan is desired, it should be installed prior to the engine, and should be larger in area than the engine itself and of ample capacity.

# CHAPTER 14 — COOLING SYSTEMS

Basically there are two types of engine cooling systems; raw water cooling and closed cooling systems. Raw water cooling uses the water that the boat floats in, and is also known as "sea water cooling". A closed cooling system uses fresh water or liquid coolant (a combination of fresh water and anti-freeze with perhaps other additives just as in an automobile) circulated through the engine and then passed through a cooler and recirculated. Such a system is often called "fresh water cooling".

A thermostat or temperature regulating device is usually included in the cooling system to control the temperature of the coolant. The coolant should be at least 135 degrees for either the raw water or closed cooling system. In salt water use, the raw water cooling system should keep the engine temperature under 160 degrees in order to minimize salt precipitation and corrosion. With a closed cooling system, temperatures can be increased to 185 degrees. When an engine is raw water cooled, it should be provided with a pump that is of the self-priming type which will operate whenever the engine is operating. A temperature gage should be used to check the temperature of every cooling system.

Just like the automobile engine, the boat engine requires fluid cooling of all the normal jacketed areas of the engine. However, unlike the automobile, additional cooling must be provided to the exhaust manifolds, to the exhaust elbows between the engine and the tail pipe, and sometimes to the transmission and reduction gear. On many boats a separate oil cooler is used, usually of a water cooled type. The exhaust line between the engine and the transom or stern is usually also cooled by the flow of used water leaving the boat's cooling system. Depending on the type of cooling system there may be variations in the methods used to cool the engine.

## RAW WATER SYSTEMS

The typical raw water cooled engine uses a pump (see Fig. 14-1) driven by the engine to draw in water through a

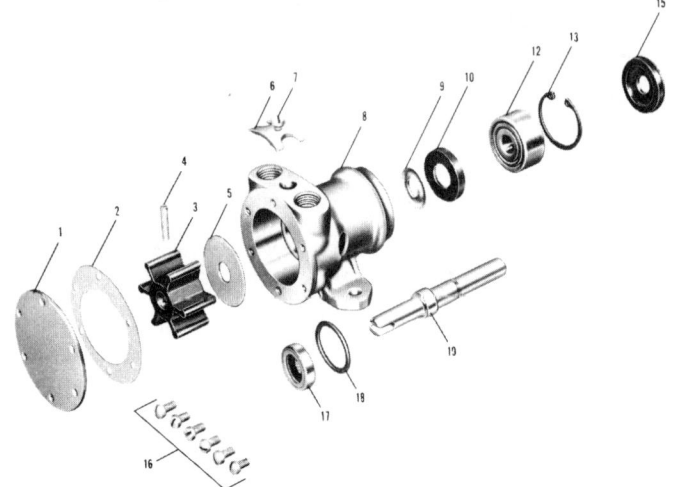

FIG. 14-1 — A typical marine engine water pump.

FIG. 14-2 — A water pick-up or inlet to provide cooling water to the engine. (Courtesy of Glenwood Marine Equipment)

scoop or water pick-up (see Fig. 14-2) located on the outside of the hull below the waterline. Usually the water pick-up is one size larger than the inlet of the water pump to assure adequate cooling water. The position of the water pick-up will vary depending on the boat, but the location should be as close to the motor as possible. In boats operating at normal speeds, the pick-up can be located at any convenient area adjacent to the motor underwater. However, on high speed boats which may leave the water and become air-born at times, the pick-up should be at the stern in a clear area where a positive flow of water will be assured. It is usually located away from the propeller and not behind any underwater appendages. In competition boats which will turn only in one direction, the pick-up should be placed on the side the turn is being made. Thus on a counter-clockwise course, the pick-up

would be on the left or port side. In some cases, the water pick-up has been incorporated into the underwater equipment such as a rudder, strut or skeg on racing boats (see Fig. 14-3). Since the water pick-up is usually a thru-hull fitting, see the section later in the chapter for installation recommendations.

The raw water cooling system in its most basic form draws in water through the water pick-up, directs it through the engine, and passes it out through the boat's exhaust system. In certain high-speed race boats not intended for idling, such a type of "forced water" cooling can be used. Because of the boat's forward momentum, sufficient water can be forced through the boat's cooling system as long as the water pick-up is properly located and sized. A water pump is not used in this case since the race boat people consider this a waste of power and an unnecessary addition of weight.

However, for normal pleasure boat operation where a wide variety of

FIG. 14-3 — A rudder with integral water pick-up. Water enters at the bottom of the rudder, flows through a tube in the rudder, and exits out the top opening. Hoses at the opening feed the water into the boat. This item is specifically intended for high speed competition boats that have little in the water but the propeller and rudder.

speeds will be common, including idling, a water pump is a necessity. This more common system may include the addition of an oil cooler in the line ahead of the engine. The cooling water enters the engine driven pump where the water is passed through the exhaust manifolds and enters the engine block at preferably the lowest possible point in the block. The water is circulated through the block and then passed into the exhaust line beyond the manifolds, leaving the block at preferably the highest point. The water discharged into the exhaust

line should enter into the line at least 6″ below the manifold outlet to prevent water from entering the engine and damaging it (if not fitted with risers). This exhaust water cools the exhaust line and helps muffle the sound. The spent cooling water leaves the boat normally at the stern through an exhaust port located at or just above the waterline in most boats.

For better temperature control, a thermostat may be used in the system which can be used to recirculate a portion of the water back to the exhaust manifolds and engine jackets (see

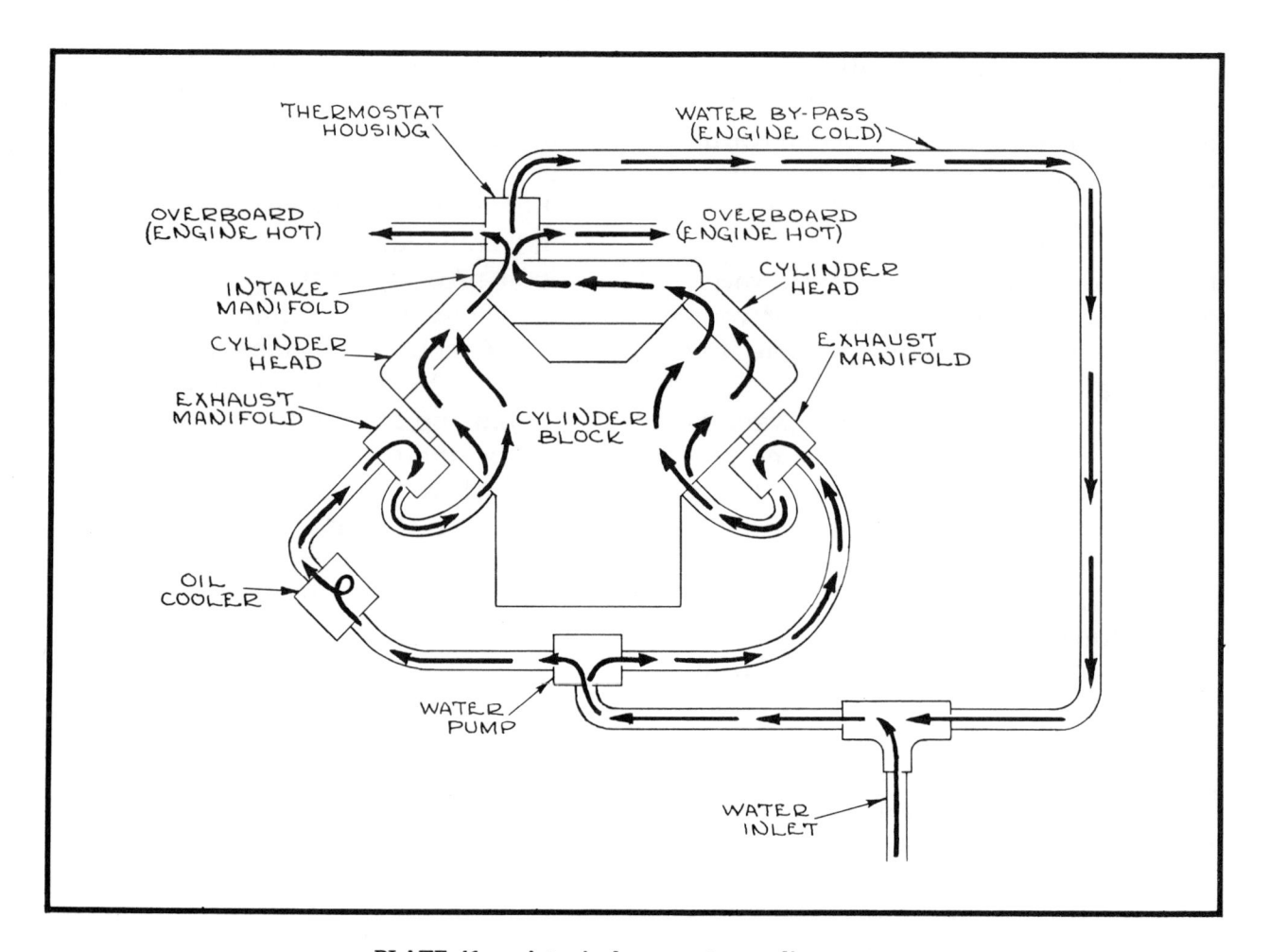

**PLATE 41 — A typical raw water cooling system circulation diagram.**

155

Plate 41). This is handy during starting for faster warm-ups. However, thermostats with raw water cooling tend to cause troubles due to corrosion, and often a gate valve in the line is used instead. With the gate valve, the operator can determine the suitable opening of the valve to control the amount of water that is recirculated (if any) and use this to control temperature, which under most conditions frequently proves to be fairly constant. In this instance, the thermostat can be dispensed with.

There are a couple of other variations on the raw water cooling system. One uses a diverter to pump cooling water directly to the exhaust manifold, while a portion of the cooling water is diverted to the engine jackets and thermostat (see Plate 42). When warm, the thermostat allows the water to pass on to the exhaust manifold and overboard into the exhaust line with the balance of the cooling water. However, during warm-up the thermostat diverts the water back to the pump where it is recirculated back into the engine. The difference here is that DIRECT water is entering the engine without being preheated by the manifolds first. Some engine manufacturers use this system, but the proportion of cooling water being diverted must be carefully determined.

A variation on the above system includes the two-pump system. One pump draws in water and distributes some of it directly to the manifolds in the same way, and sends the rest of it to another high volume circulating pump similar to that used on automobiles. This pump circulates this volume of water through the block and heads. A thermostat diverts the water

back to the pump where it is recirculated, or diverts the water not required on to the exhaust manifolds and out the exhaust line depending on temperature conditions. The purported advantage of this more sophisticated system is that more uniform temperatures can be maintained in the entire engine for supposedly better efficiency.

## ENGINE PLUMBING

A high grade of marine quality multiply heavy-duty hose should be used from the water pick-up gate valve or seacock to the pump. Hose clamps should be made from all stainless steel of the worm screw band type. Never restrict any line in the cooling system. Hoses and pipes must never be smaller than the inlet size of the pump. Gradual bends of maximum radius are desirable for the inlet hose to prevent kinks and collapsing. Never use elbows or other restrictive fittings at the inlet or anywhere in the cooling system plumbing. A constant-primed pump is assured if the inlet water hose is higher at some point than the pump. In other words, there should be a high loop somewhere ahead of the pump. Check valves at the inlet may be used to provide the pump with water at all times. With a properly set up system, however, these are not ordinarily necessary.

When the smaller trailerable type of inboard boat with raw water cooling is used in salt or brackish waters, some method of flushing out the motor with fresh water during lay-ups is desirable. This can readily be done by providing a coupling in the hose immediately after it leaves the pump. The use of a standard type hose coupling will en-

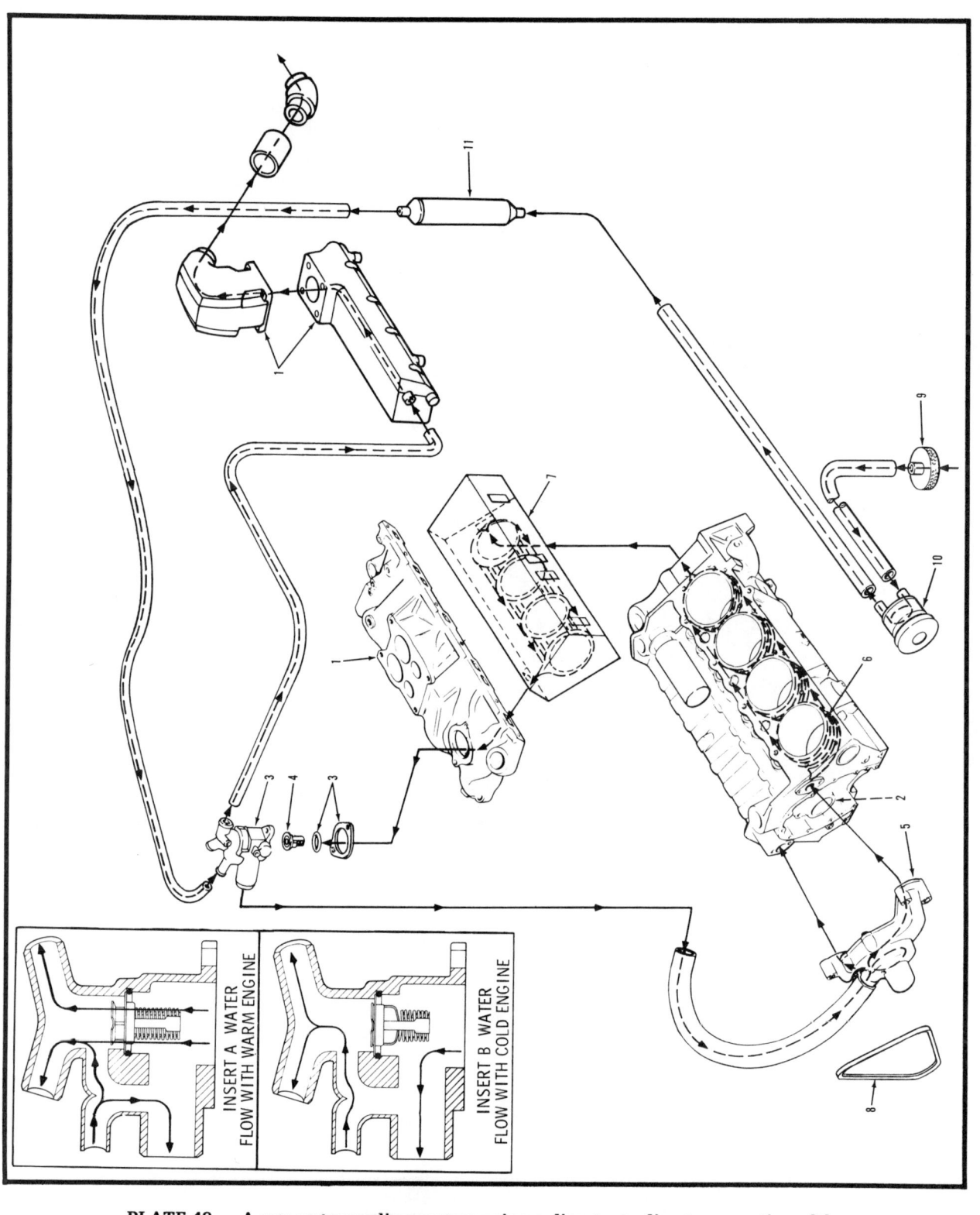

**PLATE 42** — A raw water cooling system using a diverter to direct one portion of the water directly to the manifolds and another portion to the engine block. When the engine is cold, a thermostat allows water to be recirculated through the engine block for faster warm-up. (Courtesy of OMC, Waukegan, Ill.)

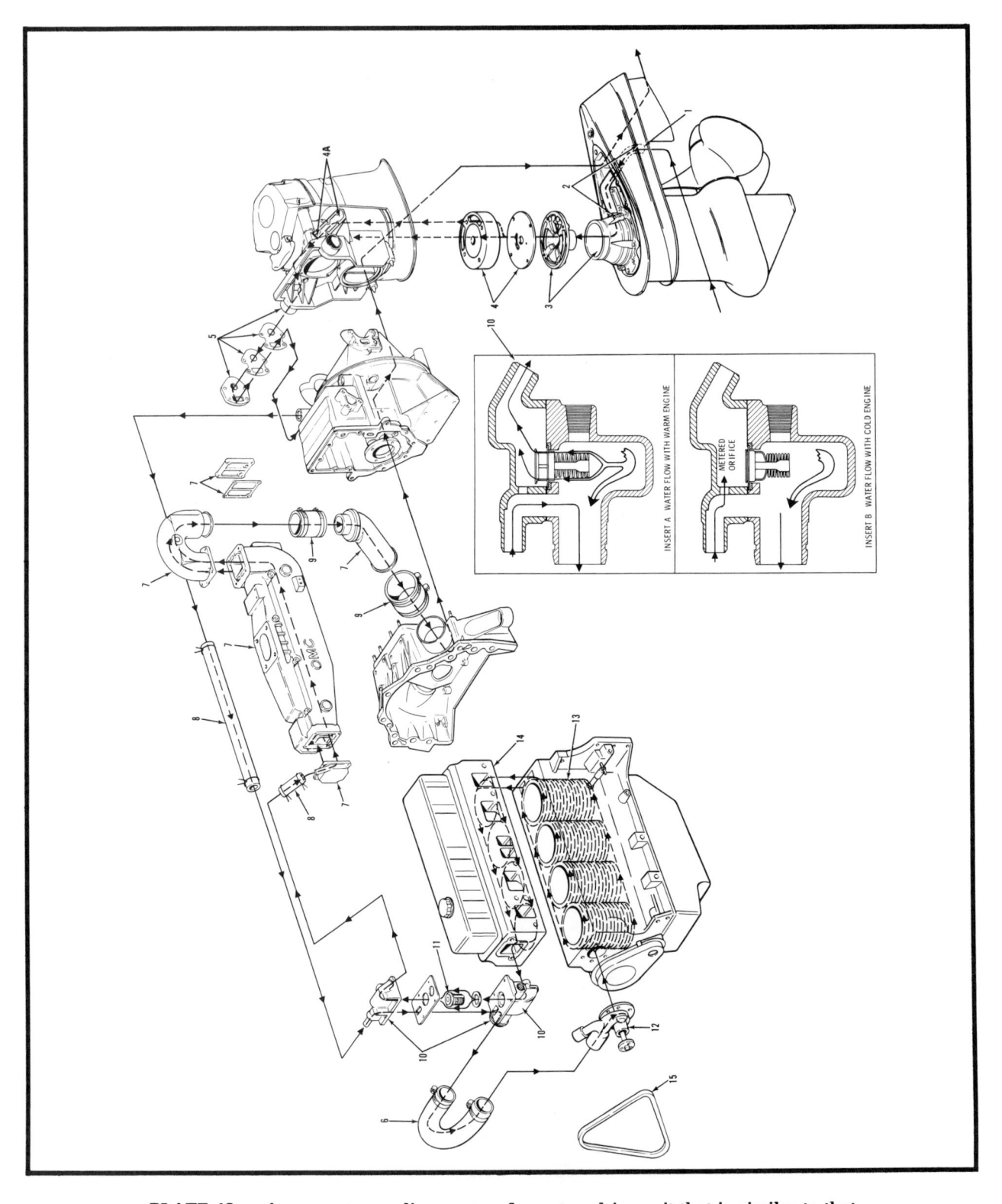

**PLATE 43** — A raw water cooling system for a sterndrive unit that is similar to that shown in PLATE 42. Note that the water intake is through the sterndrive pick-up and used water is expelled out the sterndrive via the exhaust. (Courtesy of OMC, Waukegan, Ill.)

able a garden hose to be used for flushing out the motor. When this method is used, running the motor is not required. The rubber impeller pumps common on many motors should never be run without water being pumped through the pump since the impeller may burn up.

## THRU-HULL FITTINGS

Various fittings in the boat will pass through the hull either above or below the waterline. Special attention should be given to all such fittings, especially those below the waterline. Obviously, failure of one of these fittings could cause the boat to sink. The common thru-hull fittings concerning the engine on an inboard installation include the water pick-up and the exhaust line. A typical thru-hull fitting is shown in Fig. 14-4. A general rule is that all thru-hull fittings should be equipped with some type of valve at or adjacent to such a fitting that can be shut down to keep the water from coming through the fitting. However, certain exceptions

FIG. 14-4 — A typical thru-hull fitting. This one is made from bronze. (Courtesy of Gross Mechanical Laboratories, Baltimore, Md.)

and variations concerning this rule sometimes apply.

Two types of valves are ordinarily used, either the typical gate valve, or the seacock, which is a full-way type valve especially intended for marine use. A seacock is ALWAYS preferable to a gate valve, although more expensive. A gate valve is much slower in operation, more troubleprone, and the tendency is to use cheaper gate valves which may contain metals not suitable to salt water conditions. Because the gate valve is an in-line installation, there is a possibility of placing a strain on the thru-hull fitting which could lead to an eventual failure. There must be a connection between the gate valve and thru-hull fitting, and this could fail making the gate valve useless.

The seacock, on the other hand, is quick to operate, usually requiring only a quarter turn from full open to full closed positions. When properly installed, seacocks are quite reliable and trouble-free. The seacock must be independently mounted in place so that no strain results. The seacock is bolted through the hull into solid hull members or backing blocks, with plates or large washers used under the nuts on the inside of the hull. The seacock becomes integral with the thru-hull fitting (see Fig. 14-5). The seacock should be bedded in a marine sealant or mastic. Since most seacocks are bronze, they must be insulated by non-conductive mountings when used on metal hulls. There should be ready access to any seacock or valve.

While seacocks are highly recommended aboard boats, there are some arguments which indicate that gate valves or NO valves may be justified. In smaller trailerable boats, especially if

159

used only on fresh water, the use of gate valves may be acceptable to some owners as a means of reducing costs. Then too, on many small runabouts not kept in the water at all times, and which have only a water pick-up below the waterline as the only thru-hull fitting, a valve is often NOT used. The argument goes that if the line fails, an

FIG. 14-5 —A marine seacock and integral thru-hull fitting is generally advisable at all openings below the waterline as opposed to other types of valves. (Courtesy of Gross Mechanical Laboratories, Baltimore, Md.)

obvious stream of water will shoot up while under way, and this can be quickly plugged since on a small boat the fitting will be readily accessible. Admittedly, this is cutting costs to the bare bones, and while such a practice is NOT advised, it is still common.

Another argument concerns the use of seacocks or gate valves on exhaust lines where they exit the boat. In theory, the exhaust line could fail at this point, and perhaps water could enter and flood the boat, especially if the exhaust ports are at or below the waterline. However, such valves can cause trouble, especially if the valves are copper based metals and the engine is a diesel. Not only must the skipper remember to open the exhaust valve before starting the engine each time, but sulphur in diesel exhausts can corrode the valve which could cause it to fail even if closed. Because the exhaust line is often quite large in diameter, a large gate valve or seacock would be required, and these are quite expensive. Therefore, many exhaust installations are not fitted with a gate valve or seacock, and as a precaution, the exhaust ports are located far enough above the waterline to minimize the hazard.

Different types of water pick-ups are available to suit various types of boats and hull materials. Usually the thru-hull fitting has pipe threads which can fit directly into the seacock or valve, or be adapted to standard pipe fittings or pipe-to-hose fittings into the plumbing system. The thru-hull water pick-up may have a built-in water scoop which must be located forward and well away from the propeller, or a separate scoop strainer is fitted over the thru-hull fitting on the outside of the hull.

## WATER FILTERS

In many boats that are raw water cooled, the addition of cooling water intake filters or strainers is necessary or desirable. Where waters are quite sandy or silt laden, or infested with weeds or pollution, the debris must not be allowed to enter the engine's cooling system. Water strainers connected in the cooling line before the pump and oil cooler (if used) keep the system free of possible blockages which could result in overheating and engine damage. Both single and duplex strainers are available (see Fig. 14-6 and Fig. 14-7). The duplex filter is desirable since the boat's engine can be kept running while the clogged filter is shut down and cleaned, and the other filter then used for filtering.

Various types of water strainers are available, with one type being combined with a seacock.

## CLOSED COOLING SYSTEMS

The closed cooling or "fresh water" system is more complicated than the raw water cooling systems, but offers important advantages. Today's powerful high speed motors are considerably lighter in weight than past engines. As such there are many thin walled sections with relatively small water passages, not to mention various aluminum components in certain cases. Add salt water to these conditions and the average motor will have a relatively short life. Another disadvantage of raw water cooling is the variance in temperatures throughout the system. It is true that thermostats have controlled

FIG. 14-6 — This raw water strainer is integral with a seacock at the thru-hull opening. (Courtesy of Gross Mechanical Laboratories, Baltimore, Md.)

FIG. 14-7 — This duplex raw water strainer allows one filter to be cleaned without shutting down the engine, simply by moving the lever to the alternate filter. (Courtesy of Gross Mechanical Laboratories, Baltimore, Md.)

this to a great extent. However, there is still a considerable difference between the temperature of the incoming water and the water circulating through the engine. These differences create "hot spots" and can cause steam locks and cracking under certain conditions. At excessive temperatures the salt will precipitate out of the ocean water and eventually ruin the block or other components. Even in so-called "fresh water", a closed cooling system may be desirable since fresh water conditions are often quite brackish, or contain mud, silt, sand, and chemicals that can be forced into the cooling system and cause problems. Hence the desire and need for closed cooling systems aboard boats even though the cost and complexities are greater.

Various types of closed cooling systems are available, but the major element in all systems is the heat exchanger. A heat exchanger can be compared to the radiator on an automobile. The difference, however, is that instead of having air directed over the radiator to cool the water in it, a supply of cool water is used instead, which removes the heat of the engine's cooling water, transfers this to the water passing through the heat exchanger, and passes it back into the sea. The heat exchanger device keeps the engine's coolant separate from the sea water.

In effect, the closed cooling system is two systems in one. The sea water portion of the system is much like the raw water cooling system. Sea water enters through a water pick-up and is pumped through the heat exchanger and out through the boat's exhaust line or a separate discharge if the exhaust is the dry type. The fresh water portion of the system uses the engine's pump to circulate the coolant through the heat exchanger and engine passages. A thermostat or temperature control valve controls the amount of water that passes through the heat exchanger, or that is recirculated through the engine.

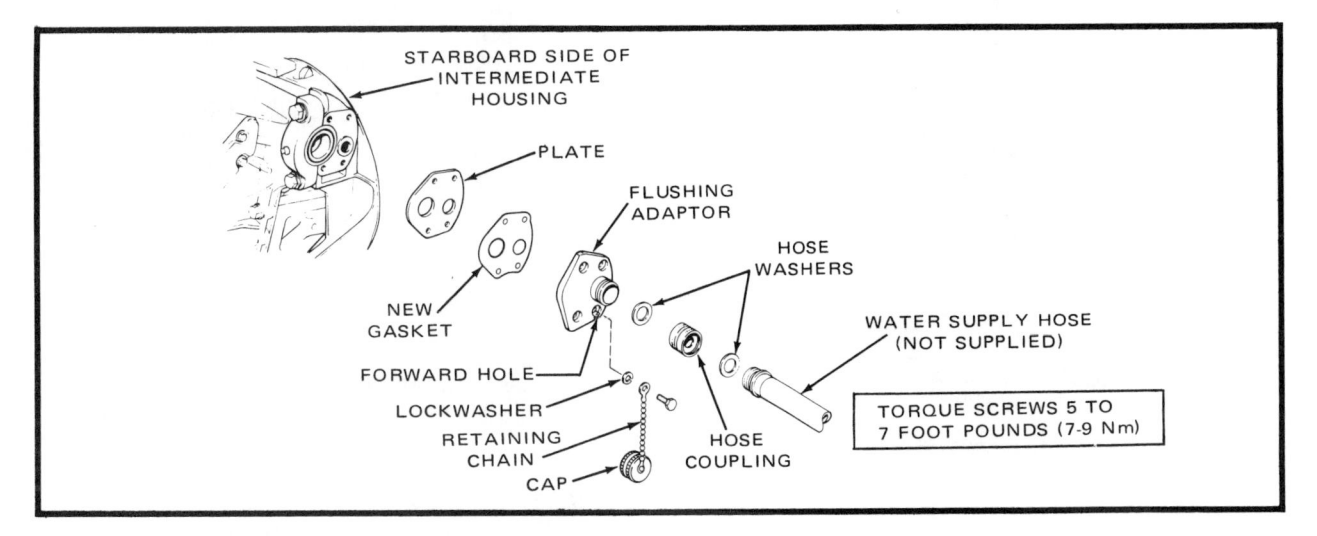

PLATE 44 — The flushing adapter kit available for this sterndrive engine allows the engine to be flushed out with a garden hose adapter through the drive unit. (Courtesy of OMC, Waukegan, Ill.)

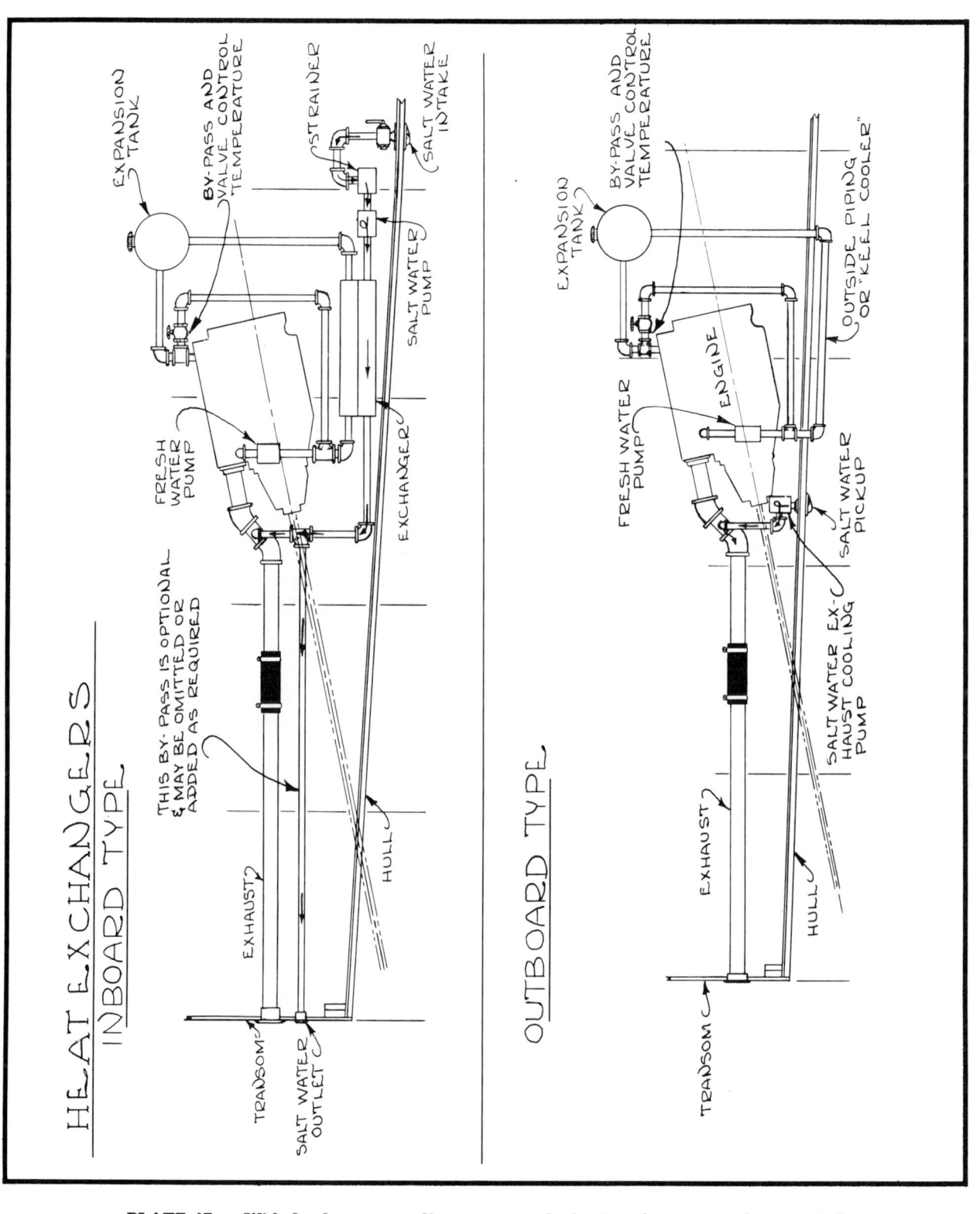

**PLATE 45 — With fresh water cooling systems, the heat exchanger can be mounted either inside the boat or as an appendage on the outside of the hull. For medium to high speed boats, the keel cooler located on the outside of the hull usually creates too much drag and is not practical.**

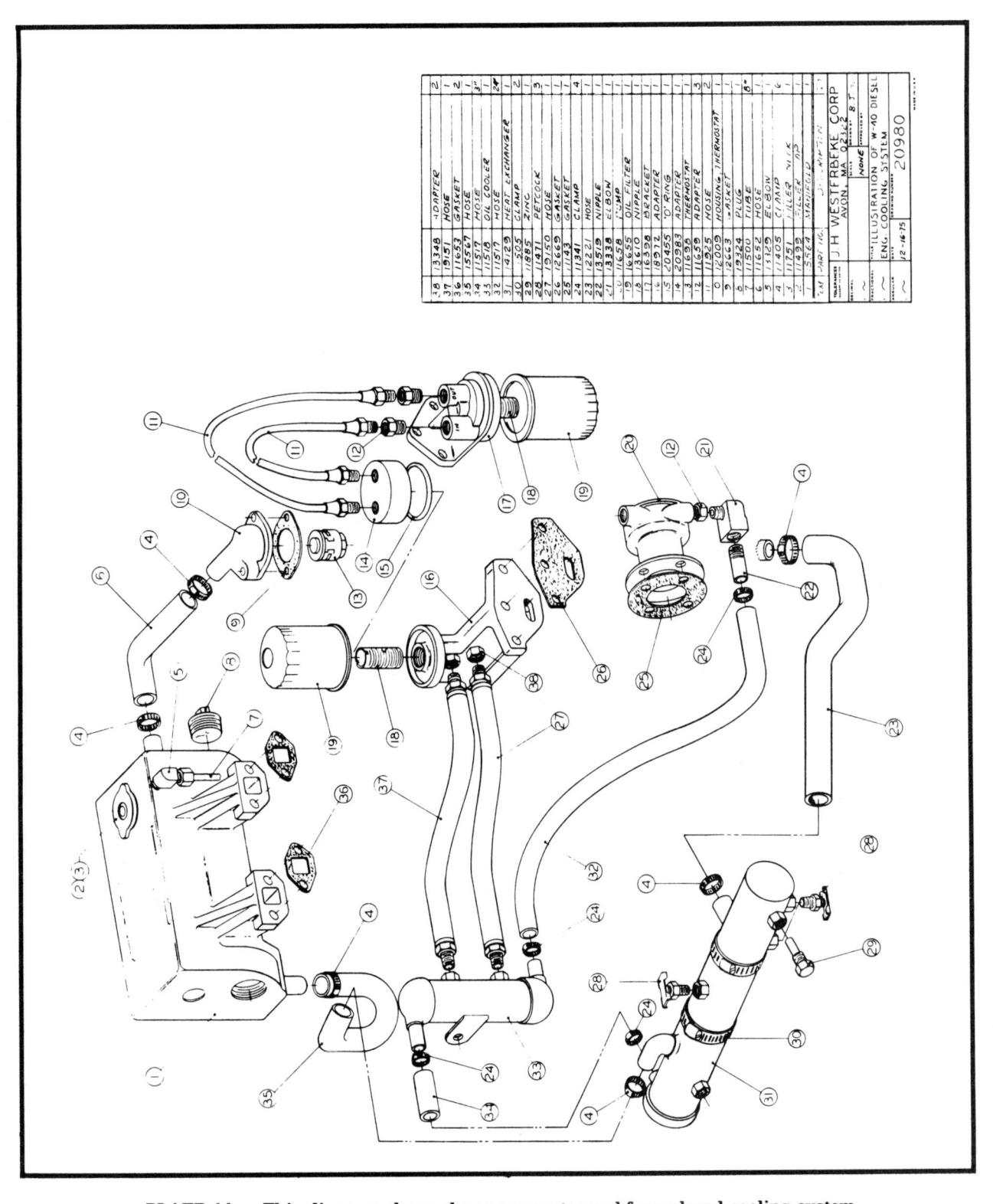

| | | | | |
|---|---|---|---|---|
| 38 | 13348 | ADAPTER | 2 | |
| 37 | 9151 | HOSE | 2 | |
| 36 | 11653 | GASKET | 1 | |
| 35 | 15567 | HOSE | 3" | |
| 34 | 11517 | HOSE | 1 | |
| 33 | 11517 | HOSE | 24 | |
| 32 | 4129 | HEAT EXCHANGER | 1 | |
| 31 | 505 | CLAMP | 2 | |
| 30 | 11885 | ZINC | 1 | |
| 29 | 11471 | PETCOCK | 3 | |
| 28 | 13519 | HOSE | 1 | |
| 27 | 12260 | GASKET | 3 | |
| 26 | 1143 | GASKET | 1 | |
| 25 | 11341 | CLAMP | 4 | |
| 24 | 13338 | HOSE | 1 | |
| 23 | 12221 | HOSE | 1 | |
| 22 | 13519 | NIPPLE | 1 | |
| 21 | 11658 | ELBOW | 8" | |
| 20 | 16655 | PUMP | 1 | |
| 19 | 13610 | OIL FILTER | 1 | |
| 18 | 16372 | NIPPLE | 1 | |
| 17 | 20455 | BRACKET | 1 | |
| 15 | 20983 | ADAPTER | 1 | |
| 14 | 20983 | "O" RING | 1 | |
| 13 | 11635 | ADAPTER | 1 | |
| 12 | 11638 | THERMOSTAT | 3 | |
| 11 | 11025 | ADAPTER | 2 | |
| 10 | 12009 | HOSE | 1 | |
| 9 | 12663 | HOUSING THERMOSTAT | 1 | |
| 8 | 13924 | GASKET | 1 | |
| 7 | 11500 | PLUG | 8" | |
| 6 | 11652 | TUBE | 1 | |
| 5 | 15129 | HOSE | 6 | |
| 3 | 11751 | ELBOW | 1 | |
| 2 | 11492 | CLAMP | 2 | |
| 1 | 5564 | FILLER NECK | 1 | |
| | | FILLER CAP | | |
| | | MANIFOLD | | |

J H WESTERBEKE CORP
AVON MA 02362
ILLUSTRATION OF W-40 DIESEL
ENG. COOLING SYSTEM
20980
12-16-75

**PLATE 46** — This diagram shows the components used for a closed cooling system for a small diesel engine together with lubrication oil cooling. Sea water passes through the heat exchanger although not indicated. (Courtesy of J. H. Westerbeke Corp, Avon, Mass.)

In addition to this, an expansion or "surge" tank is used in the fresh water portion of the system which is much like the reservoir on the radiator of an automobile, and also uses a similar type pressure cap. As with the automobile, the pressure cap prevents boiling and loss of coolant. The expansion tank provides the extra volume necessary as the water temperature increases along with its volume. This is especially important in the short time just after an engine is shut down.

There are basically two closed cooling system configurations; one with the heat exchanger located within the hull, and the other with the heat exchanger located on the outside of the hull (see Plate 45). When the heat exchanger is located on the outside of the hull it is called a "keel cooler". The difference between the heat exchanger and the keel cooler is that the heat exchanger has a housing consisting of tubes within a tube to contain the water. With the keel cooler the tubes are exposed to the sea water and no housing is necessary (see Fig. 14-8 and Fig. 14-9).

The keel cooler type of heat exchanger has both advantages and shortcomings. An advantage is that no sea water pump is required, which can be an important consideration where silt, sand, mud, and debris are a problem. However, on wet exhaust systems a separate pump would still be required to cool the exhaust line, as well as the manifolds, if these are not cooled by the closed cooling system. Because keel coolers are located on the outside of the hull, they cause a certain amount of drag or resistance. In boats operating in the speed ranges of up to 10 to 12 knots, the added drag is usu-

ally not critical. However, for faster hulls, the use of an external keel cooler could prove impractical. Because the keel cooler is located outside of the hull below the waterline, the boat must be hauled out for any maintenance on the keel cooler, and it will be more vulnerable to damage and snagging of lines.

With metal hulls, heat exchangers of either type are frequently not used in the closed cooling system. Instead, through clever design, the cooling can be built into the hull by the use of double skins, or encapsulated areas such as in the keel or skeg appendage, or by grids that circulate water against the hull plating. The engine's cooling water is circulated through these areas and the sea water transfers the heat from the closed system. Obviously, anyone planning such a system must be able to estimate flow rates and cooling capacity requirements to suit any given installation for it to operate properly. There is more to any closed cooling system than merely putting a pipe into the cooling medium and hoping that the amount of heat disipated will do the job.

In closed cooling systems, the exhaust manifold may be cooled either with the fresh water or coolant in the closed system, or directly from the sea water. While it is more desirable to use the closed system to cool the manifolds, it does require more volume and hence a system of greater capacity with additional expense and complexity. Since manifolds are sometimes considered expendable and relatively easy to replace, many elect the simpler system with raw sea water used to cool this portion of the engine. Regardless of the type of cooling system, provi-

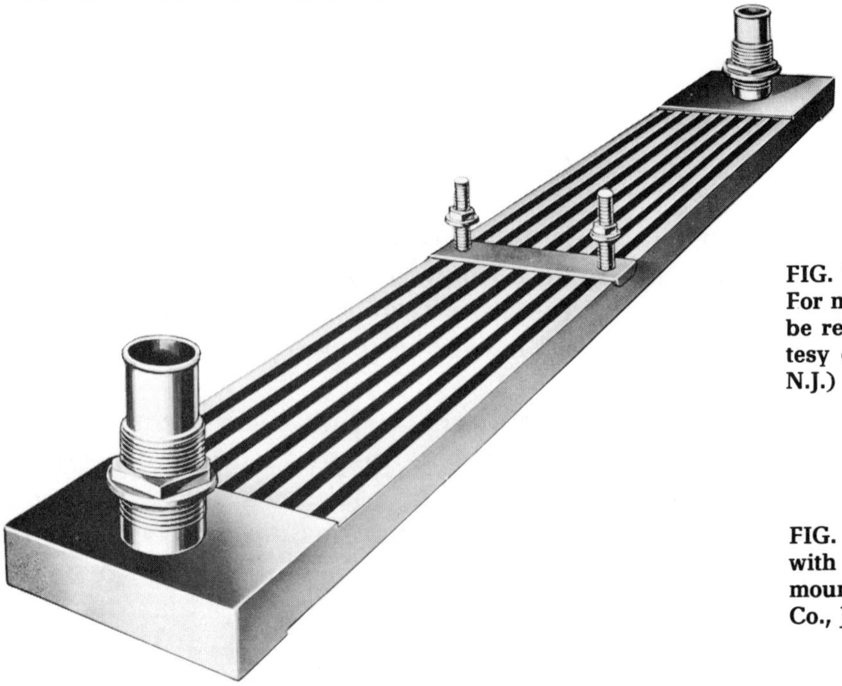

FIG. 14-8 — An exterior-type keel cooler. For minimum resistance, this type should be recessed into the hull slightly. (Courtesy of Walter Machine Co., Jersey City, N.J.)

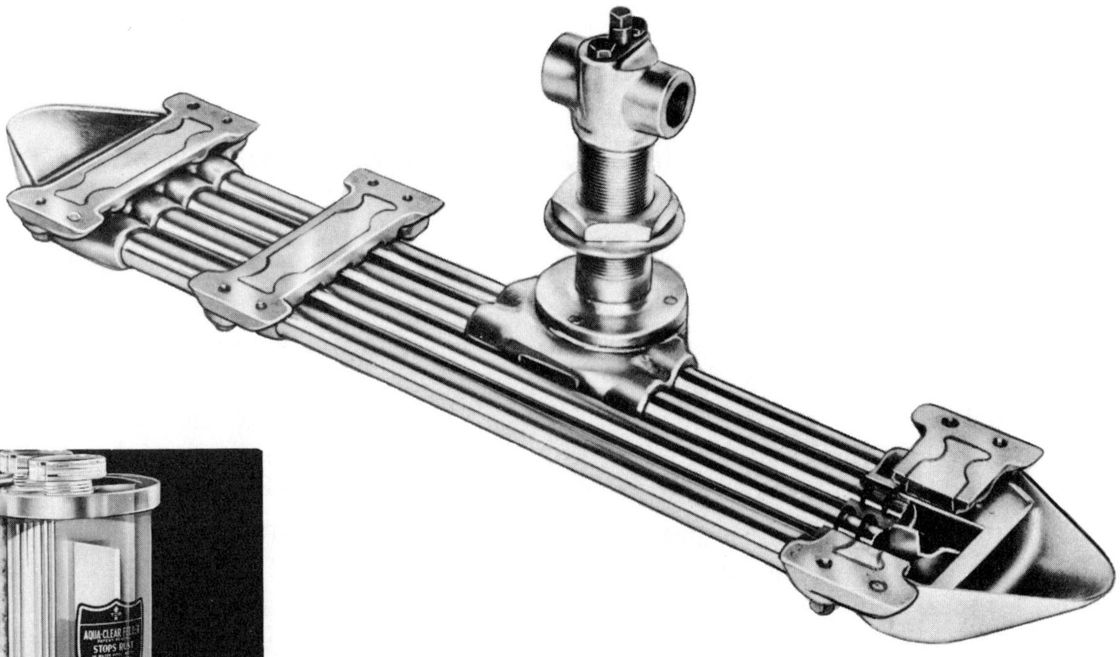

FIG. 14-9 — An exterior-type keel cooler with streamlined end plates for surface mounting. (Courtesy of Walter Machine Co., Jersey City, N.J.)

FIG. 14-10 — A feeder with crystals for use in brackish waters in lieu of fresh water cooling. When used properly, these feeders protect the engine from the effects of saltwater corrosion. (Courtesy of Sudbury Laboratory, Sudbury, Mass.)

sions should be made to drain the system to avoid damage from freezing during layups.

## FEEDERS

Another method used to eliminate the harmful effects of salt or brackish water on the engine is to use chemical crystals in a feeder (see Fig. 14-10). This feeder is installed in the raw water cooling system as close to the inlet in the bottom of the boat as possible. The water flowing around the crystals slowly dissolves them and deposits a microscopically thin film on any and all metal surfaces, whether iron, steel, copper, brass, bronze, aluminum, stainless steel, or lead. Since this film will not build up on itself, it can never interfere with the heat transfer or the flow of water. The film rather effectively prevents the damage through corrosion caused by dissimilar metals used in the same system. The crystals must be changed periodically, however, their cost is not great.

# CHAPTER 15 — EXHAUST SYSTEMS

As in the automobile, the primary function of the boat's exhaust system is to get rid of the products of combustion from inside the engine in a safe manner that will not seriously detract from the engine's performance. However, the exhaust system in a boat must be considerably different from that in an automobile. The cooling of an auto exhaust is not important since it is under the car where plenty of air movement eliminates any danger of fire. In a boat, however, a hot exhaust pipe cannot be tolerated due to the fire hazard, except in one special case which will be discussed later.

There are two basic exhaust systems used aboard boats; the wet system, and the dry system, or "dry stack" exhaust. The primary difference between the two systems is that cooling water is injected into the exhaust line of the wet system and leaves the boat through the exhaust outlet, whereas on the dry system, heat insulation along with air movement keeps exhaust temperatures within safe limits, and cooling water is not used. In either system, however, wet or dry sections or components may be included, depending on the particular installation. With either system there are many variations and it is not possible to cover them all. However, those discussed and illustrated are common types which can usually be adapted in one form or another to a given boat.

With either the wet or dry systems, a primary requisite is that the exhaust lines must never DECREASE in size from the exhaust outlet or manifold size, although the size can be increased. Exhaust lines should be increased ½" in diameter beyond every 10' of length of run. Any resistance or backpressure created in the exhaust system will cause the engine to lose power and efficiency, as well as increase engine temperatures and perhaps result in engine damage. This means that angles and bends in the line must be kept to a minimum, and sharp changes in direction should not be made. Where changes in direction are necessary, long sweep elbows and 45 degree "ells" should be used, and the sizes of these components are preferably increased in size to minimize backpressure. Bends in hoses should have a radius that is no less than five times the hose diameter.

All exhaust systems must be gastight throughout their lengths inside the boat for safety. Each engine should be exhausted by its own separate system; don't join the exhaust of twin engines into a single system nor use the engine's exhaust line for a generator exhaust. Supports, hangers, brackets, and other fittings in contact with the exhaust system should be of noncombustible material that will not transfer heat to adjacent combustible materials. Where an exhaust line passes through a bulkhead, a clearance of 2″ should be provided around a line in a wet system, and a clearance of 9″ should be provided around a line in a dry system. All exhaust systems should be made of non-corrosive materials compatible with exhaust gases. Since diesel engine exhaust contains sulphur, copper bearing metals (with the possible exception of Monel) should not be used as they will react and deteriorate over time. Engines which are mounted on flexible mounts should have a flexible section in the exhaust line between the exhaust manifold or riser, and the exhaust line. The use of rubber hose in a wet system or a flexible metallic bellows in the dry system fulfills this requirement.

A means of monitoring the exhaust temperature is recommended on all boats. On most small boats using a wet system, a water temperature gage is commonly used. However, if the engine uses a heat exchanger with a separate pump for injecting water into the exhaust system, a separate gage should be provided for this portion of the system in the event that the pump or water injection system fails. In addition to engine temperature gages, some boats have alarm systems which actuate if the exhaust temperature exceeds a safe level, while in other cases it is possible to arrange for an automatic shut-down of the engine by use of a temperature operated switch when engine exhaust temperatures become too high.

Ideally the length of any exhaust system should be kept to a minimum. The exhaust outlet must be located and positioned to prevent water from entering the engine whether it is of the wet or dry type. The outlet in all cases

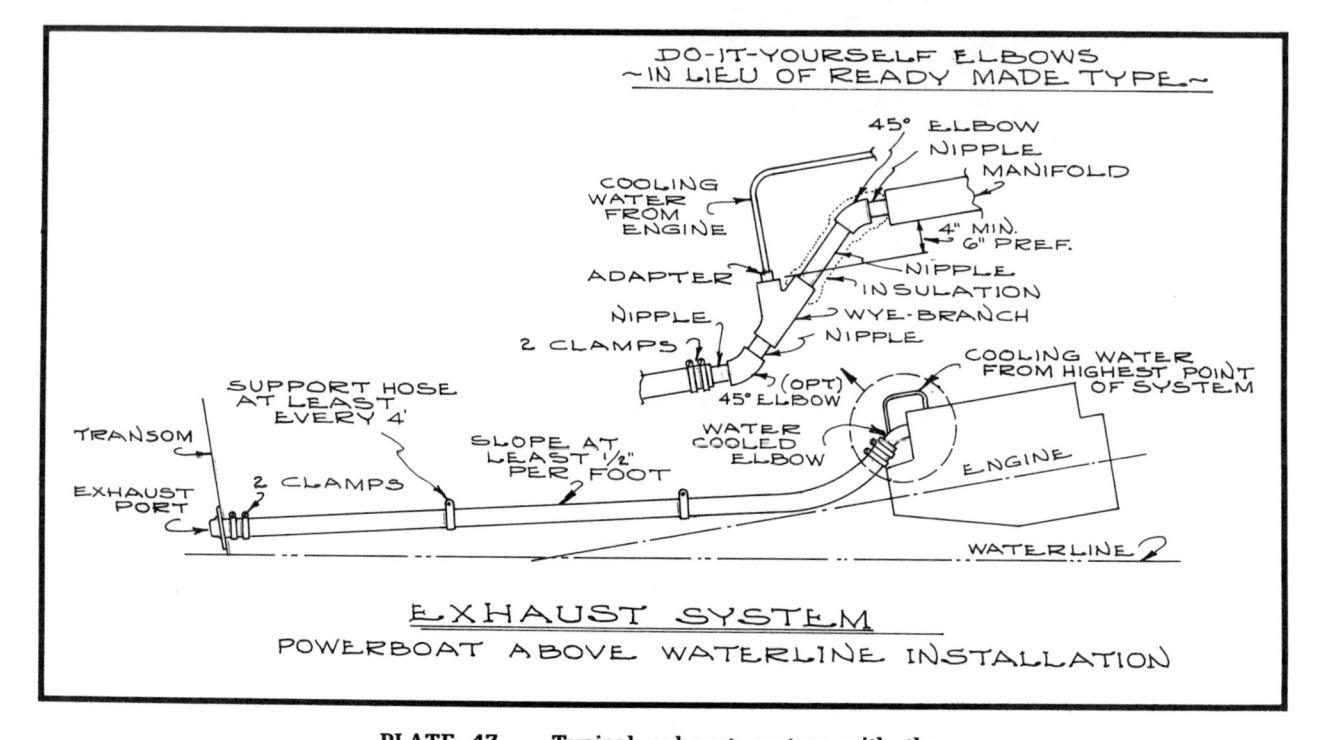

**PLATE 47 — Typical exhaust system with the engine located above the waterline.**

should preferably be above the waterline when the boat is at rest, and positioned so that under the worst heeling or loading conditions, water will not enter the exhaust system. In any exhaust system, a drain cock and trap should be provided at the lowest portion of the line for condensate to prevent damage from freezing during lay-ups.

## WET SYSTEMS

The wet exhaust system is by far the most common aboard pleasure boats. Some of the reasons for this are that the water in the system helps muffle the sound and makes the boat cooler. When flexible hose is used in the system, vibration will be less of a problem than with a dry system. With most wet systems, the noxious fumes and exhaust smoke are exited out the stern or transom where they are not as bothersome. Several variations are possible with wet systems depending on whether the engine is located at, above, or below the waterline, and if the installation is on a powerboat or sailboat. A muffler or silencer may be installed in the exhaust system also to further minimize noise.

Depending on the powerplant, the exhaust system may be integral with the engine, or provided with the engine by the manufacturer. This is often the case with sterndrive and jetdrive powerplants, and with some sailboat

FIG. 15-1 — A water cooled exhaust elbow eliminates the hot spot between the point where the exhaust leaves the manifold and the cooling water enters into the exhaust line.

installations. In all cases, the specific instructions and recommendations provided by the motor manufacturer should be followed with regard to the exhaust installation. In other installations, or where specific instructions are not provided, the following will provide guidance to making a proper exhaust installation for various types of boats.

A typical installation for an inboard powerboat with the motor above the waterline is quite basic (see Plate 47). A water cooled exhaust elbow (Fig. 15-1) is connected to the aft end of the exhaust manifold. The cooling water (either from the engine in a raw water cooling system, or from a separate pump if a closed cooling system is used) is injected into the elbow so that it enters the exhaust line at least 4″ (and preferably 6″ or more) below the lowest level of the manifolds.

When the engine is at or near the waterline where a possible back surge of water could enter the engine, water cooled risers are used at the aft end of the exhaust manifolds (see Fig. 15-2). The rise of the elbow keeps water from entering the engine, and similarly, the cooling water enters the riser on the low side to be injected into the exhaust line beyond the engine to keep it from also entering the engine. A typical system is illustrated by Plate 48.

From the elbow or riser, the exhaust line runs aft in a downward slope which should be at least ½″ for each

FIG. 15-2 — Where a back surge of water could possibly enter the exhaust line, a water cooled riser is used on the end of the manifold as shown. (Courtesy of Nicson Engineering, Santa Fe Springs, Calif.)

foot of run. Note that the slope must be measured with the vessel in normal trim at rest and that more slope is always desirable. At one time, the exhaust line connections were standard threaded pipe connections since standard metal piping was commonly used for the exhaust line. However, in most current installations, non-metallic "steam" hose of the approved "Neoprene" braided type is used. This type of hose is quite flexible in long lengths, but it must all be cooled and cannot be directly connected to a hot spot on the motor. The approved type can withstand a temperature of 280 degrees and will not collapse. Connections to metal fittings with this type of hose are made by the use of all-stainless steel or comparable non-corrosive worm screw band clamps at least ½" wide. Clamps of the spring tension type often used on automobiles are not suitable. Two clamps per junction are recommended,

spaced one clamp width apart and one clamp width from the end of the hose, but 1" from the end of the rigid pipe or fitting. While flexible hose can usually make most bends in an exhaust system, pipe fittings or metal exhaust connections are also auitable. The standard pipe fittings, such as a 45 degree elbow, would use a nipple into each end to which the adjoining flexible hose would be attached. Special metal exhaust fittings are also available with barbed ends over which the hose fits. Clamps are used to secure the hoses to the fittings.

Where the cooling water is injected into the exhaust line, the water should enter the exhaust system so that it is as parallel to it as possible. Never inject the water at right angles, as the water could back up into the engine as well as erode the exhaust pipe opposite the point of injection. The water flow rate into the exhaust system must be ade-

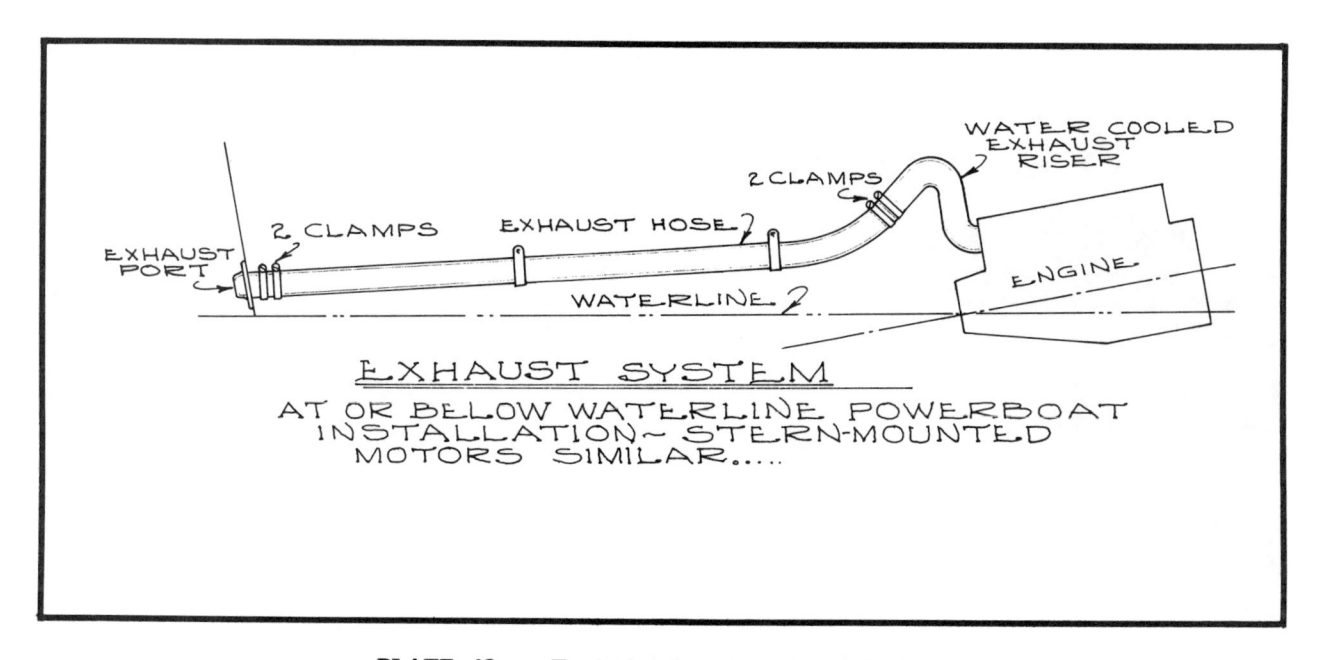

**PLATE 48 — Typical exhaust system with the engine at or below the waterline using a riser.**

172

quate to cool the system, especially if flexible hose is used in any portion. A recommended flow rate is based on a formula as follows:

Gallons of water per minute =
$$\frac{\text{cubic inch displacement X engine RPM}}{660,000}$$

As an example, an engine with 325 cubic inches at 3000 RPM divided by 660,000 would require a flow of water into the exhaust equal to 1.48 gallons per minute.

On the wet exhaust system, the ex-

haust normally leaves the boat at the stern or transom just above the waterline. On transom sterned boats, the outlet should be located well away from the centerline so that there will be less of a tendency for the fumes to come back aboard the boat. In a fast planing boat, the outlet at the transom will almost never be below the waterline underway even if located below the waterline at rest. However, such an installation will cause problems at slow speeds or idling. Because water has a great effect on reducing engine

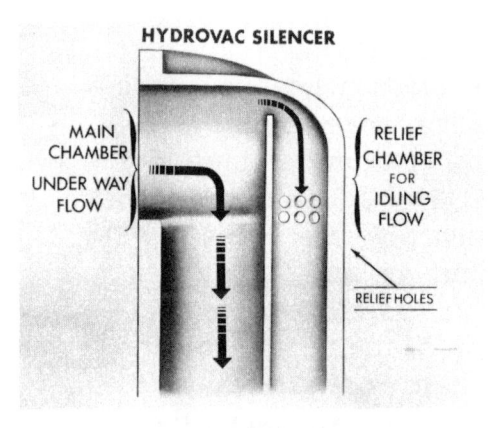

**FIG. 15-3 — This muffler fits on the transom of the boat at the exhaust outlet above the waterline. When underway, the exhaust is directed down into the water for muffling. At idle, the force of the water diverts the exhaust out the relief chamber passages. (Courtesy of W. H. Salisbury & Co., Skokie, Ill.)**

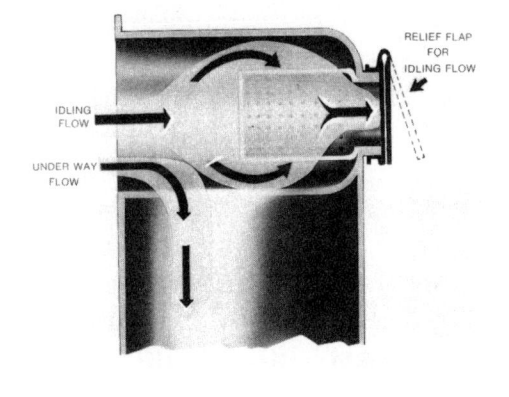

**FIG. 15-4 — This muffler is similar to that shown in FIG. 15-3, however, the relief device at idle is somewhat different. (Courtesy of W. H. Salisbury & Co., Skokie, Ill.)**

exhaust noise, however, there are special devices available which allow the exhaust to actually exit through the water while planing, and yet have the ability to allow operation under slow and idling speeds (see Fig. 15-3 and Fig. 15-4). This type of muffler can be used on just about any planing type boat with a transom exhaust outlet.

There are several types of exhaust outlets or "ports" as they are called. Both metal and non-metallic types are available (see Fig. 15-5 and Fig. 15-6). One type that provides an extra precaution for preventing water from entering the exhaust line consists of a flexible or hinged flap that opens under exhaust pressure when the engine is running, and yet closes when the engine is not running, or when running slowly, to prevent water from surging into the line (see Fig. 15-7). A valve or seacock at the exhaust port can be used, with the disadvantages and advantages as previously discussed in Chapter 14.

A variation of the water cooled system with exhaust ports just described is the over-transom exhaust used mostly on smaller high speed sport runabouts. The over-transom exhaust is much like an exhaust riser in effect, with a cooling water jacket along its length. The over-transom exhaust pipe connects directly to the exhaust manifolds and rises steeply to pass over the transom of the boat (see Fig. 15-8). The cooling water is deflected to pass out the end of the unit along with the exhaust. Because the exhausts are quite short and water is not injected into the exhaust until nearly the outlet, such units have little muffling ability and are quite noisy.

Mufflers or silencers are often included in the exhaust system even

FIG. 15-5 — A typical metal exhaust port intended for transom mounting. (Courtesy of Glenwood Marine Equipment)

FIG. 15-6 — A synthetic exhaust port such as this one will not rust or corrode in use. (Courtesy of Globe Rubber Works, Rockland, Mass.)

FIG. 15-7 — Flaps such as this over the exhaust ports will prevent a backsurge of water from entering the exhaust line. Underway, the exhaust forces the flaps open. (Courtesy of W. H. Salisbury & Co., Skokie, Ill.)

FIG. 15-8 — These over-transom exhausts on an automobile conversion are popular on competition and sport runabouts. Cooling water from the engine enters just aft of the manifolds and passes out the end of the units with the exhaust. (Courtesy of Glenwood Marine Equipment)

though the water in the wet system does eliminate a good percentage of the engine noise. Since the muffler will have water (and perhaps salt water) going through it, all mufflers should be made from non-corrosive materials. Both metallic and non-metallic types are available to suit a wide range of installation requirements. Several types are shown in Fig. 15-10. Cast iron and galvanized steel mufflers are often used, however, these are not normally as durable as other types. The rubber "Neoprene" muffler is often used since it is non-corrosive, light in weight, and easy to install. The muffler should not contact the hull structure as

FIG. 15-9 — Another example of over-transom exhausts. This header-type manifold and riser system is suitable for high-speed competition boats. (Courtesy of Nicson Engineering, Santa Fe Spring, Calif.)

this will increase exhaust noise. In general, the muffler should be as close to the exhaust manifold as possible.

When the motor is at or below the waterline, such as is common in sailboat installations, variations in the wet exhaust system are necessary in order to provide the proper downslope to the exhaust line. Because the engine may be below the waterline, the exhaust gases must be lifted vertically to a point where adequate downslope can be provided to the line. Three methods that are often used for this situation include the standpipe muffler system, the water jacketed riser, and the water-lift system.

In the standpipe system (see Plate 49 and Plate 50), a vertical muffler called a standpipe is located well above the waterline near the boat's centerline. Exhaust gases enter the bottom of the standpipe and flow through a pipe inside to nearly the top. Cooling water from the engine is injected into the standpipe and mixes with the exhaust gases. A diverter in the standpipe, or the height of the exhaust pipe in the standpipe, prevents this water from passing into the exhaust pipe and down into the engine. The mixed exhaust gases and cooling water leave and pass through the exhaust line out the hull. Because the standpipe outlet

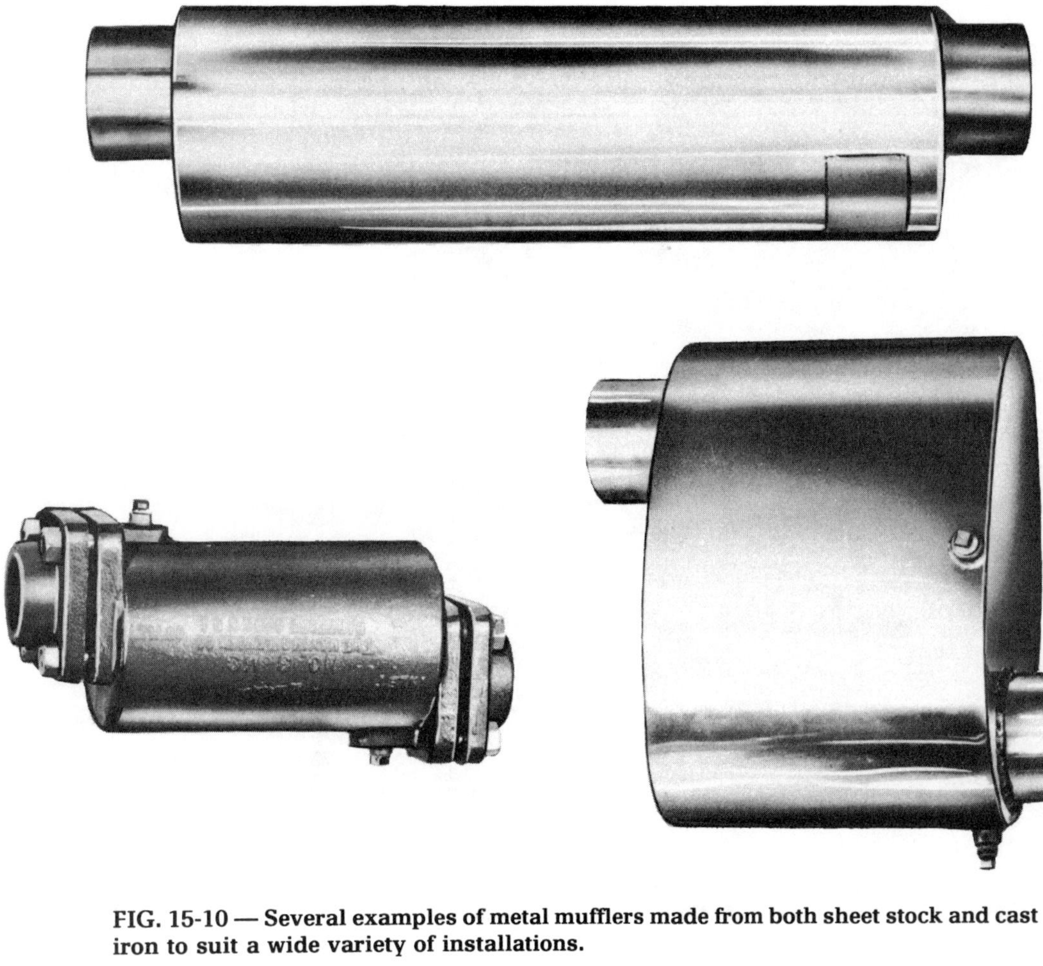

FIG. 15-10 — **Several examples of metal mufflers made from both sheet stock and cast iron to suit a wide variety of installations.**

is low, water cannot back up into the exhaust system from the outside. The exhaust pipe between the engine and the standpipe may be either a water jacketed hose or pipe, or may be dry. In this latter instance, the pipe must be insulated as in a dry system. If the standpipe is rigidly mounted, a flexible section should be used at some

point in the line between the engine and the standpipe. Depending on the system, a muffler may be installed in the line aft of the standpipe.

With the water jacketed riser, the standpipe is not used. Instead, the riser, which must have it's high point at least 12″ above the waterline and preferably higher, is used to keep water

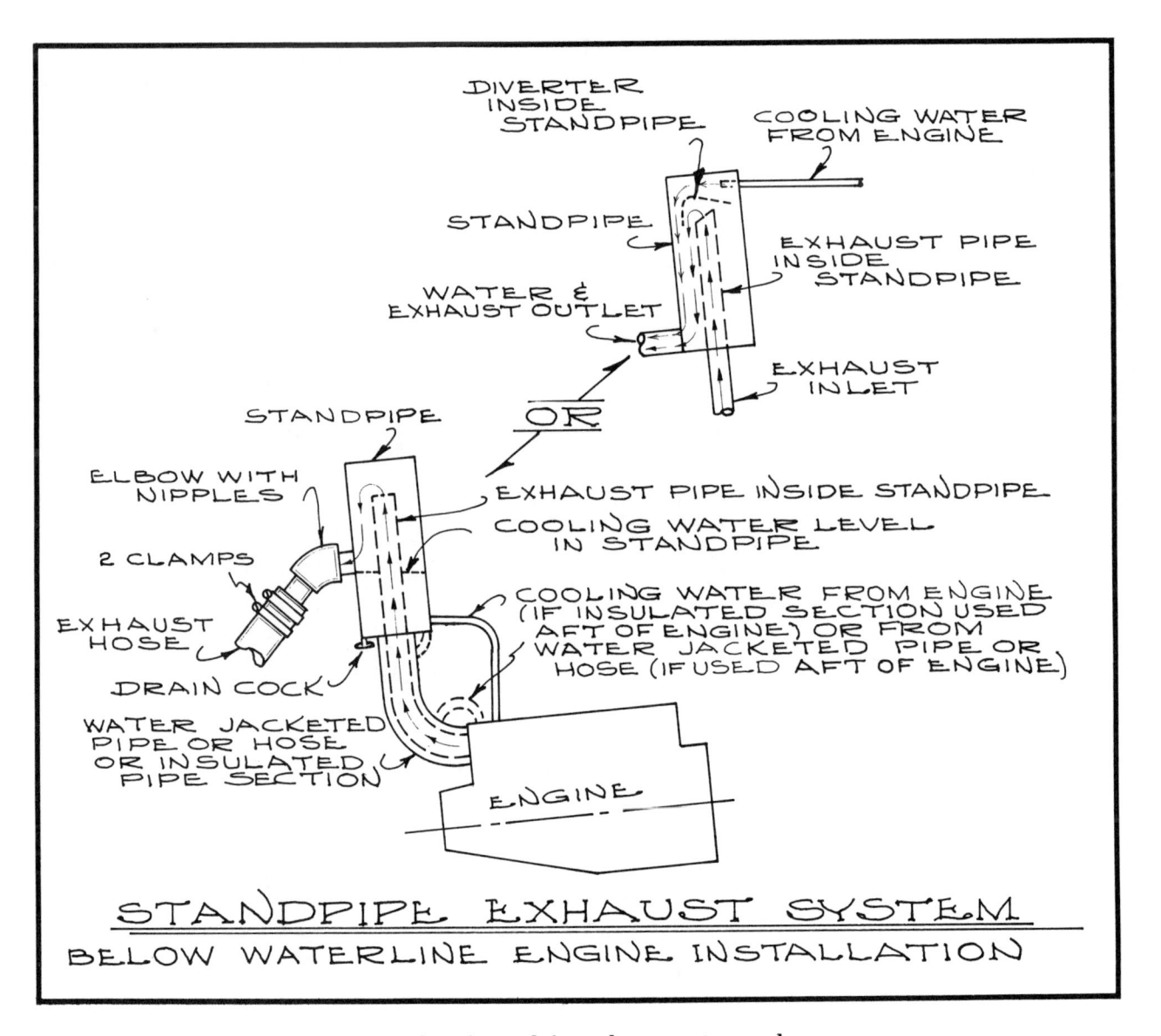

STANDPIPE EXHAUST SYSTEM
BELOW WATERLINE ENGINE INSTALLATION

PLATE 49 — A standpipe exhaust system such as used on sailboats having the engine well below the waterline.

177

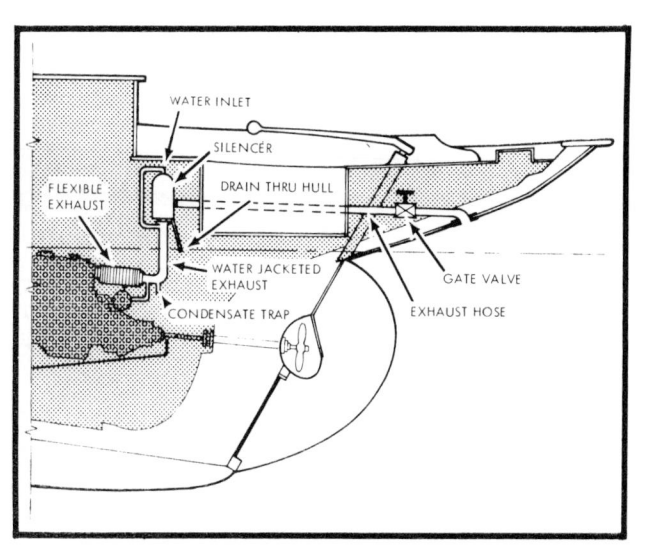

**PLATE 50 — A schematic of a typical standpipe exhaust system in a sailboat. (Courtesy of J. H. Westerbeke Corp., Avon, Mass.)**

from backing up into the exhaust system (see Plate 51). Cooling water from the engine is injected into the riser at a low point, which exits the riser on the downward side into the exhaust line. Like the standpipe system, there may be a dry section between the riser and the motor which may require insulation or a flexible section. A muffler is also optional.

The waterlift system uses a somewhat different approach to below waterline installations. The main component of the system is the water-lift muffler (see Plate 52) which is actually a container or "can". The exhaust line to the stern of the boat goes

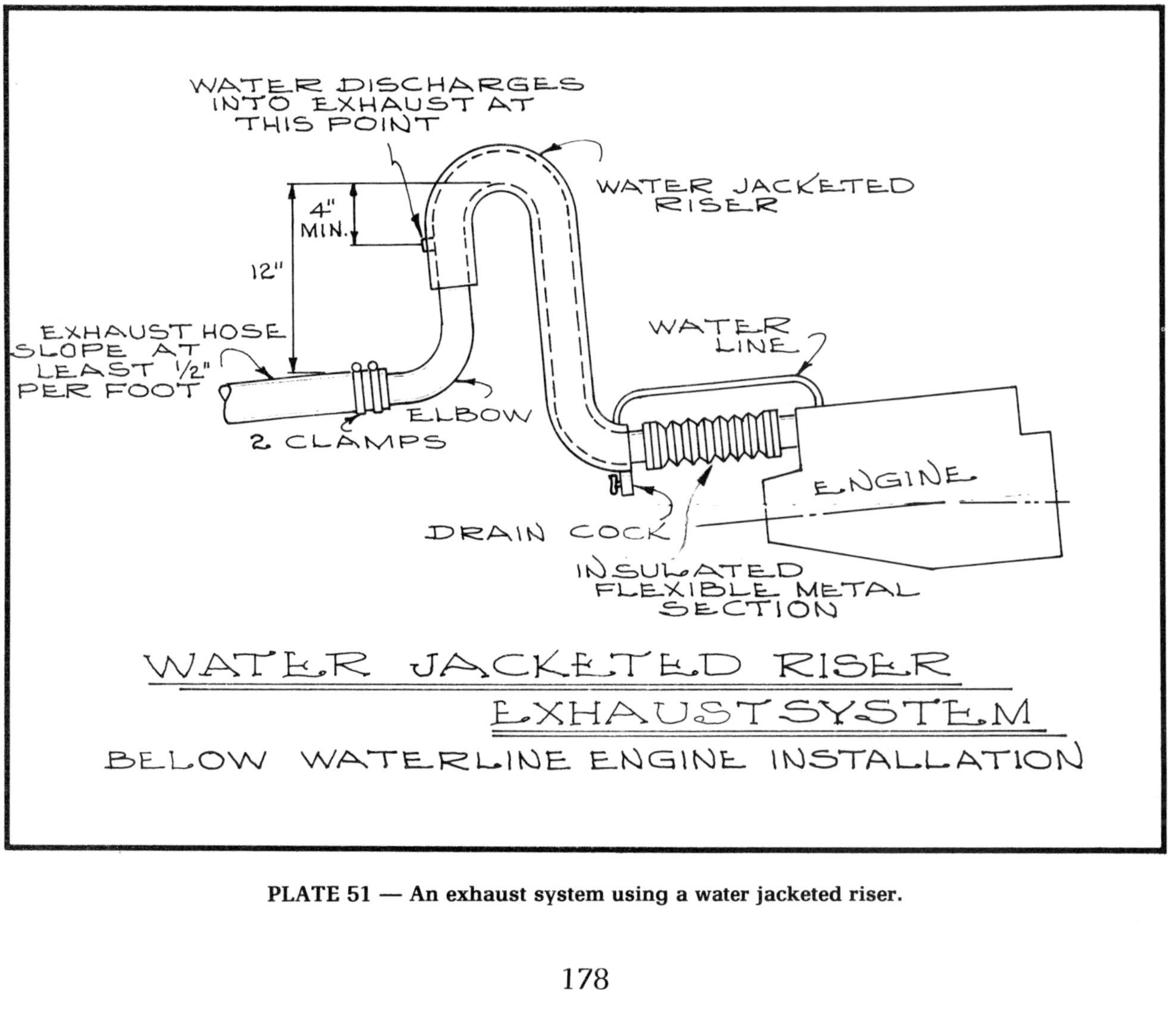

**PLATE 51 — An exhaust system using a water jacketed riser.**

178

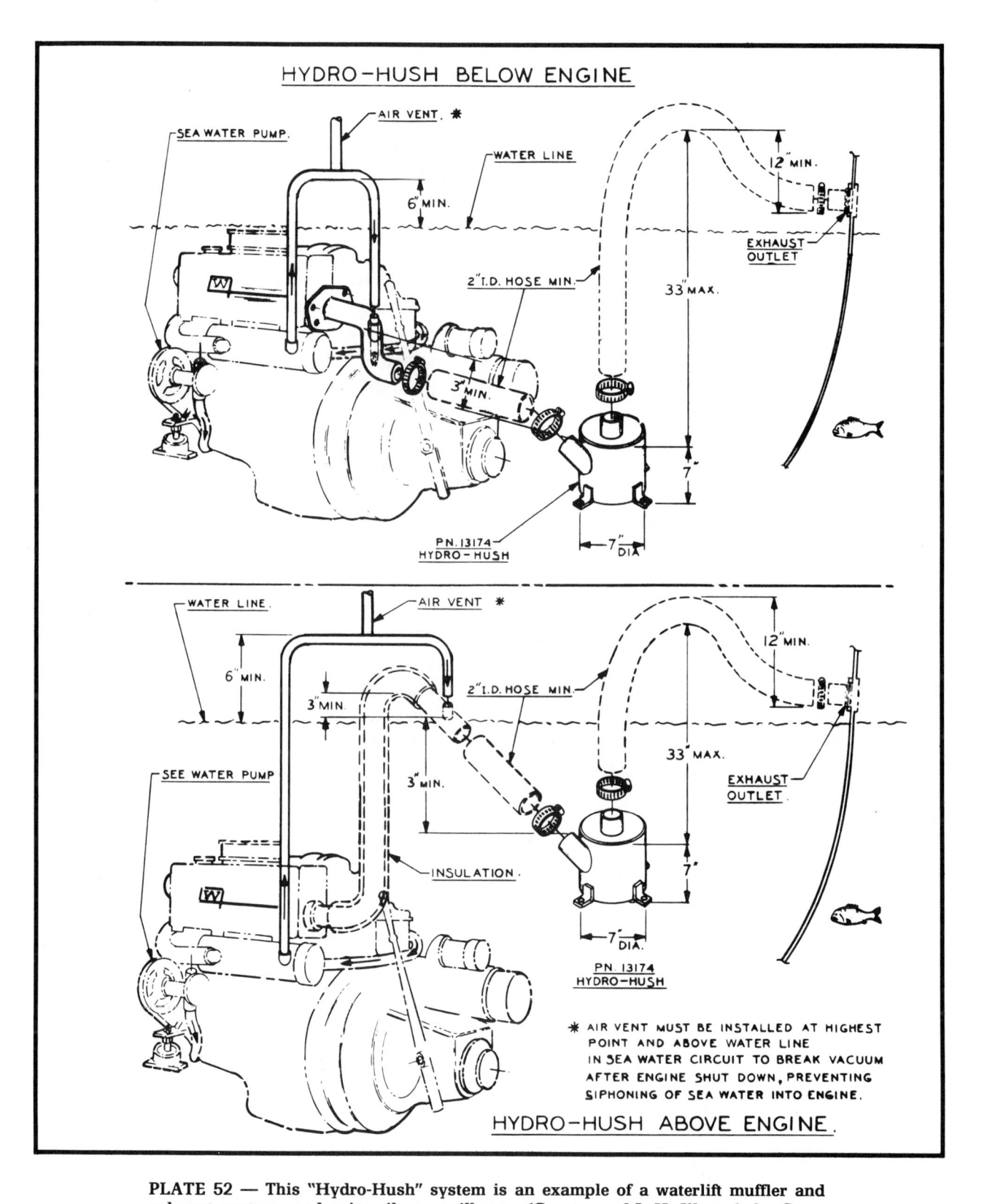

HYDRO-HUSH BELOW ENGINE

SEA WATER PUMP.

AIR VENT. ✱

WATER LINE

6" MIN.

2" I.D. HOSE MIN.

12" MIN.

EXHAUST OUTLET

33" MAX.

3" MIN.

7"

PN. 13174 HYDRO-HUSH

7" DIA.

WATER LINE.

AIR VENT ✱

6" MIN.

3" MIN.

2" I.D. HOSE MIN.

12" MIN.

SEE WATER PUMP

3" MIN.

INSULATION.

33" MAX.

EXHAUST OUTLET

7"

PN. 13174 HYDRO-HUSH

7" DIA.

✱ AIR VENT MUST BE INSTALLED AT HIGHEST POINT AND ABOVE WATER LINE IN SEA WATER CIRCUIT TO BREAK VACUUM AFTER ENGINE SHUT DOWN, PREVENTING SIPHONING OF SEA WATER INTO ENGINE.

HYDRO-HUSH ABOVE ENGINE.

**PLATE 52 — This "Hydro-Hush" system is an example of a waterlift muffler and exhaust system used primarily on sailboats. (Courtesy of J. H. Westerbeke Corp, Avon, Mass.)**

179

into the top of this unit and down nearly to the bottom, while the line from the engine enters the side. Exhaust and water are both allowed to enter the muffler, which is about a quarter filled with water at all times. Because of the pressure created by the exhaust of the engine, the water and gases are lifted up and out of the muffler when water reaches the outlet level, and into the exhaust line where they leave the boat.

To be effective and efficient, the waterlift muffler must be installed carefully and properly. The muffler must be mounted as close to the centerline as possible, and somewhat below the engine's exhaust outlet unless a riser is installed ahead of the muffler. An air vent of syphon break must be installed to prevent water from syphoning back through the engine and filling up the muffler with water. Installation dimensions are also critical and will vary with the unit. The waterlift muffler can lift water from 2' to 4' depending on the unit, and an additional muffler is not required.

## DRY SYSTEMS

In most dry exhaust systems or "dry stacks", the exhaust exits the boat via a vertical stack with the outlet well above the level of the highest portion of the boat, be it the deck, cockpit, or cabin. Depending on the type of engine, engine exhaust temperatures may exceed 1000 degrees. Hence, any portion of a dry exhaust system presents a hazardous situation unless properly installed. As a general rule any portion of the dry exhaust system must be insulated and located well away from any combustible material (9" to 10"

should be considered a minimum distance). All surfaces of the dry exhaust system should be insulated or protected with guards so that surface or adjacent temperatures do not exceed 160 degrees Farenheit.

A common insulation method is the use of various types of lagging. One form of lagging uses asbestos rope or thick tape wrapped around the pipe and then wrapped with fiberglass tape or screen to prevent the asbestos from flaking off. An air space between the asbestos and the pipe can be used for additional insulative capacity. This can be accomplished by wrapping with heavy screen or expanded wire mesh prior to wrapping with asbestos (see Plate 55). Spacers can be used on the pipe between it and the mesh to create a "chimney" effect between the pipe and the insulation for the circulation of air as long as the ends are open. Another insulation method is similar to that used for steam pipes in shoreside systems using a lagging adhesive or compound. Lagging compound can be made by using a teaspoon of plaster-of-Paris to a pound of ground asbestos made into a heavy paste by mixing with water. This mixture is reinforced over the pipe with screen, expanded mesh, or wire. Another solution to the hot pipe situation is to use a pipe within a pipe to form an insulative flue. The outer pipe should allow at least 1" of space around the exhaust pipe at all points, and must be open at both ends. Where the pipe passes to the outside, however, there must be some means of keeping water from entering. In addition to insulation, protective guards may be necessary for the safety of crew members.

On vertical dry stacks, a funnel or

"dummy stack" is often used to conceal the exhaust outlet. Regardless of this, rain and other water must not be allowed to enter the dry stack. The stack can be angled so that the exhaust exits in a more horizontal direction, and a flap over the opening is recommended. Nevertheless, a drain cock and condensation trap should be installed at the lowest portion of the exhaust system to get rid of any condensation which could freeze and cause damage during lay-ups. The outlet of the dry stack should also be fitted with a suitable spark arrestor.

A dry exhaust system should not be rigidly mounted to the engine, especially if the engine uses flexible

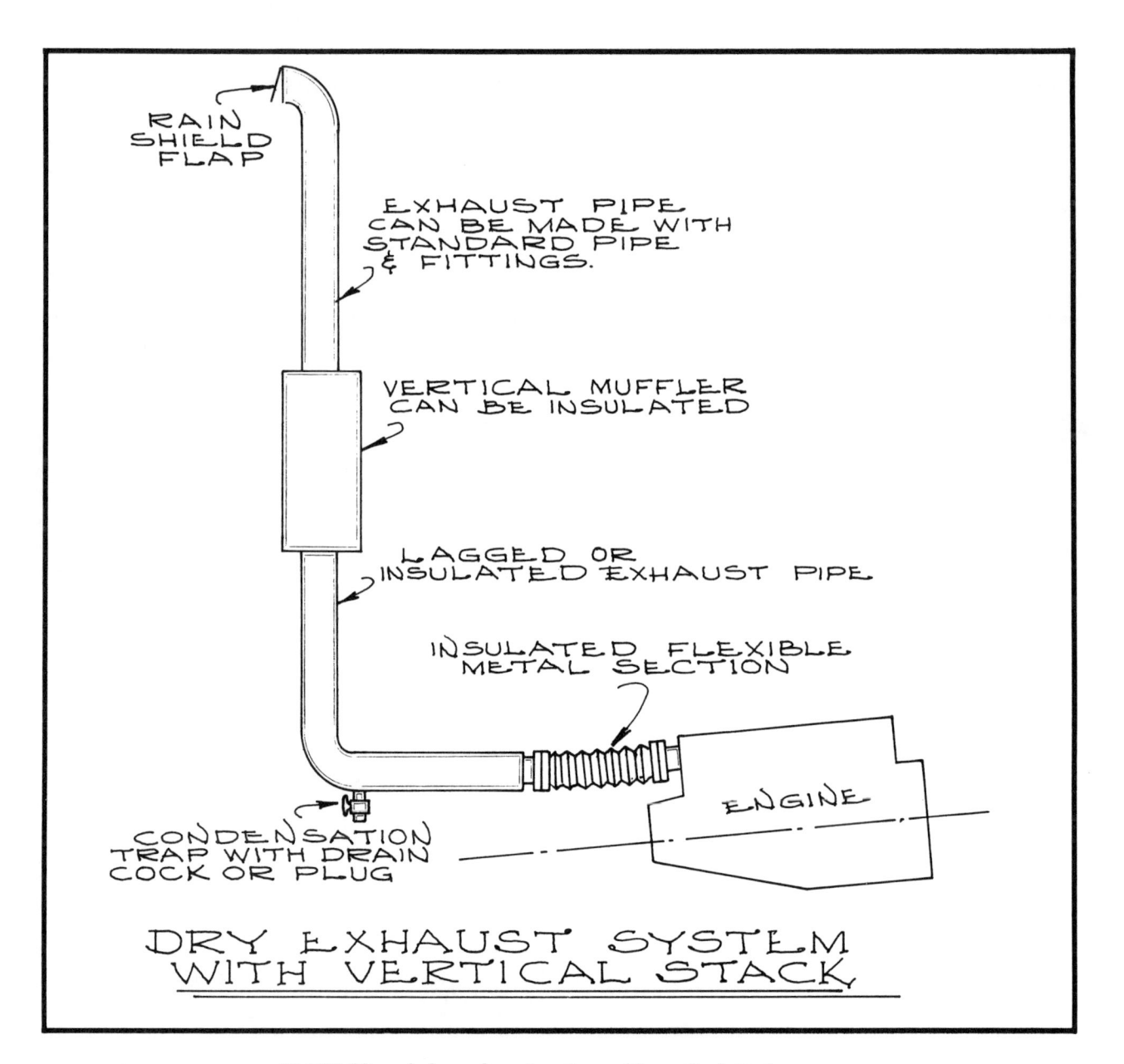

**PLATE 53 — A dry exhaust system with vertical stack.**

mounts. A typical method is to join the exhaust to the engine by means of a flexible metal bellows section (see Plate 53). If these are used, they should be installed to be free from strain, and the stainless steel type is recommended for durability. Where a long horizontal run is necessary, a water jacketed pipe is recommended (see Plate 54). Cooling water can be directed to the pipe jacket and then to the muffler or other outlets where it can be ejected overboard.

Another type of dry exhaust system is often used on competition high speed racing boats. Basically, these boats used header-type exhaust pipes or manifolds which expel the exhaust nearly adjacent to the engine. Since these are often in open cockpit boats with only the driver in the boat, and are used only for regulated competition, their use is tolerated. This is one case where a hot exhaust system without any form of auxiliary cooling is used aboard a boat. Obviously such an installation offers no noise reduction whatsoever.

## EXHAUST BACKPRESSURE

The backpressure of the exhaust system is one of the most important considerations of an adequate exhaust

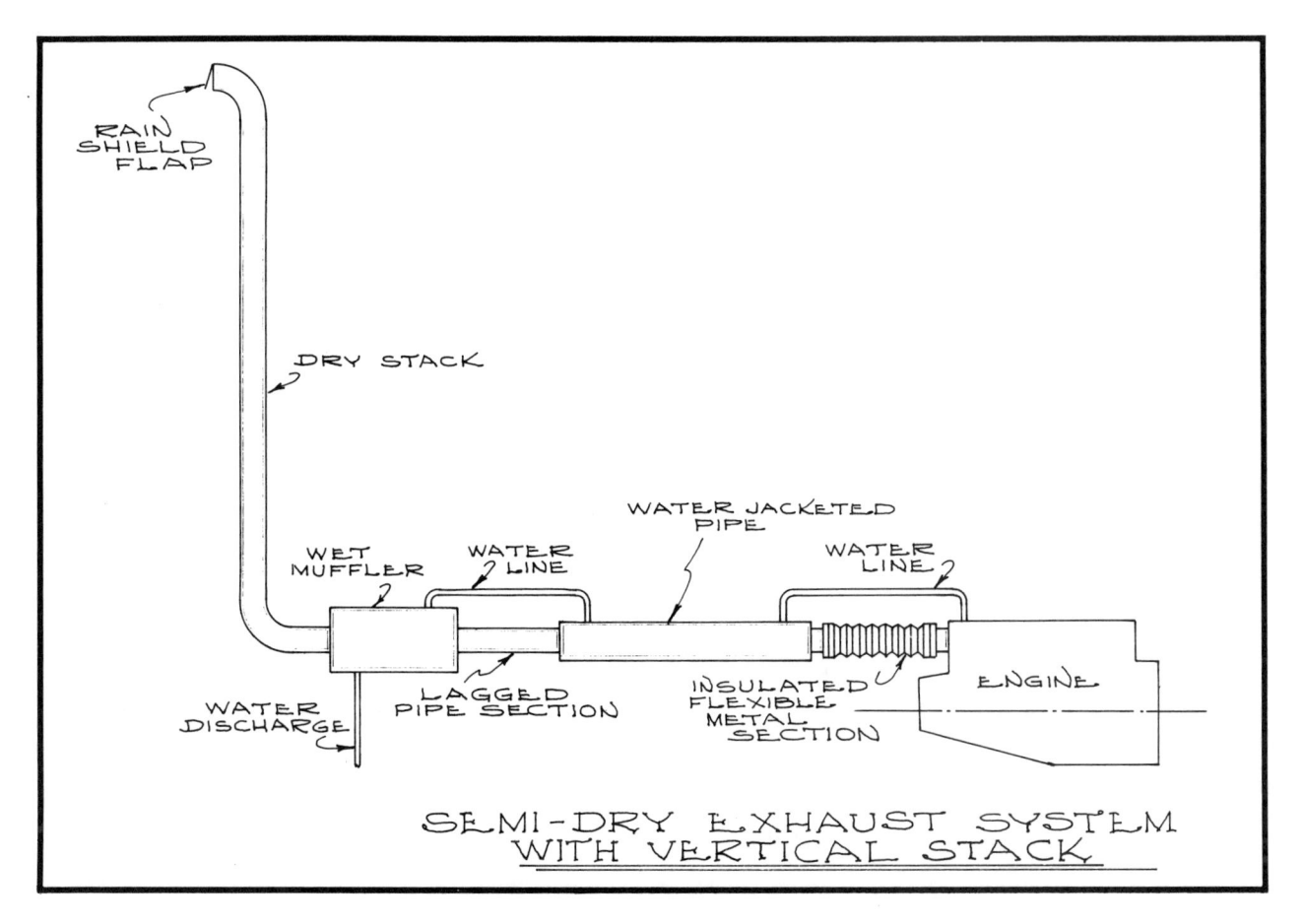

**PLATE 54 — A semi-dry exhaust system with vertical stack.**

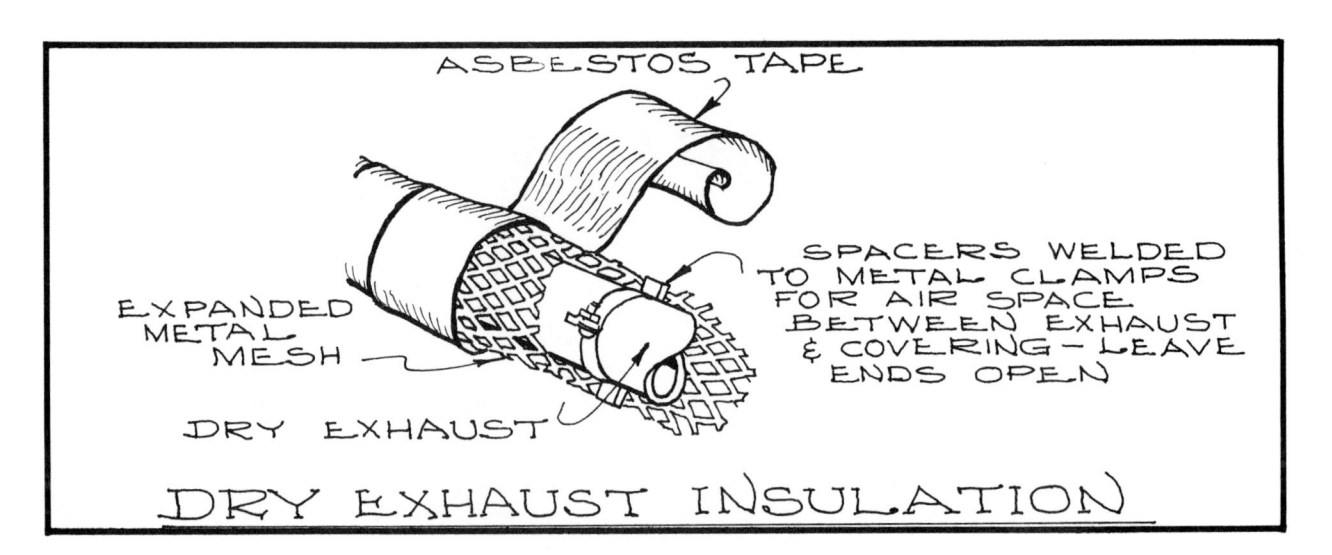

**PLATE 55 — One method of insulating a dry exhaust line.**

system. If the system is excessively long, or includes many changes in direction, or is otherwise questionable with regard to restriction, the backpressure should be checked before putting the boat into operation. The results of excessive backpressure may not show up immediately in a new installation, however, excessive backpressure will lower the power and perhaps lead to engine damage.

With some engines, there is a tap provided in the exhaust system to measure backpressure. Alternately, a tap can be drilled into the manifold or elbow with an adapter to connect a manometer or pressure gage. The engine should be run at full load and readings taken. The engine manufacturer usually gives figures which indicate the proper maximum backpressure allowable. If the engine exhaust exceeds these figures, modifications to the exhaust are necessary to provide a freer flow. Restrictions are normally caused by too long a line without an increase in the size, sharp bends and turns, and dips or pockets in the line where water will set.

# CHAPTER 16 — RUDDERS & STEERING

When building a boat, the size, shape, type, and location of the rudder is usually specified by the designer of the boat. Not all inboard boats however, use rudders, such as sterndrive and jetdrive boats. Depending on the design, the rudder required may be a ready-made item, or details may be provided so that the builder can make his own rudder. On an existing boat that will be re-powered, the present rudder will probably be adequate for the job if it is currently satisfactory and the proposed installation is similar to the existing one. However, if the powering change will be from a single engine to a twin engine, or vice versa, then changes to the rudder and steering system will probably be necessary. If changes in rudders are necessary, competent professional advice regarding the size and type of the rudder should be sought, preferably from a qualified naval architect familiar with the type of boat, or from the manufacturer of the boat. Due to the many possible boat types and rudder configurations there is no set formula for determining rudder size without knowledge of the design.

There are basically two types of rudder systems; those mounted under the boat called "inboard" rudders, and those mounted outside and behind the boat called "outboard" rudders (see Plate 56 and Plate 57). Many shapes and types are available in either con-figuration, as illustrated, and will vary considerably depending on the speed and type of boat. Generally, the faster the boat's speed, the smaller the rudder can be. Sailboats and low speed power boats will have considerably different and larger rudders than high speed planing powerboats. However, the rudder principle is the same in all cases. The rudder is a blade in the water connected to a stock or shaft to which force is exerted to turn it one way or the other. This in turn deflects the water moving over the rudder and moves the stern of the boat to make it turn. Note that it is the back of the boat that does the turning, since it pivots about the bow in order to change direction, which is just the opposite of an automobile.

Rudders may be either the unbalanced type, or designed with some degree of balance to make turning easier (see Plate 58). An unbalanced rudder has the rudder stock or pivot point at the extreme forward end of the rudder and all the blade area is aft of this pivot point. On a balanced rudder, there will be a certain portion of the blade area forward of the rudder stock or pivot point which will decrease some of the force necessary to pivot the rudder. However, the portion of the blade forward cannot be too great a percentage of the rudder area as this will make steering too easy as well as dangerous, with constant attention to

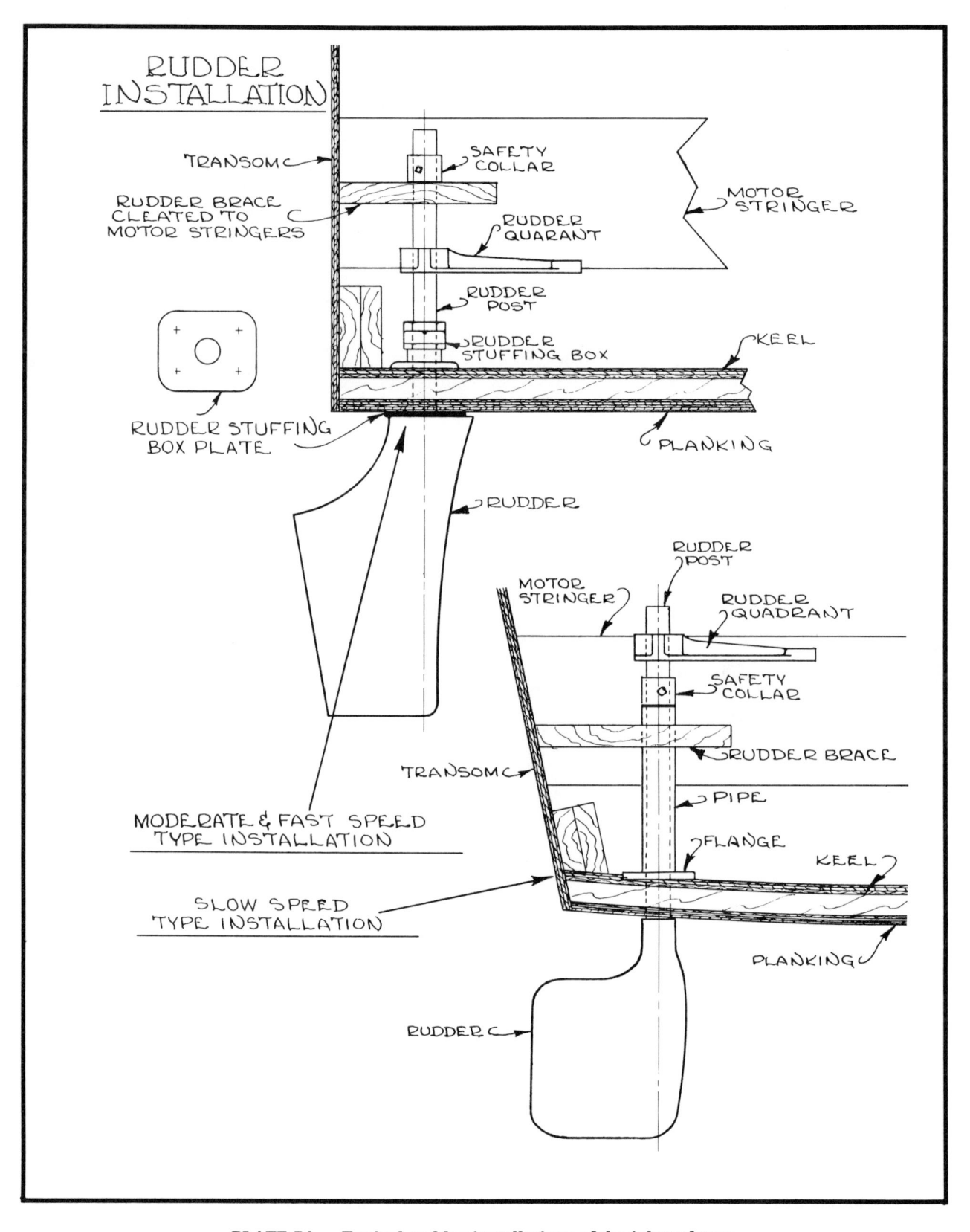

**PLATE 56 — Typical rudder installations of the inboard type.**

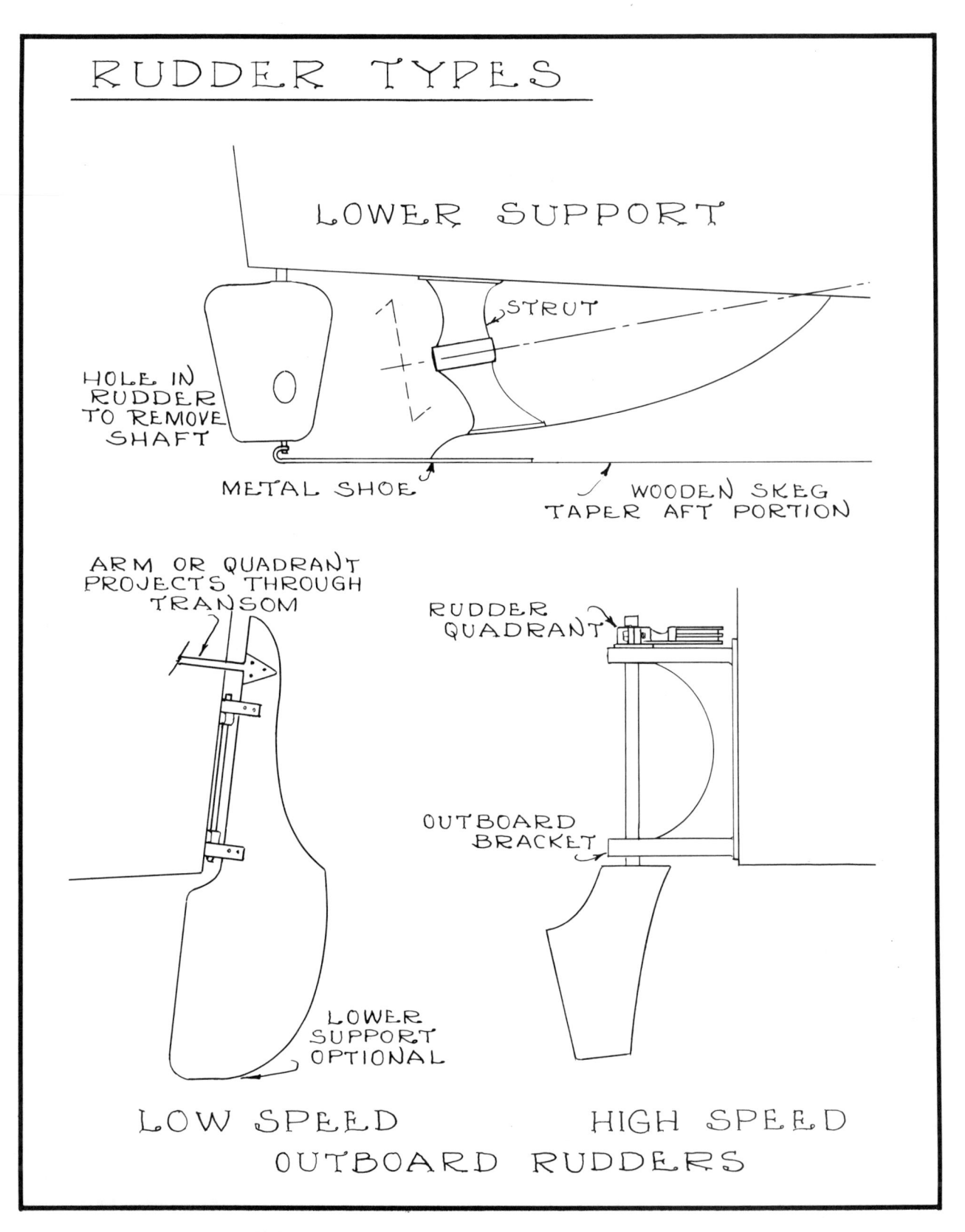

# RUDDER TYPES

## LOWER SUPPORT

STRUT

HOLE IN
RUDDER
TO REMOVE
SHAFT

METAL SHOE

WOODEN SKEG
TAPER AFT PORTION

ARM OR QUADRANT
PROJECTS THROUGH
TRANSOM

RUDDER
QUADRANT

OUTBOARD
BRACKET

LOWER
SUPPORT
OPTIONAL

## LOW SPEED          HIGH SPEED
## OUTBOARD RUDDERS

**PLATE 57 — Typical outboard rudder configurations.**

the helm being required. In general, the balanced rudder will have an area forward of the pivot point of up to 20% of the total rudder area.

Since an appendage under the boat such as a rudder can add considerable drag or resistance to the hull, careful attention is required regarding the size and shape of rudders used, especially on high speed boats. In cross section, the rudder used for slow and moderate speed boats is usually of the "streamline" or airfoil shape as shown by Plate 58. With this rudder the thickest portion will be 25% to 35% along its length (or "chord" as it is called) from the forward or leading edge. The shape is such that fullness is provided along the contours so that they are convex and not straight or concave. This fullness minimizes resistance and provides the necessary lifting forces for turning efficiency. Rudders which vary from this shape may loose efficiency, stall when turned, and also "chatter" or vibrate. While it would seem that sharp leading and trailing edges would be helpful, actually a slight rounded edge or radius is desirable at the leading edge for less resistance. The radius at the trailing edge can be less, but sharp edges are not practical since they damage easily.

On high speed craft, a wedge shaped rudder is often used, tapering to a fine leading edge forward. This section provides constant pressure to the rudder blade at all areas at higher speeds, and

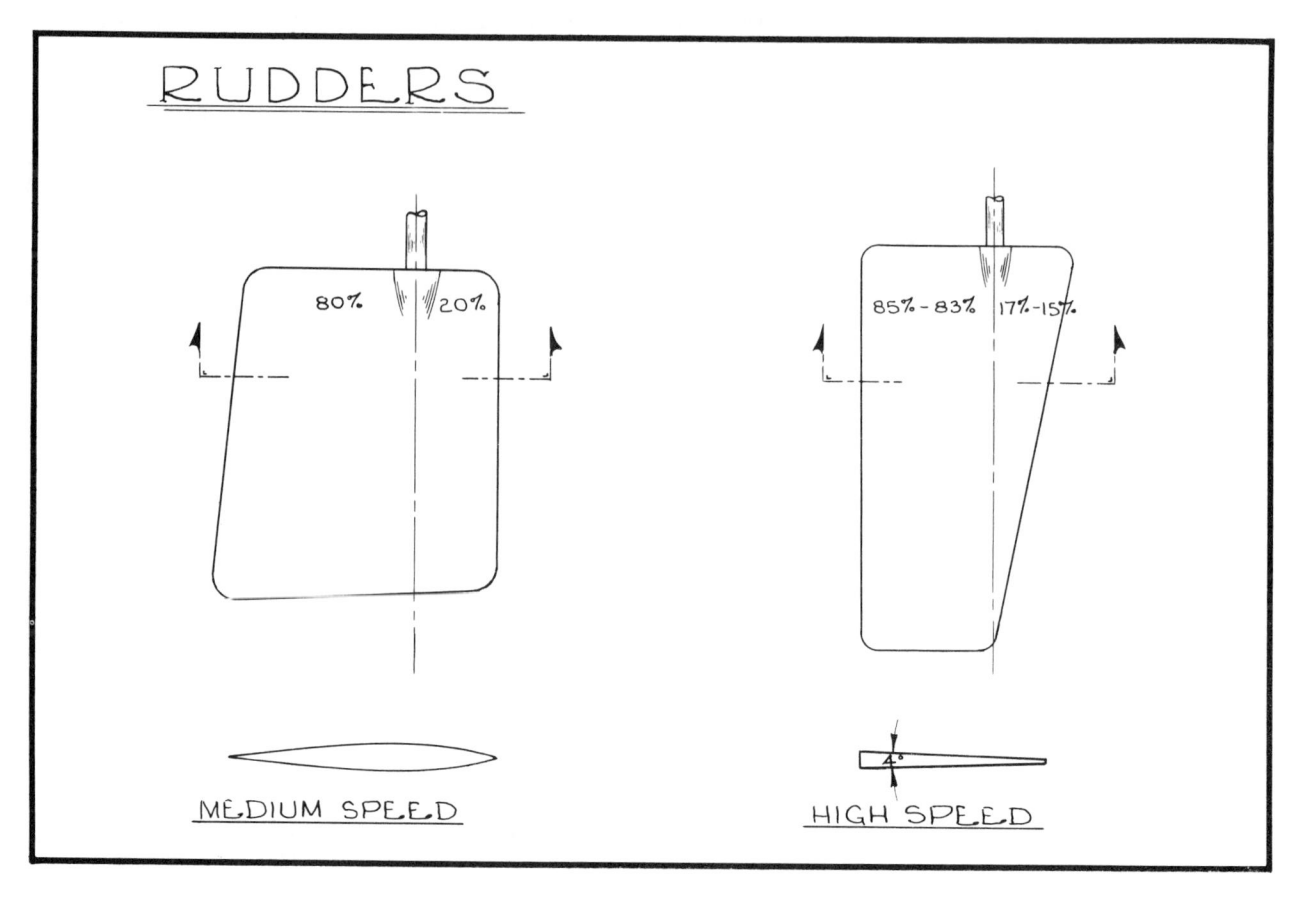

PLATE 58 — Typical sections through balanced rudders.

187

prevents "burbling" caused by the rudder acting in half air instead of in solid water. The degree of wedge may vary, however 4 degrees included angle is a good average. Most powerboat rudders are made from metal, and certain modifications to the above requirements of both slow-to-medium speed rudders and high speed rudders may be required to suit the method of manufacture.

On slow and medium speed boats, especially if single screw, a single rudder at the centerline is used, supported where it passes through the hull if of the inboard type, and also at the bottom by a skeg, keel extension, or "deadwood" on most boats of this type (see Plate 57). If the rudder is the outboard type, these are usually hung onto the stern or transom with fittings called "gudgeons and pintles". Ready-made or custom-made fittings may be required. Rudders mounted on skegs together with the propeller are afforded considerable protection from damage by the boat's skeg or deadwood and are therefore considered highly safe and reliable.

On high speed powerboats, the drag created by big rudders and skegs or other underwater appendages can drastically reduce or hinder performance. Consequently, rudders are much smaller in area and are usually of the spade type; that is, hung below the boat by the stock without any other underwater support. Usually such a rudder is mounted directly behind the propeller on either single or twin engine boats so that maximum propeller thrust can be used to aid turning. Be-

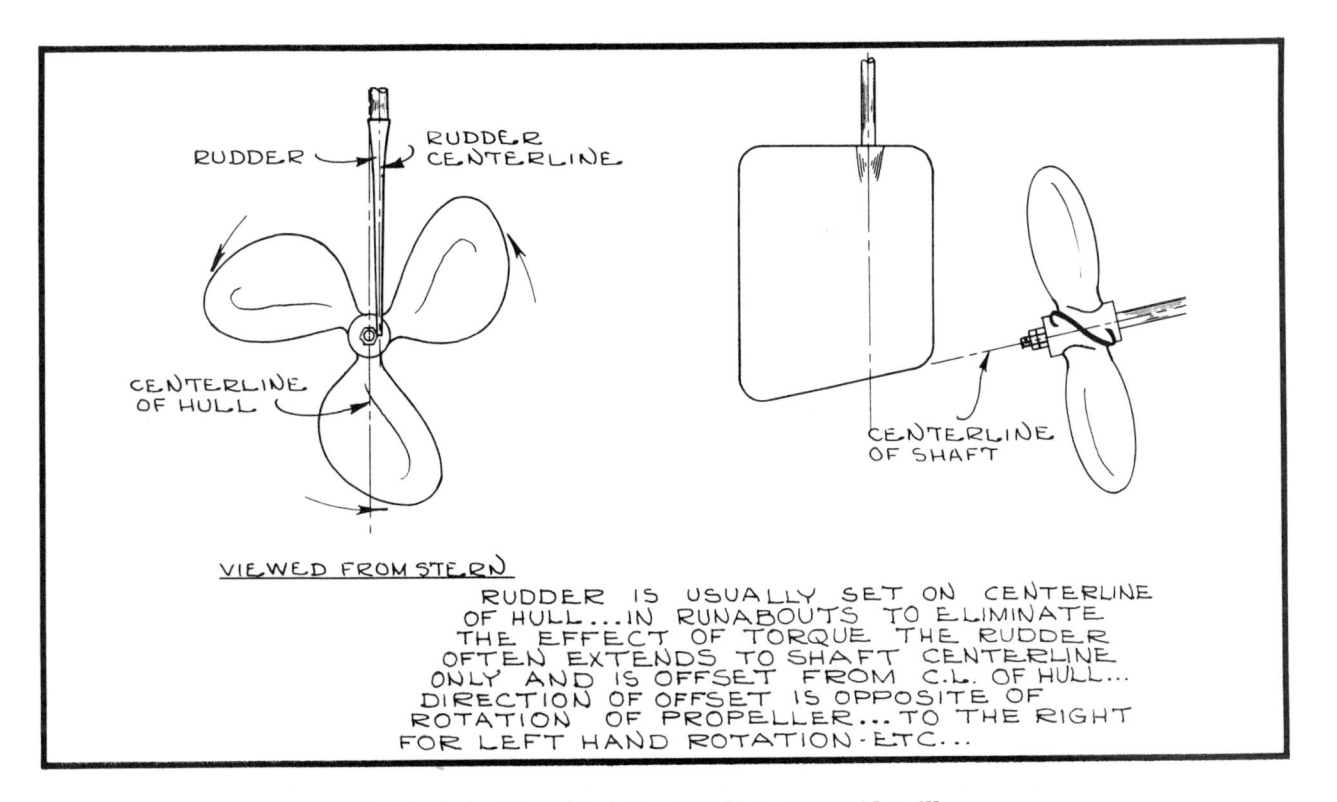

RUDDER IS USUALLY SET ON CENTERLINE OF HULL...IN RUNABOUTS TO ELIMINATE THE EFFECT OF TORQUE THE RUDDER OFTEN EXTENDS TO SHAFT CENTERLINE ONLY AND IS OFFSET FROM C.L. OF HULL... DIRECTION OF OFFSET IS OPPOSITE OF ROTATION OF PROPELLER...TO THE RIGHT FOR LEFT HAND ROTATION-ETC...

**PLATE 59 — Offsetting the rudder to one side will compensate for torque reaction.**

188

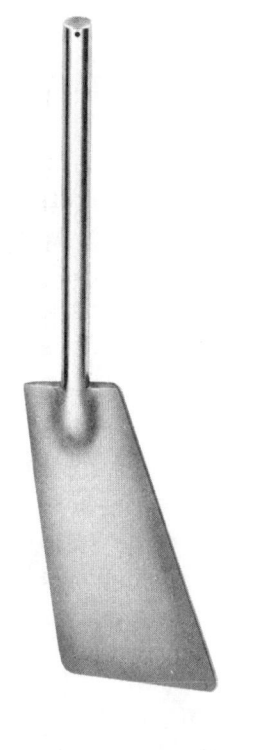

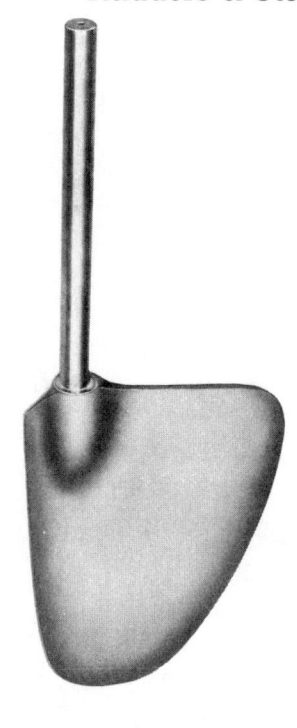

FIG. 16-1 — A wedge-type rudder as used on high speed boats. (Courtesy of Glenwood Marine Equipment)

FIG. 16-2 — This type of rudder is used on cruisers operating in the medium to higher speed ranges.

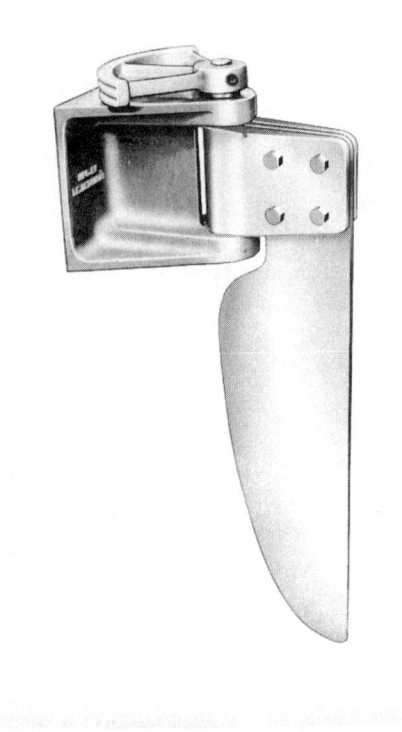

FIG. 16-3 & FIG. 16-4 — These outboard transom mounted rudders are of the unbalanced type and are used mainly on competition boats.

cause of the smaller rudder area, turning is most effective at high speeds. At slow speeds, these rudders are much less effective, and if the boat has twin screws, the engines are often used for directional control. Hence the reason why high speed planing boats are slow to respond to the helm at slower speeds, and the perpetuated myth that ALL types of boats will handle better with twin engines than single engines. Because spade rudders have no protection from a skeg or deadwood, they are quite vulnerable to damage, along with the propeller, shaft, and strut, especially if of twin screw. Also, the spade rudder stock requires considerable support and strength to withstand the rudder forces since there is no lower support.

## POWERBOAT APPLICATIONS

Rudders should be installed so as to turn about 35 degrees from dead center in either direction, and not over 40 degrees. More action than this can result in stalling, or an immediate loss of control, and a drastic increase in strain on the rudder which could damage the rudder or cause it to fail. Stops are therefore provided at some point in the system to prevent greater rudder angles.

The deeper the rudder, the more the hull will tend to bank or lean inboard in a turn. Normally this is not a disadvantage, except that there is often a commensurate loss of speed in sharp turns. Hence, competition boats capable of high speeds prefer flatter turn-

**FIG. 16-5 — This slow speed boat uses an outboard mounted rudder that may not be much to look at, but it is simple, reliable, and effective.**

190

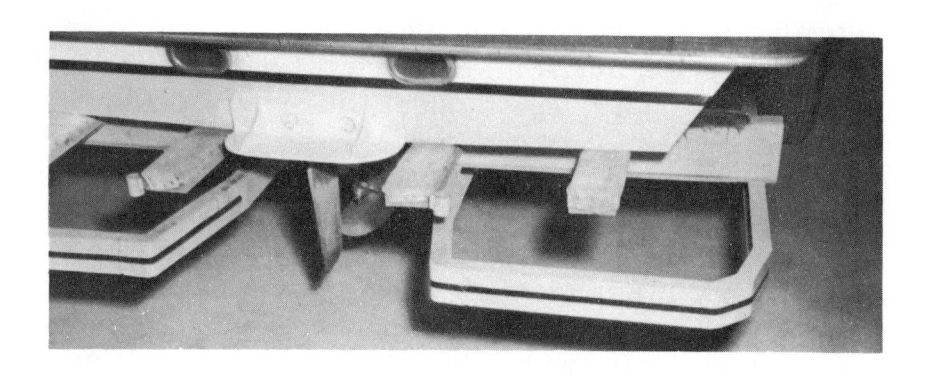

FIG. 16-6 — When the rudder is beyond the transom, a plate should be mounted over it in line with the bottom to prevent air from being sucked in during turning to eliminate steering problems.

ing angles. If the rudder is too deep, stresses on the spade-type rudder can be considerable. This is why an upper steady-rest bearing is necessary to support the spade rudder stock. On the faster boat, rudder proportions usually will be about twice as deep as the width or "chord".

The rudder must not be located where it will suck air. Since the rudder depends on a constant flow of solid water for turning ability, the presence of air will cause an immediate loss of steering action, and possibly cause propeller cavitation or "ventilating" as well. In many cases, especially on the shorter high speed runabout or racing-type boat, the rudder will necessarily have to be located beyond the transom of the boat to suit the propeller shaft angle and clearances. Such a condition will almost always result in the above described condition, and if it occurs, an extenson or "plate" must be used over the rudder from the bottom of the boat to prevent air from being sucked in on a turn (see Fig. 16-6). The problem is evidenced by a severe stream of water or "rooster tail" flying up from the transom area, together with a loss of turning ability.

A power boat will always tend to turn better in the direction the propeller rotates due to the propeller's torque reaction. Offsetting the rudder slightly to one side, as shown by Plate 59 will compensate for this torque reaction to some degree in high speed boats. In the smaller single engined runabout type, this is why it is desirable for the driver of the boat to be seated on the side which the propeller rotates. If the propeller turns clockwise, or right handed, the driver should sit on the right or starboard side to help overcome the torque reaction. Another advantage to offsetting the rudder from the propeller is that it makes removal of the propeller shaft possible without first removing the rudder. On powerboats of slow to medium speed where the rudder is supported at the lower end, a portion of the rudder may be cut away, or a hole may be cut through the rudder, so that when the rudder is turned, the shaft can be removed.

## TWIN SCREW APPLICATIONS

When twin engines are installed, twin rudders are usually recommended, although in slow to medium speed craft in the larger sizes which have a fairly large centerline mounted rudder, a single rudder may suffice. However, the efficiency of rudders not installed directly in the propeller slipstream is not as good. In almost all twin screw applications, spade-type rudders will be used and are similar to any other spade-type application. However, the rudders should be adjusted to compensate for the difference in the turning radius of the two rudders as shown by Plate 60. The illustration shows a typical boat turning with twin rudders, with the relative proportions enlarged for clarity. Note that the outboard rudder on a turn requires less of a turning angle than the inboard rudder. Obviously, the angle would vary depending on the turning radius of the boat and spacing of the rudders. To compensate for this, it is possible to slightly "toe-in" the actuating gear (quadrants or tiller arms as will be discussed) when they are mounted forward of the rudder stock, or "toe-out" if the gear is mounted to the aft side of the rudder stock.

It is preferable to make arrangements for physical adjustments on test runs. For best efficiency it is also good practice to adjust the rudders to ascertain their best tracking position. This is done by holding a straight course, and disconnecting one rudder at a time to allow it to determine its most efficient trailing position. Generally this will be a degree or so from being parallel with the centerline of the boat. Turnbuckle adjustment rods with cable steering, or other adjustment devices, can be used to make adjustments during test runs.

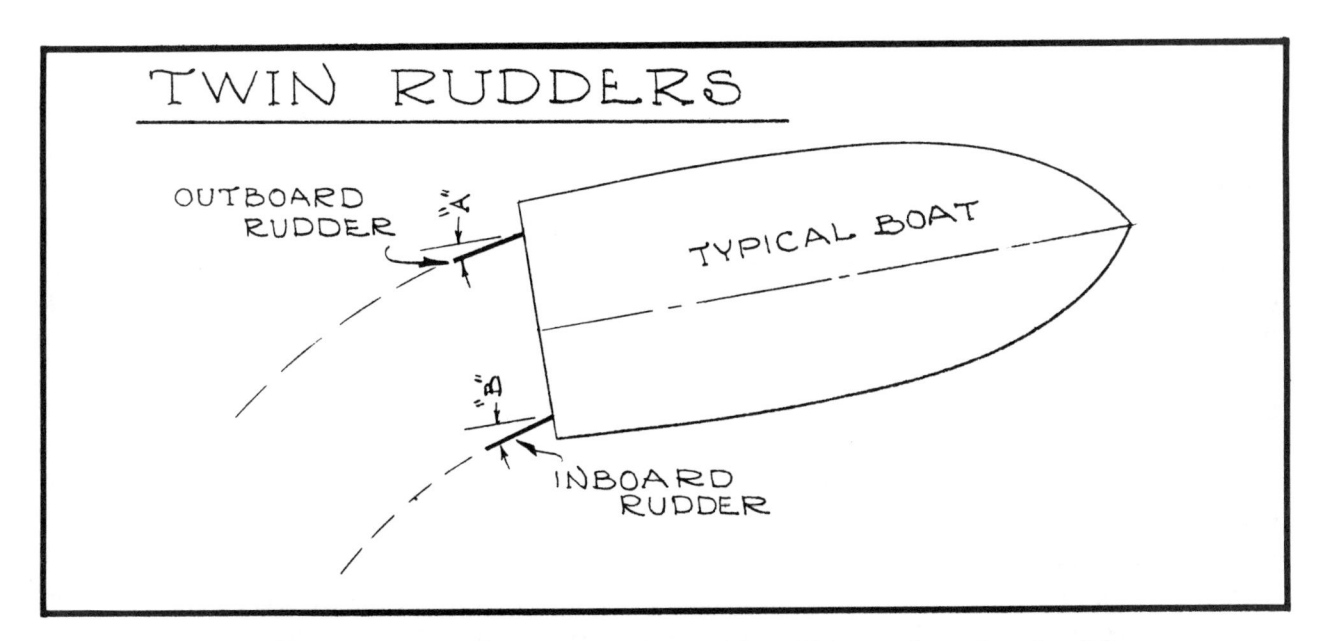

PLATE 60 — Note the difference in angularity required between the outboard and the inboard rudder with twin rudders on a typical turn. Angle "A" of the outboard rudder is less than that of Angle "B". Twin rudders should have this difference in angularity for efficiency on turns. A toe-in of five to ten degrees on the quadrants or tiller arms when the rudders are centered will compensate for this when the quadrant or tiller arm is forward of the rudder stock.

## INBOARD RUDDER INSTALLATION

The rudder stock on the inboard mounted rudder must pass through the bottom of the boat to the inside much the same way as a propeller shaft does on the engine. Since the hole is through the bottom of the boat, some means must be provided to keep water from entering, just as with the propeller shaft. There is more than one way that this can be accomplished. If the hole for the rudder is near the waterline, a tube can be used that leads vertically into the hull to well above the waterline which will keep water out of the boat if it is properly sealed where it joins to the hull.

However, the most common method is to use a fitting called a rudder port which contains a packing or stuffing box just like that used on the propeller shaft (see Fig. 16-7). Various types and sizes of rudder ports are available ready-made to suit a wide variation in rudder stock sizes and hull configurations. While the rudder port provides a water-tight seal at the hole, it also has the job of providing bearing support for the rudder stock or shaft. The mounting flange of the rudder port should preferably be bolted through the hull for strength, being well bedded with sealant. Many rudder ports have a length of tube that extends down through the hull and slightly past the bottom of the hull which can be trimmed to length. Ideally, the rudder port should be located above the waterline, or blocked up so that it is above the waterline. This enables the packing to be replaced without risk of water coming aboard. However, in most powerboats this is not always practical or possible.

FIG. 16-7 — A typical rudder port with stuffing box is used where the rudder shaft passes through the hull to prevent leaks and provide a rudder bearing. (Courtesy of Glenwood Marine Equipment)

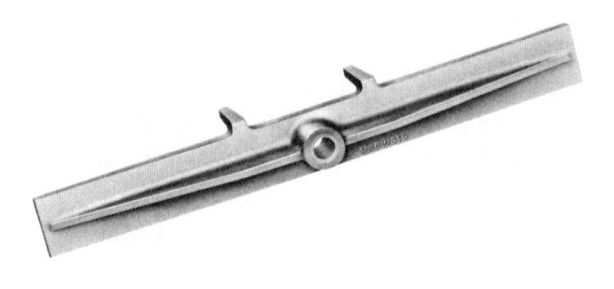

FIG. 16-8 — This rudder post bracket supports the upper end of the rudder post. The bracket usually secures to the motor stringers or other suitable blocking near the stern. (Courtesy of Glenwood Marine Equipment)

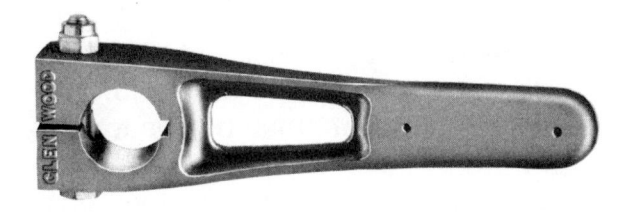

FIG. 16-9 — A typical rudder tiller arm that fits to the rudder shaft. (Courtesy of Glenwood Marine Equipment)

With rudders having a lower support, the other bearing point provided by the rudder port will usually provide sufficient strength and support for the rudder stock. However, on spade type rudders, an additional bearing point is necessary inside the boat above the rudder port. There should be ample distance between the rudder port and upper bearing for rigidity, and this is sometimes difficult to achieve due to cramped conditions. An upper steady rest bracket with a bearing, such as the flange bearing or pillow block type, is highly desirable in this situation, as high on the stock as possible. The steady rest can be a piece of wood with a suitably sized hole in it for the rudder stock, or ready-made units are available. (see Fig. 16-8). In either instance, adequate support and securing of the steady rest is important. In many cases, the steady rest can span across the motor stringers which is a good method. If a suitable bearing is not available, it is possible to use a steady rest made from dense, heavy hardwood such as oak, teak, or lignum vitae, with a tightly drilled hole for the stock.

In addition to the rudder support, a means must be provided to prevent the rudder from falling out of the boat. This is usually done by installing a safety collar over the shaft above the steady rest. The safety collar.has a set screw, split ring, or other device to lock it in place. A washer or two is used between the steady rest and the safety collar, which may be of the oil-impregnated type for smooth action as long as graphited washers are not used.

It is not desirable to run the collar directly on the rudder port stuffing box, since it is necessary to adjust the packing gland and replace the packing at times. Since the weight of the rudder is on this collar, there is no way to keep the rudder from falling if the collar is raised or removed from the shaft for checking purposes, unless there is a lower skeg.

In lieu of a rudder port, a rudder tube may be used which may have bearings inside for shaft support. Such a tube may be made from metal with a mounting flange, or in the case of fiberglass hulls, it may be a rigid fiberglass tube bonded directly in place to the hull. In metal boats, such a shaft tube is common, being welded in as part of the hull.

Because the rudder stock does not rotate at high speed like a propeller shaft, the critical alignment required for a propeller is not necessary for the rudder stock. However, this does not mean that a sloppy installation is acceptable. The alignment of the various components should be true in order to prevent binding in the system and to provide smooth action. In some cases, lubrication of the components is desirable, and hence Zerk-type grease fittings may be installed so that waterproof grease can be used in the system.

## RUDDER ACTUATING EQUIPMENT

Obviously some means must be provided to turn the rudder in order to turn the boat. On many sailboats, especially with outboard rudders, this is readily done by a simple lever or "tiller" connected to the top of the rudder actuated by the helmsman. This is probably the most basic steering system as it is a direct control type requiring no other equipment. Consequently, tiller steering is cheap, simple, reliable, and easy to maintain and repair.

However, as rudder forces become greater because of the speed of the boat or the rudder area, other means are necessary to actuate the rudder, usually by means of a more powerful steering system connected to the rudder. Basically, the problem is one of leverage, which means that some form of lever arm must be fitted to the rudder stock to transmit the leverage of the steering system to the rudder. Usually this is accomplished by use of a rudder tiller arm or rudder quadrant (see Fig. 16-9 and Fig. 16-10), depending on the type of steering gear to be used. Several types and sizes are available to suit many installations, and most are ready-made units of metal. Another variation is the radial-type wheel shown by Plate 61. With all these devices, a lever arm is formed, which together with the mechanical advantage provided by the steering gear, will provide the necessary force to turn the rudder as long as the system is carefully planned and installed.

The quadrant, tiller arm, or radial wheel may be fastened to the rudder stock in a number of ways. In some cases, the rudder stock is squared, and the fitting is clamped in place. In other instances, a keyway is used together with a clamp ring or split clamp ring to hold it to the shaft. In other cases, set screws alone are used, which may be considered satisfactory if the shaft is counterbored to receive the set screw.

FIG. 16-10 — A typical rudder quadrant used with various types of cable steering that fits to the rudder shaft. (Courtesy of Glenwood Marine Equipment)

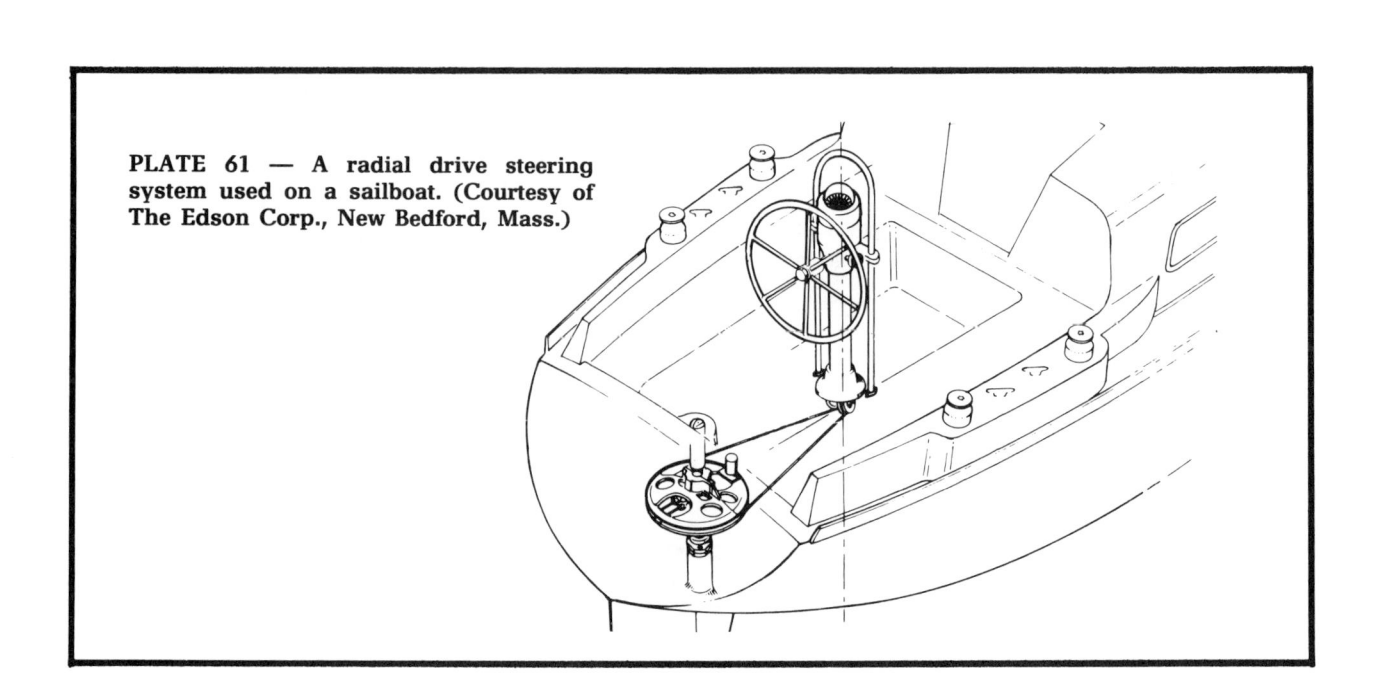

PLATE 61 — A radial drive steering system used on a sailboat. (Courtesy of The Edson Corp., New Bedford, Mass.)

## STEERING GEARS & CONTROL SYSTEMS

There are several types of steering gears and steering control systems possible. Much depends on the type of boat and the operator's requirements. The most common and popular types will be discussed along with general installation and usage requirements. In many cases, certain steering gears and control systems are proprietary items available from different manufacturers as ready-to-install units. When this is the case, the specific installation and usage requirements should be per the manufacturer's recommendations. Since the rudder is one of the most important pieces of equipment aboard a boat, the installation, selection, and maintenance of the completed system should be carefully done.

With the exception of boats which use a manual tiller to the rudder, most rudders are actuated by means of a steering wheel that can be either re-motely located or directly hooked to the boat's steering gear. Two systems of the latter type include a rack-and-pinion type and a worm gear type, both of which are directly coupled to the rudder stock (see Fig. 16-11 and Plate 62). A wheel or helm is used to rotate a shaft which accuates the rack-and-pinion or worm gear, that in turn moves the rudder. Both of these systems are most commonly used on sailboats. With the rack-and-pinion type, a gear on the shaft runs in a geared rack which is shaped like a typical quadrant. This geared quadrant has a hole to fit directly onto the rudder stock on inboard rudders, or a geared quadrant with a slotted arm is available for use on outboard mounted rudders (see Plate 63).

The worm gear steerer is often used where the rudder stock is heavily raked aft and there is not room for a quadrant. A universal joint is often fitted to the shaft to provide a more suitable angle for the wheel. The worm gear steerer is often called a "non-reversing"

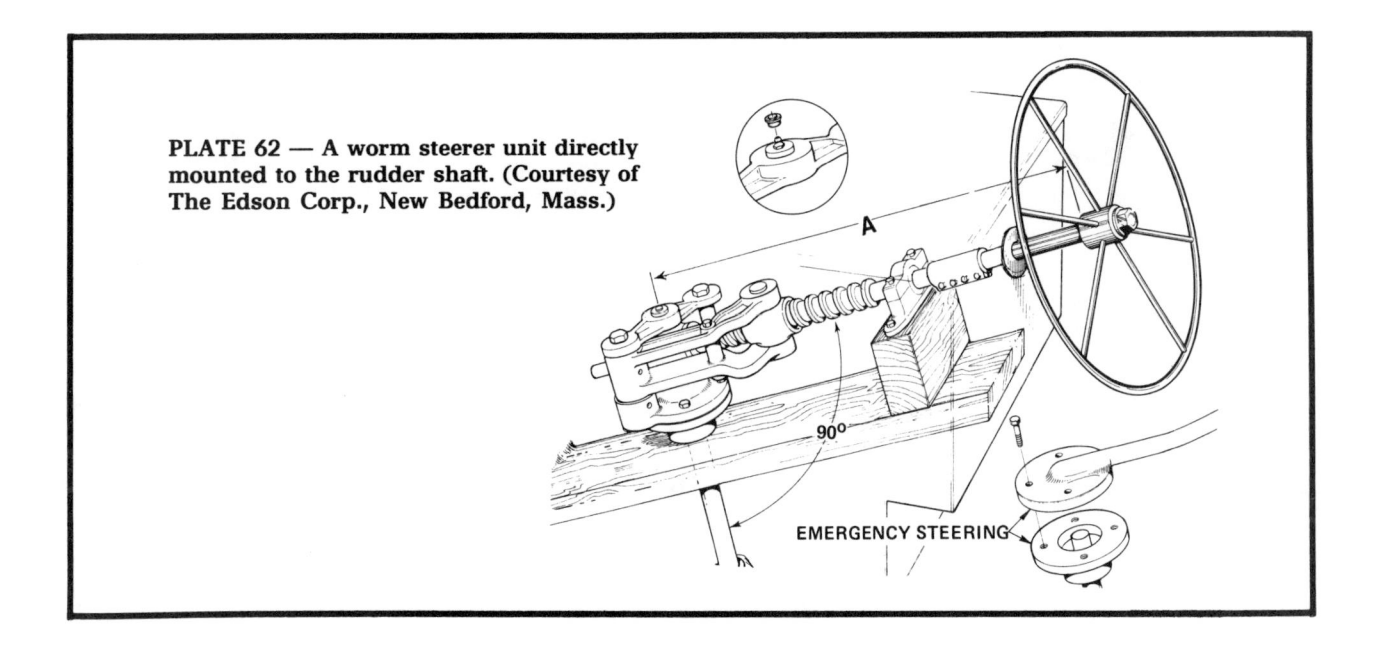

PLATE 62 — A worm steerer unit directly mounted to the rudder shaft. (Courtesy of The Edson Corp., New Bedford, Mass.)

A

90°

EMERGENCY STEERING

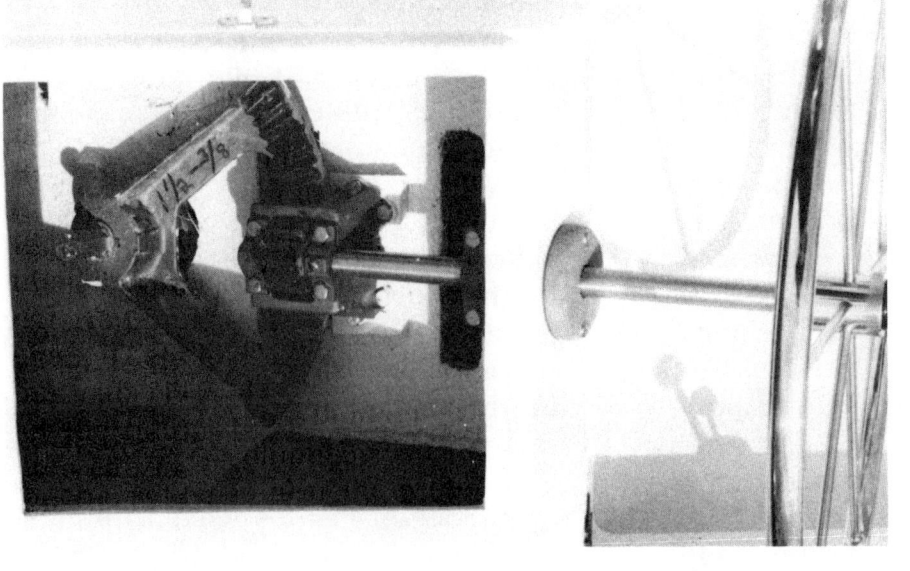

FIG. 16-11 — A rack-and-pinion steering system as used on a sailboat. (Courtesy of The Edson Corp., New Bedford, Mass.)

type, meaning that the feedback from the rudder will not turn the wheel when the helmsman lets go. This is often desirable on cruising sailboats and on boats where directional stability can make control more fatiguing.

Other types of steering systems locate the wheel or "helm" at some other

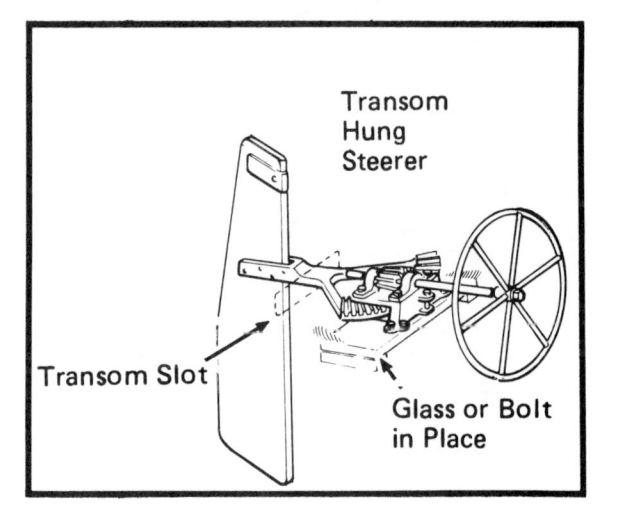

PLATE 63 — A rack-and-pinion steerer featuring a slotted quadrant which directly connects to an outboard rudder. (Courtesy of The Edson Corp., New Bedford, Mass.)

location away from the actual steering gear, and are said to have "remote" steering. In many cases, especially aboard power boats with flying bridges, two or more steering "stations" are desired. Not all types of steering can be adapted to this use, however, and a type should be selected that is suitable. Also, if an automatic pilot is desired in the steering system, the automatic pilot and the steering system adaptation must be compatible.

Typical steering control systems used aboard pleasure boats are the drum-and-cable, chain-and-cable, push-pull cable, geared mechanical types, and the hydraulic or "power assist" types. All have their advantages and disadvantages, and one may be more suitable for a given installation than another. The ultimate selection lies with the operator's desires, budget, and requirements of use. Depending on the type of system, the rudder will be actuated either by a tiller arm, quadrant, or a radial wheel unit.

The drum-and-cable type is inexpensive and relatively easy to install

197

and maintain. This type of steering is often used on racing boats since it is reliable and offers positive control. Some "head scratching" must be used in planning so that leads are fair and straight and the system runs free, but the actual installation is not beyond the abilities of the average person. The ends of the cable fit into the grooves of the quadrant and secure with cable clamps or other devices. The cable, when in the grooves, should be on the same horizontal plane as the lead pulleys on either side, with the pulleys set somewhat aft of the quadrant so that the cables will track in the quadrant grooves at all times. Two drum-and-cable systems are shown by Plate 64. The cables may lead on either or both

sides of the hull. Depending on the drum, either a single length or two lengths of cables may be required. In either case, at least one turnbuckle is required in the cable to make adjustments and take up slack. Two turnbuckles are even more desirable, with one on each side of the drum. Because the cable is "fixed" at the drum whether a single or double cable is used, adjustment for slack is desirable on both portions of the cable. Such cables, however, should not be overly tight as this places undue strain on the system and can cause binding.

Pulleys or sheaves used with cable steering can be of the fixed or pivoting type that can be adjusted to varying lead positions. All such pulleys should

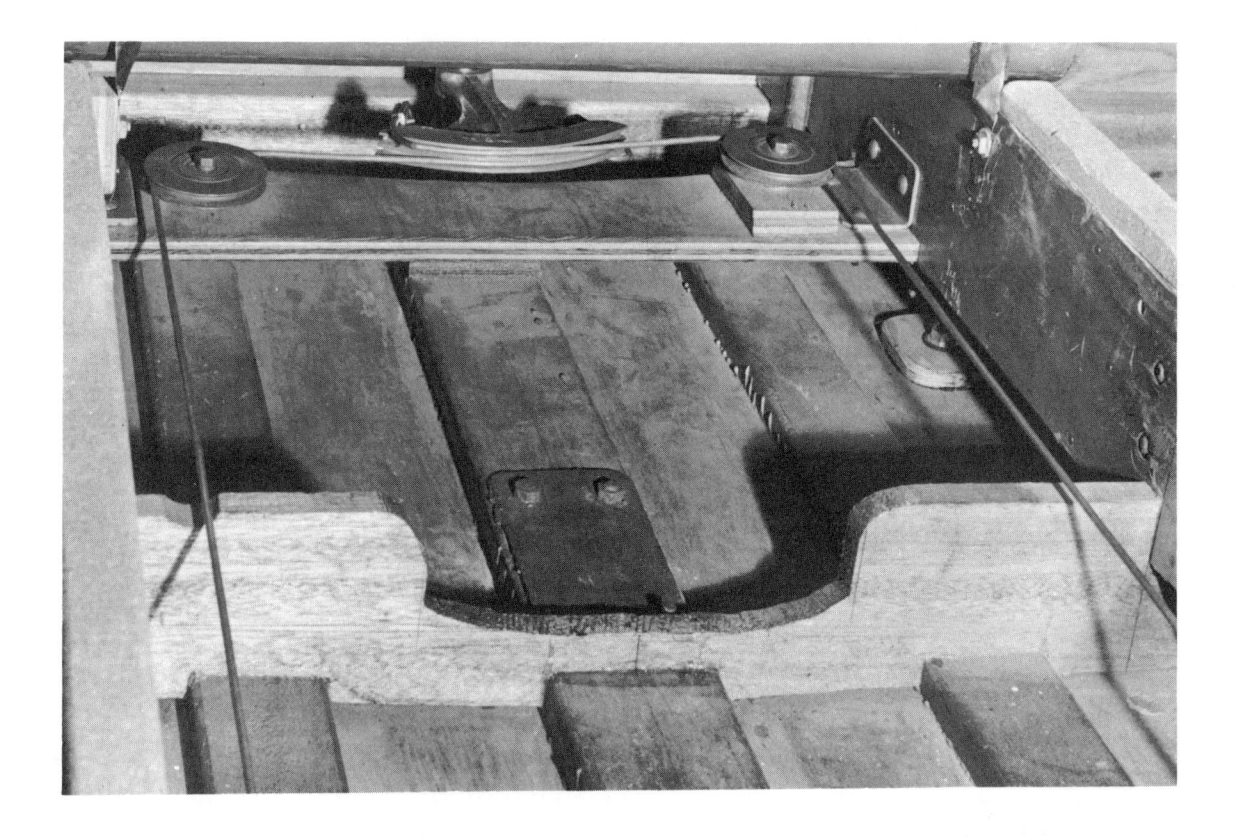

FIG. 16-12 — A cable steering system using pulleys, and a quadrant on an inboard runabout. Note the husky mountings of the pulleys and the plate backing up the bolts of the strut along the keel batten.

198

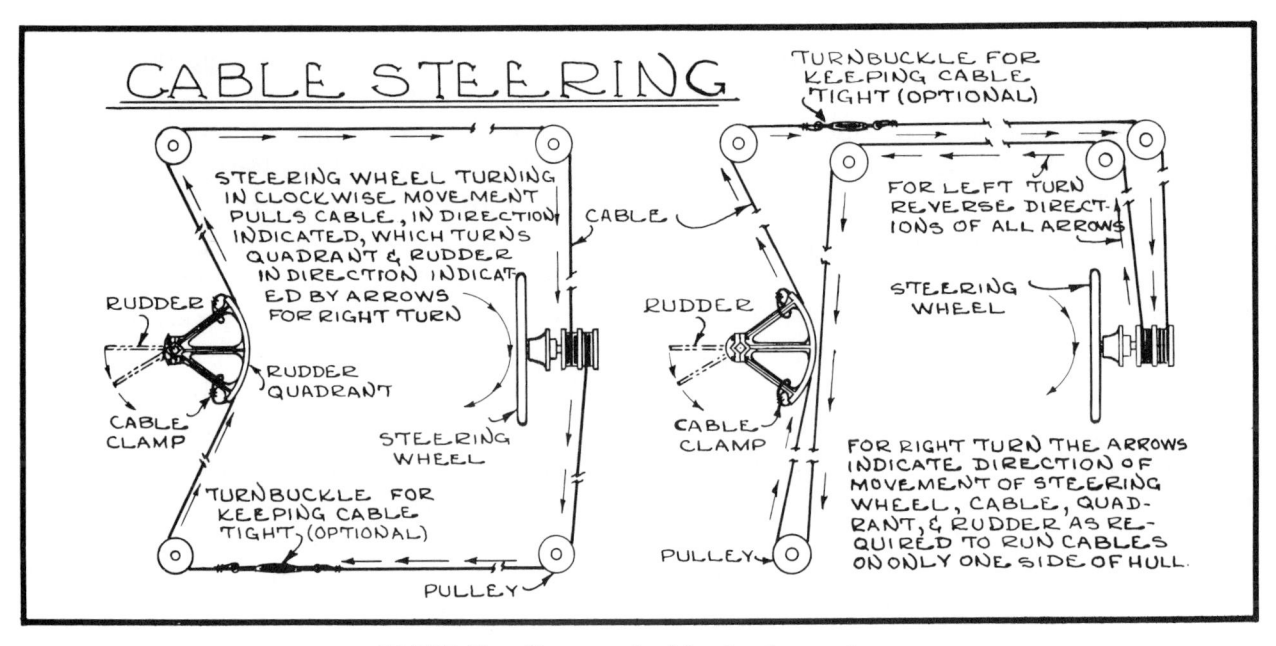

**CABLE STEERING**

TURNBUCKLE FOR KEEPING CABLE TIGHT (OPTIONAL)

STEERING WHEEL TURNING IN CLOCKWISE MOVEMENT PULLS CABLE, IN DIRECTION INDICATED, WHICH TURNS QUADRANT & RUDDER IN DIRECTION INDICATED BY ARROWS FOR RIGHT TURN

RUDDER

CABLE

CABLE CLAMP

RUDDER QUADRANT

STEERING WHEEL

TURNBUCKLE FOR KEEPING CABLE TIGHT (OPTIONAL)

PULLEY

FOR LEFT TURN REVERSE DIRECTIONS OF ALL ARROWS

RUDDER

STEERING WHEEL

CABLE CLAMP

PULLEY

FOR RIGHT TURN THE ARROWS INDICATE DIRECTION OF MOVEMENT OF STEERING WHEEL, CABLE, QUADRANT, & RUDDER AS REQUIRED TO RUN CABLES ON ONLY ONE SIDE OF HULL.

**PLATE 64 — Drum and cable steering systems.**

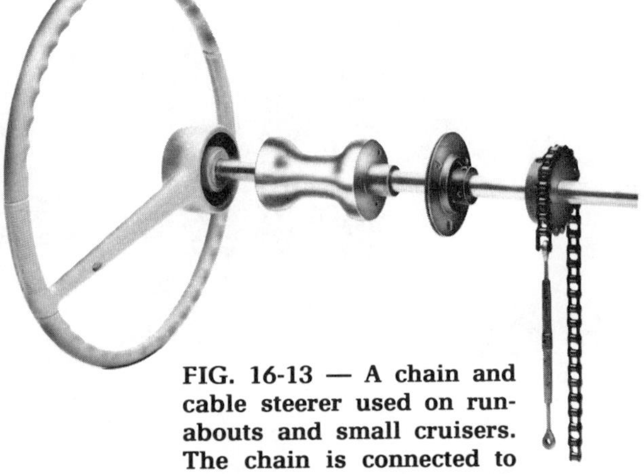

**FIG. 16-13 — A chain and cable steerer used on runabouts and small cruisers. The chain is connected to cables that lead aft via pulleys to the rudder quadrant. (Courtesy of Glenwood Marine Equipment)**

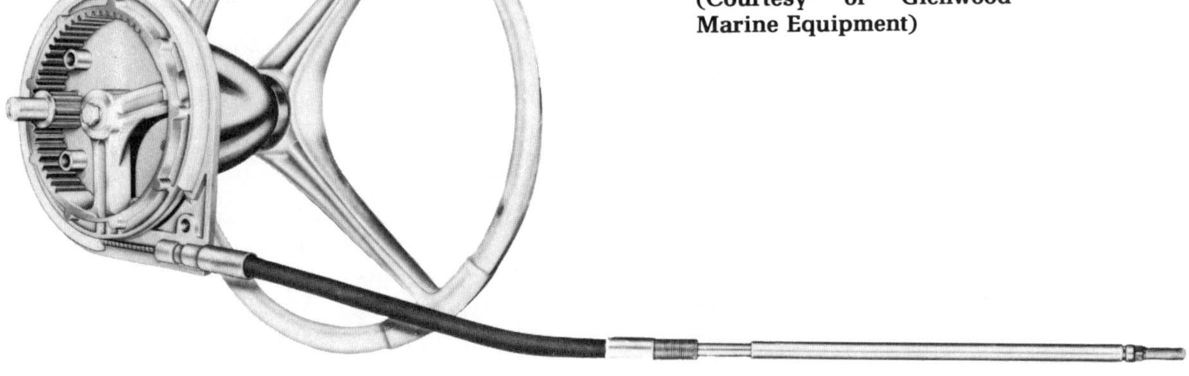

**FIG. 16-14 — A single push-pull steering system. (Courtesy of ACCO, Rockford, Ill.)**

be rigidly bolted to solid structural members as considerable strain is applied in operation. The cables used must be of flexible wire rope, preferably of the 7 X 19 variety in stainless steel. Another type of cable often used is the so-called "tiller cable" which is a steel flexible wire rope covered with a vinyl plastic sheath for flexibility and ease of operation. In most boats, either 3/16" or ¼" size will be adequate except for larger boats which may require one size larger. Pulley sizes should be at least 16 times the wire diameter, and preferably more, to prevent undue strain on the cable at turns. This would

mean that a ¼" cable would use a pulley with a diameter of at least 4". A typical installation on a powerboat is shown by Fig. 16-12.

The chain-and-cable type of steering is similar to the drum-and-cable type (see Fig. 16-13). The main difference is that the wheel is connected to a shaft fitted with a chain sprocket which gear-drives the chain. The ends of the chain are connected to cables which in turn lead to the rudder quadrant in the same manner as the drum-and-cable type (see Plate 65). Where more power is required, the wheel shaft can be reduction gear-driven to the chain

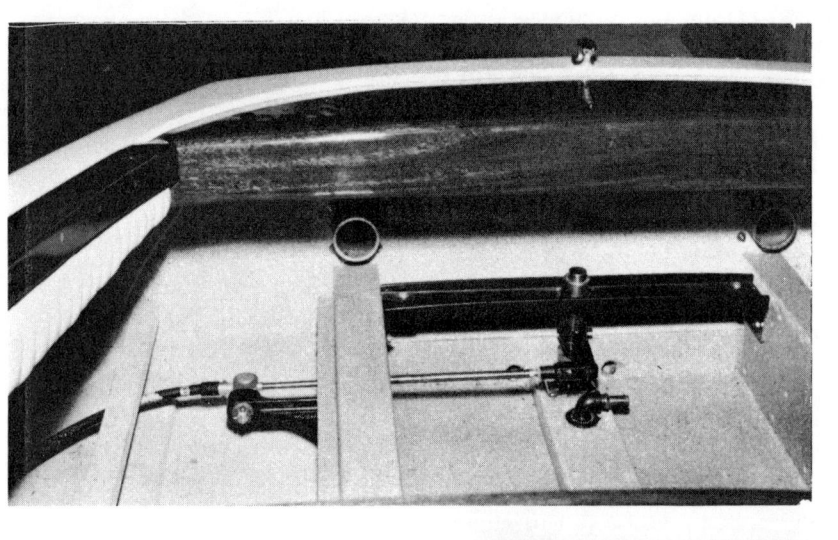

FIG. 16-15 — The assembly of the push-pull steering system at the stern where it connects to the rudder tiller arm. The end of the cable is rigidly connected to the motor stringer in this example, with the actuating rod linked to the tiller arm via a clevis. Note the rudder post bracket between the motor stringers.

FIG. 16-16 — A rack-and-pinion type steerer as seen from the backside of the dashboard on an inboard runabout looking aft. Note the push-pull cable leading from the end of the tube.

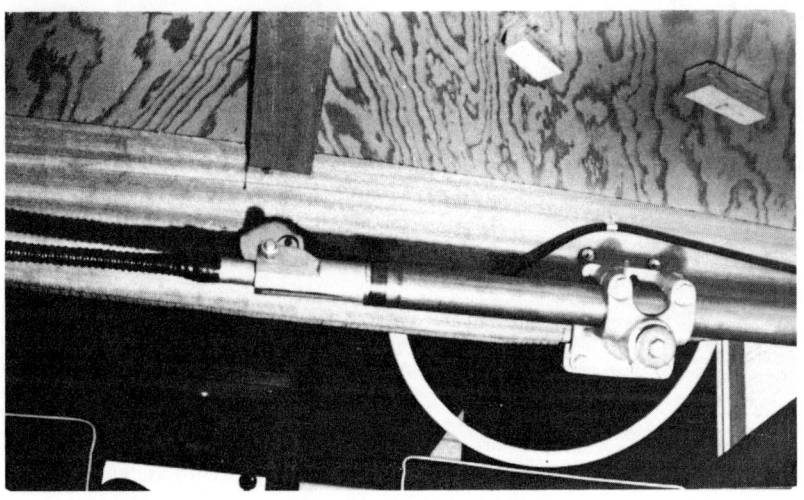

sprocket also. The chain-and-cable system can also be connected to a radial drive unit as long as the cable makes a straight lead into the radial drive wheel. Installation of the system is otherwise similar to the drum-and-cable type.

A popular system aboard power-boats, and frequently used on sail-boats, is the push-pull cable steering system. The typical push-pull cable consists of a semi-flexible cable running inside of a flexible sleeve that is fixed at either end where it is attached at the steering wheel and to the rudder or steering actuator. Several types of push-pull systems are available, and most are proprietary systems that are sized to suit, purchased ready made for installation (see Fig. 16-14). Actuation of the push-pull cable by the steerer may be by several means, including

ring gears, rack-and-pinion (see Fig. 16-16), and a type that adapts the chain-and-cable type to actuate a push-pull cable. A variation on the push-pull system is the so-called "pull-pull" system (see Plate 66). This method uses the same chain sprocket steerer used in the chain-and-cable system. Two cables of flexible wire rope are used running inside a plastic tubing conduit or sheath separately, leading from the steerer to the rudder quadrant or radial drive wheel. The plastic sheaths must be secured at each of their ending points. Unlike the typical push-pull cable which is usually of the single type, the pull-pull system uses a smaller and more flexible standard wire rope that is in equal tension on either side.

The advantages of the push-pull and pull-pull types are that the flexibility of

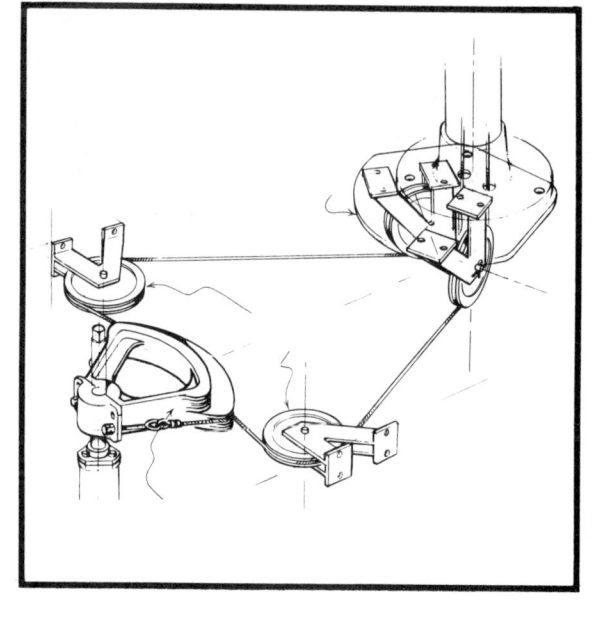

PLATE 65 — A chain and cable steering system using a pedestal steerer commonly associated with larger sailing craft. (Courtesy of The Edson Corp., New Bedford, Mass.)

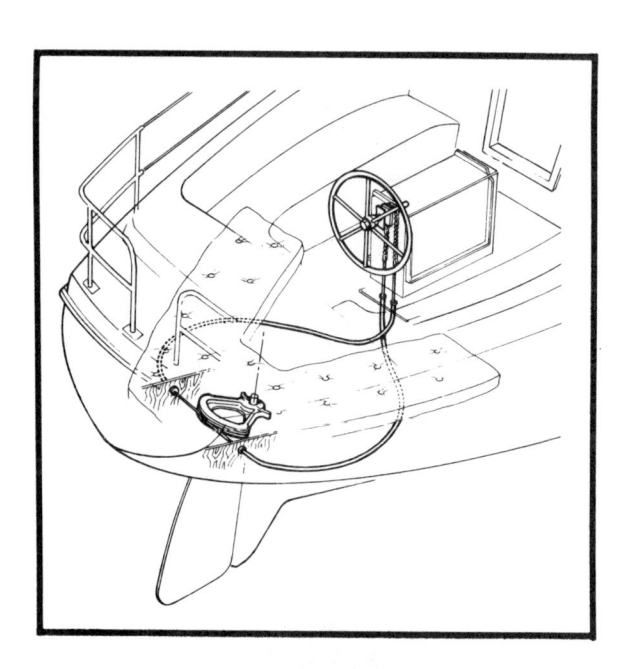

PLATE 66 — A "pull-pull" steering system using a chain and sprocket steerer and twin cables in sleeves to the rudder quadrant. (Courtesy of The Edson Corp., New Bedford, Mass.)

the cables allow installation in a wide variety of situations where other types of steering would be difficult if not impossible. The cable can be lead around corners and other obstructions with relative ease. Furthermore, since there are no pulleys or other wear points, the units are much simpler, more reliable, and easier to maintain. Most of the push-pull units attach to a tiller arm at the rudder stock by means of a clevis linkage. Adaption to dual stations is quite simple with most of the proprietary units available.

A type of steering that is usually only used on large yachts and commercial boats is the geared mechanical types. These systems consist of geared steerers connected by rods or tubing which lead to the rudder. Various other geared units and universal joints can be used in the system in order to change directions and connect to the rudder. The lengths of rod or tubing in the system must be carefully supported with bearings and aligned to operate freely. Obviously, such a system takes considerable care in installation, however, it is quite reliable and smooth in operation. The extra cost and complexity of this type of system usually makes it impractical for the average do-it-yourselfer since high quality materials and installation methods are required if a long-lasting, reliable system is desired.

Hydraulic steering is becoming more common even though it is expensive. In a sense hydraulic steering on a boat is much like "power" steering in an automobile. Several types of systems are available from different manufacturers. The principle, however, is similar for most. The wheel is used to actuate a hydraulic pump that directs the fluid under pressure through lines to a hydraulic cylinder near the rudder. Depending on the direction the wheel is turned, the cylinder actuates the rudder in one direction or the other. The components in the hydraulic system are few, and the lines connecting them can be directed in any direction so that cramped quarters present few problems. Any number of additional helms can be installed simply by plugging another helm pump into the system. Similarly, an automatic pilot can also be simply installed. Installation of a hydraulic system should be per the specific instructions provided by the manufacturer, and in some cases, the work is best left to a professional or one familiar with hydraulic systems. A hydraulic system is shown by Plate 67.

## STEERER & WHEELS

Usually the steerer is part and parcel with the steering system, although there are several configurations. When the steerer and wheel are remote from the rudder, they will be mounted to the control console, dashboard, or bulkhead, or in the case of many sailboats, to a steering pedestal (see Fig.16-17 and Fig. 16-18). Except for the pedestal type, most steerers are of a "bulkhead mount". The actual steerer mechanism mounts behind the bulkhead, dashboard, or control console panel with the steering shaft protruding through a hole to receive the steering wheel or "helm". With pedestal type mounts, the pedestal can be of a ready-made type, or the builder can make his own. In the latter instance, it should be emphasized that the pedestal must be quite strong and securely mounted in place. The same applies to all steerers

202

mounted to bulkheads, dashboards, and control consoles. Forces applied to the steerer can be quite severe, so not only should the steerer be preferably bolted in place, but the adjoining structure must be quite strong and rigid as well.

Various types and sizes of wheels are available. In many cases, the manufacturer of the steering system will provide a suitable wheel sized to suit the unit. With other steering systems, the wheel size must be selected by the owner to suit. Most steering manufacturers can advise the purchaser as to the proper sized wheel for his installation that will provide the correct steering leverage. Whether the wheel should be mounted vertically, horizontally, or at some angle between depends on the type of installation and the operator's desires. In many cases, a mock-up should be made using various helm configurations in order to determine which will be the most practical and comfortable. If building a new boat,

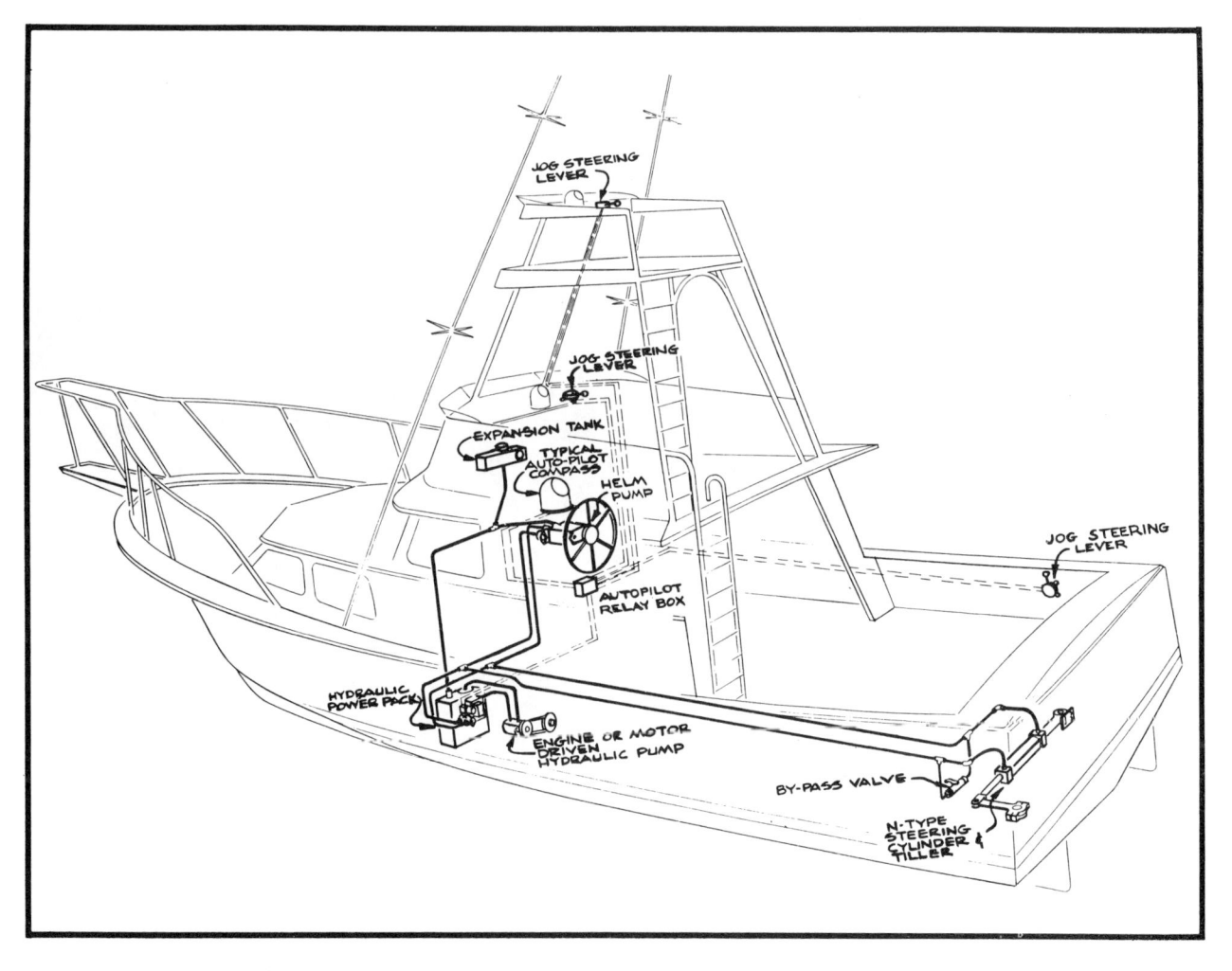

**PLATE 67 — A hydraulic steering system showing the versatility possible with steering systems of this type which allows multiple steering stations. (Courtesy of Wm. E. Hough Co., Seattle, Wash.)**

the designer may have detailed this portion of the design. However, since this is a personal matter, a full-size mock-up is still desirable. Emergency steering provisions are a good idea on any boat, however, powerboats frequently have no such provisions. If building a new boat, the designer may include such details with the plans, or the steering manufacturer may include emergency steering provisions with the unit.

## SKID FINS

On many high speed sport and competition boats, the design of the hull is such that steering is relatively ineffective even with adequate rudder area. In short, the rudder will turn the stern in the proper direction, but the hull tends

to skid more or less sideways without any appreciable change of direction. In this type of boat a skid fin, or perhaps two of them in tandem, is a requirement.

The skid fin (see Fig. 16-19) is small in area and well streamlined to present minimum drag. Yet, the fin does extend into the water enough to provide a pivot point around which the boat will turn. The questions arise, however, where the fin should be located, and whether one or two will be required. The answer to these questions is that there really is no precise answer. Much depends on the design of the hull and the speed capability. If building a boat of this type, the designer will usually have enough experience and will frequently note the location and number of fins to use. If this information is not given, someone who has experience in

FIG. 16-17 & FIG. 16-18 — Two examples of pedestal type steerers commonly used on larger sailboats. (Courtesy of The Edson Corp., New Bedford, Mass.)

this matter should be consulted for advice. On a planing boat where a fin may be required, the fin location is generally assumed to be just forward of the center of the wetted planing surface. Admittedly, such a point is difficult to determine by sight alone.

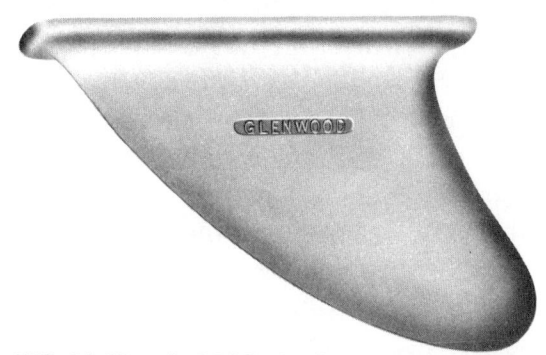

FIG. 16-19 — A skid fin is often used on high speed runabouts to aid in turning and prevent skidding. (Courtesy of Glenwood Marine Equipment)

Skid fins can be bolted or screwed to the bottom of the boat. With the typical inboard runaboat or ski boat, the fin will be located along the centerline of the hull. Fins are usually made from metal castings in either bronze or aluminum. There is some argument about the fastening methods and materials that are best. A bronze fin that is bolted to the hull will be quite strong. However, in the event that the boat hits an object or runs aground, there is a chance of causing extensive hull damage. On the other hand, if an aluminum fin is used screwed to the bottom of the boat, the fin will probably fracture or break away from the hull with little damage, although a new fin will be required.

# CHAPTER 17 — FUEL SYSTEMS

Too many novice boaters are quick to compare the fuel systems on their inboard boats with those of their automobiles. They can't understand why so much care is necessary with a boat's fuel tanks and fuel system when such care is not required in the standard passenger car. But comparing fuel systems between cars and boats is like comparing apples with oranges; they are just not the same. The typical car engine compartment is open at the bottom and operates with a continual blast of fresh air when in motion. Also, the fuel tank is usually located a long distance from engine heat. Consequently one seldom hears of a fire or explosion in a car with the exception of a collision. With boats, however, the engine of a boat usually sits down in what basically amounts to a closed-in "box" making a perfect "catch-all" for volatile fumes and dripping or leaking fuel. These dangerous vapors and fluids can concentrate to a point where a fire or explosion will occur with the first innocent spark or flame. The results can be disastrous. Consequently the correct and proper installation of fuel tanks and fuel systems is probably the most important safety element aboard a boat, especially those using gasoline for fuel.

The entire fuel system should be liquid and vapor tight. Boats are often subjected to conditions which are extreme and hazardous. Therefore, the fuel tanks and fuel system must be able to withstand the exposures of marine service including pressure, vibration, shock, hull movement, attack by oil, grease, solvents, corrosion, water, heat, cold, and other elements. Electrical continuity from the fill plates to the engine is important (especially with gasoline systems) to prevent accidental sparks due to static electricity as well as for the safety of crew members. The entire fuel system should be able to withstand fire from an external source for at least several minutes. When installing new tanks or a fuel system in a boat, a check should be made with local governing authorities or the U.S. Coast Guard for the latest approved materials and methods since requirements can change from time to time.

## TANK LOCATION & DESIGN

When building a new boat, the location of the fuel tanks is usually given on the plans or noted by the designer. The capacities and the tank locations given should be adhered to as closely as possible. If the builder wants to change the capacity or the tank locations, he should first contact the designer of the boat for his advice. In most boats, the weight of tanks and fuel is a considerable percentage of the total boat weight, and any changes in capacities or locations could affect not only the weight of the boat, but the balance as well, and make the results questionable.

With an existing boat where an owner wants to modify the tanks, such as by increasing the capacity or shifting their locations, the foregoing also applies. If the boat is well-balanced before such a change and floats at the proper waterline, then such changes should be approached with caution. With just about all boats, the ideal place to locate tanks is directly over the center of buoyancy, which happens to be somewhat aft of amidships in most boats. Locating tanks at this point will help keep the boat evenly balanced regardless of the amount of fuel in the tanks assuming that other large weights are also located for best balance. While it may be convenient to install additional fuel up in the bow or aft by the transom, such a practice may upset the balance of the hull unless

there are compensating weights placed towards the opposite end of the boat. The problem with compensating weights is what happens to the balance when the tank is near full or near empty? Obviously, the balance will be correct only when the tank is either full or empty, or at the level it was calculated to be.

Whenever possible, avoid locating fuel tanks at the forward portion of the hull. In most boats, the motion and shock loadings are much greater forward, and consequently the tank will be subjected to much greater stresses. This means that the tank must be proportionately stronger and thereby heavier, adding to the weight of the tank and further aggravating the problem of balancing the boat.

While a designer may give the sizes required for the tanks on a boat if building a new boat, the dimensions are best taken directly from the work to

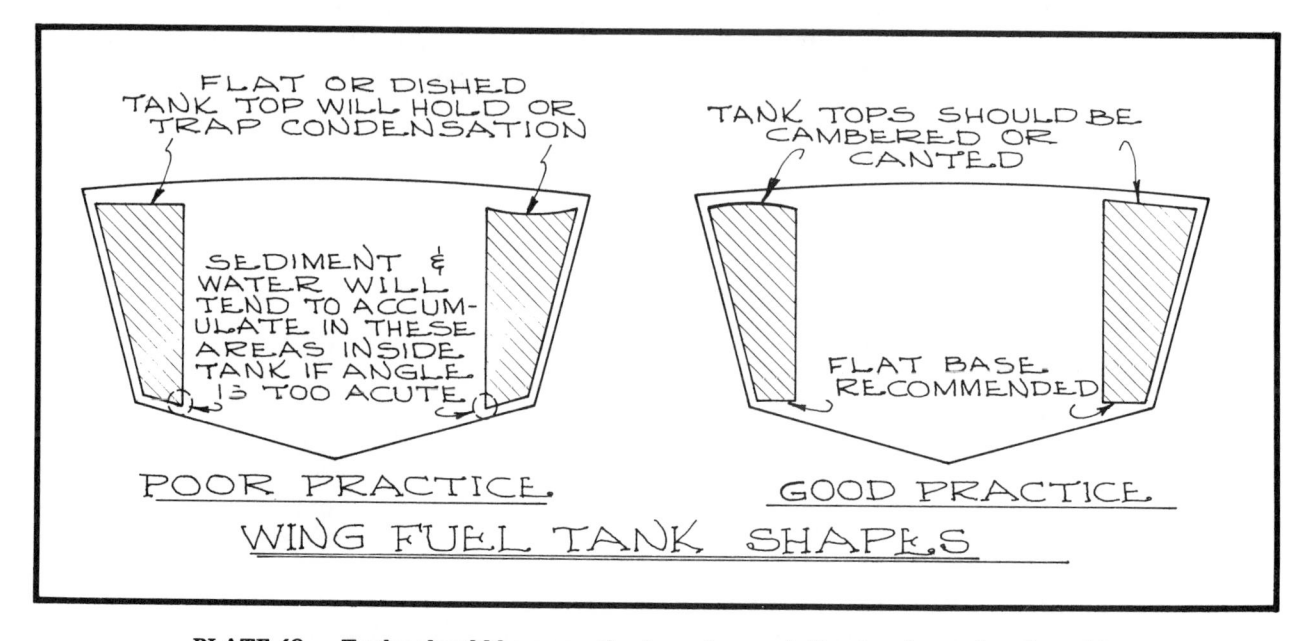

**PLATE 68 —** Tanks should be correctly shaped, especially when located outboard in the form of "wing" tanks. Tanks should have a flat base for adequate support and strength, as well as a cambered or canted top to allow condensation to drain off.

insure that the tanks will fit into the space provided. Fuel tanks used for gasoline must never be made integral with the hull. However, fuel tanks using diesel fuel are frequently integral with the hull, especially if the boat is built from steel or aluminum. In general, cylindrical tanks with convex or concave ends are the strongest. However, tanks of this shape do not use the available space as well as tanks that are shaped to fit the area.

Baffles or slosh plates should be installed vertically in all tanks where the distance in any direction exceeds about 30″ so that intervals will not exceed 20″ maximum. The baffles prevent the surge or "free surface" of the contents from making excessive noise. But more important, they prevent the movement of a tremendous weight which could affect the safety and stability on many boats. Baffles which are open should not have an open area larger than 25 to 30% of the baffle area. Limbers or drain passages should be fitted at all corners in baffles for the passage of air and fuel in the tank.

Tanks used for gasoline should have no openings or fittings in the bottom, sides, or ends. No exterior part of a tank should hold or "trap" moisture. Therefore, tank tops should be canted or cambered so that condensation and moisture will drain off. No indentations should be allowed where moisture can accumulate. The tanks should have no internal shape that will collect water and sediment inside the tank except as noted in the following. This can be prevented in many tanks which are shaped to suit a given area by providing a flat base, even if small in area, instead of a pointed bottom shape (see Plate 68). Clean-out plates can be used

on tanks for diesel fuel, however, these are preferably located on top of the tank. On diesel tanks, a sump or pocket can be installed in the bottom of a tank where water and sediment can accumulate, but the removal of such sediment should preferably be made from the top of the tank. Some diesel tanks use a drain cock at the bottom of the tank or sump to remove water and sediment from the tank, however, some authorities frown on this practice.

Insuring a positive and reliable flow of fuel to the engine is important. For this reason, the use of at least two fuel tanks arranged as shown by Plate 69 in every inboard boat is recommended. If one tank goes dry or the fuel becomes contaminated in one tank, then the contents of the other tank can be used as long as valves are installed in the lines to allow independent use. A further requirement is to provide at least one filter of ample size per engine (see Fig. 17-1). Such filters especially with diesel fuel are ideally of the duplex type so that in the event that one filter clogs, it can be shut down and cleaned

FIG. 17-1 — Every fuel system should have a filter in the supply line to remove water and contaminants from the fuel before they enter the engine. (Courtesy of Glenwood Marine Equipment)

while operating on the other. A reliable fuel system for twin engines is also shown by Plate 69. In planning any fuel system, always provide access to all components for ease in maintenance and replacement.

## TANK MATERIALS AND CONSTRUCTION

Fuel tanks should be made by persons or firms experienced in making marine tanks of the highest quality.

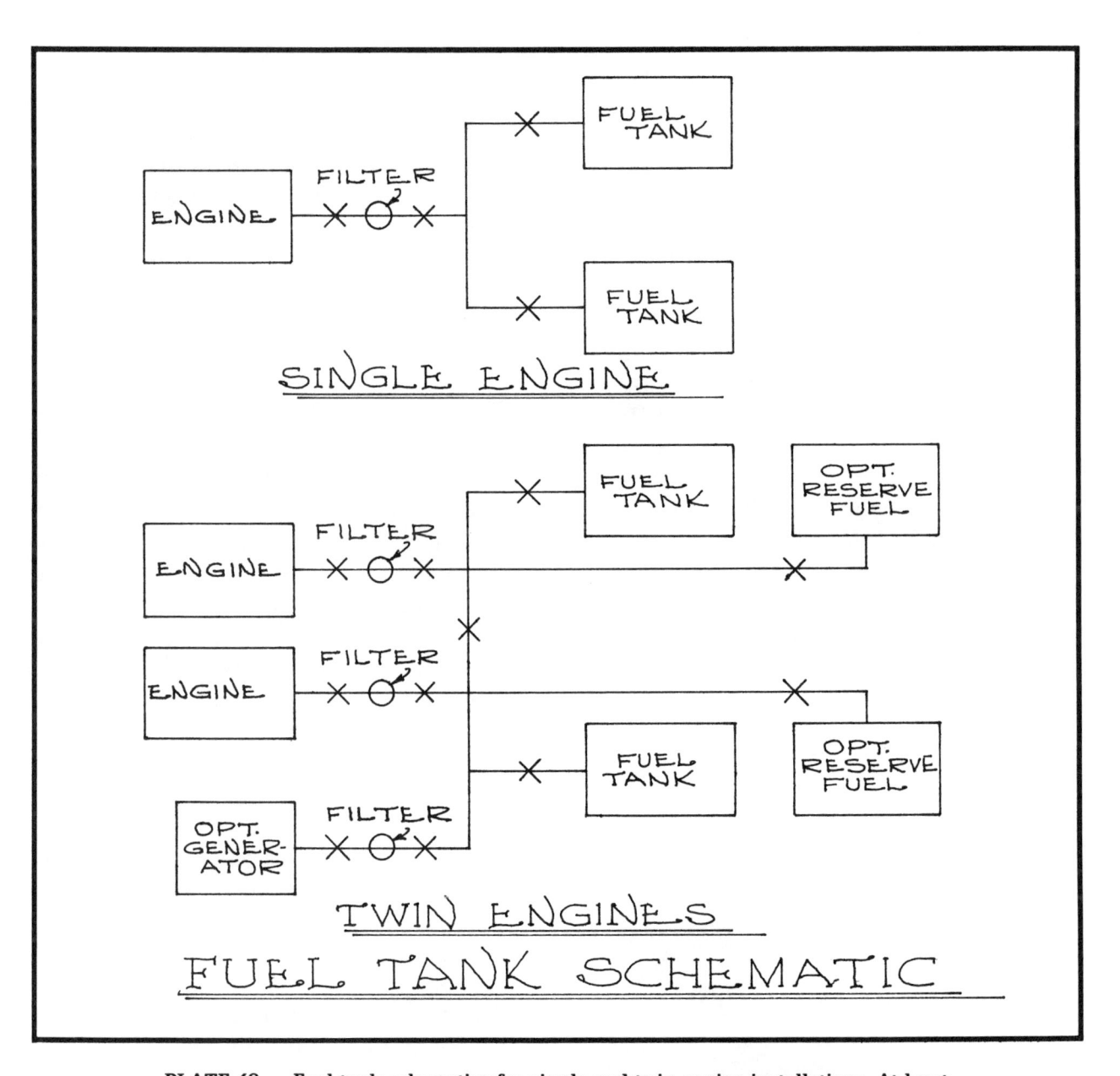

PLATE 69 — Fuel tank schematics for single and twin engine installations. At least two fuel tanks are recommended in every installation for reliability. The "X" indicates a valve or shut-off. When properly located, such valves allow independent or simultaneous use of the tanks. If a pump is used in line with the tanks, the contents of one can be pumped into another.

Don't give the job to a friend who has just signed up at the local night school welding class and needs a practice project! The structural integrity of any fuel tank, especially those used for gasoline, can be a matter of life or death. Note that tank materials and the methods of construction and design will vary depending on whether gasoline or diesel fuel is used. While gasoline is more volatile than diesel fuel, this does not mean that one can be more careless in the installation and construction of tanks used for diesel fuel. All fuel tanks should be pressure tested prior to installation, as well as the entire fuel system, for the detection and correction of leaks. The tank manufacturer should attach a label with at least his name, address, date of manufacture, capacity, material used for the construction, and the design pressure.

Tanks can be purchased ready-made from various firms, or they can be custom-made. Materials used to build tanks can include copper and various copper bearing alloys, various types of iron and steel, aluminum, and fiberglass. Round cylindrical tanks are often the cheapest and easiest to make,

FIG. 17-2 — A ready-made aluminum fuel tank suitable for either gasoline or diesel fuel. (Courtesy of Tempo Products, Cleveland, Ohio)

as well as being inherently strong. Metal tanks should be welded, brazed, or riveted and brazed, depending on the material used. All metallic tanks should be fitted with a bonding terminal. Various tank construction materials and specifications are noted by Plate 70. This listing, however, does NOT mean that all these materials should be used for both gasoline and diesel fuel.

In selecting the material to use for building tanks, several things must be considered. For example, terneplate is generally a poor tank material since it is subject to rust. Terneplate is basically sheet steel or iron which has been coated with tin alloy much like a tin can, and therefore rusts easily. Consequently, terneplate should only be used if coated inside and outside with an approved coating.

An improved tank similar to the terneplate steel tanks is made from aluminized steel. An epoxy aircraft-type fuel tank lining is then applied both inside and outside the tank. It is claimed, that unlike galvanized sheet steel tanks where welds leave bare steel exposed to possible corrosion, proper welding techniques with aluminized steel causes practically no loss of the aluminum coating. The zinc coating in galvanized sheet metal, on the other hand, can contaminate welds and leave them porous. The final coating of epoxy assures that all tank surfaces are protected. Nevertheless, such tanks are still not recommended for "below decks" installation where the tanks could remain immersed in bilge water.

"Black iron" or carbon steel tanks are only suitable for gasoline if the tanks are hot dipped galvanized after

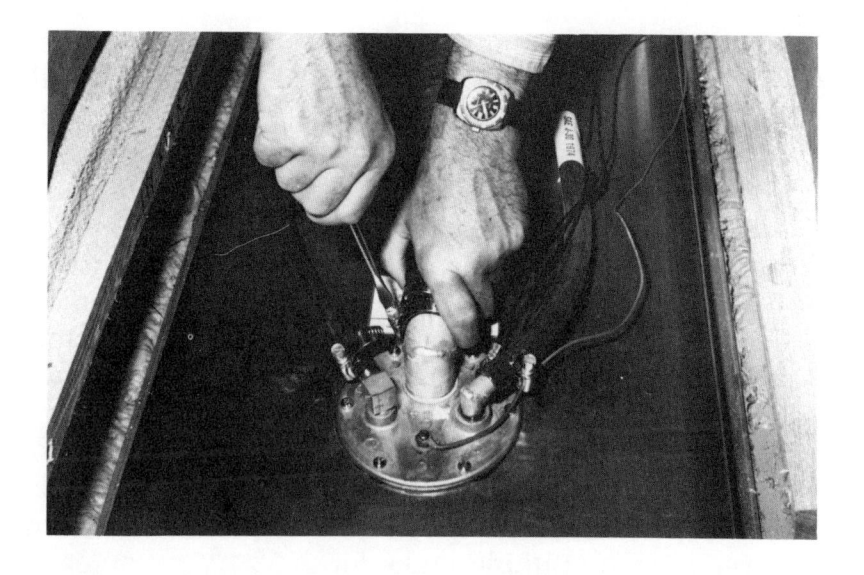

FIG. 17-3 — This combination fitting on the top of the tank shown in FIG. 17-2 includes the fuel filler pipe, fuel line pick-up to the engine, vent hose, and ground terminal.

| Material | Specification | Tank Capacities (gallons) | Required Minimum Nominal Sheet Thickness | Gauge | Welding Processes |
|---|---|---|---|---|---|
| Nickel-Copper | ASTM - B127 Class A | 1—30 | .031 in. | 22 U.S. std. | Resistance Seam Inert Gas Shielded Arc, Oxy-acetylene |
| | | 30—80 | .037 in. | 20 U.S. std. | |
| | | 80—200 | .050 in. | 18 U.S. std. | All of the above including Metal-arc, D.C. Reversed Polarity |
| | | 200—400 | .062 in. | 16 U.S. std. | |
| Copper-Nickel | ASTM - B122 | 1—80 | .045 in. | 17 A.W.G. | Inert Gas Shielded Arc, Oxy-acetylene Resistance |
| | | 80—200 | .057 in. | 15 A.W.G. | All of the above including Metal-arc, D.C. Reversed Polarity |
| | | 200—400 | .072 in. | 13 A.W.G. | |
| Copper | ASTM - B152 Type E.T.P. | 1—80 | .057 in. | 15 A.W.G. | Inert Gas Shielded Arc, Carbon Arc, Oxy-acetylene |
| | | 80—150 | .080 in. | 12 A.W.G. | |
| Copper-Silicon | ASTM B97 Types A B & G | 1—80 | .050 in. | 16 A.W.G. | Inert Gas Shielded Arc, Carbon Arc, Oxy-acetylene Metal-arc |
| | | 80—200 | .064 in. | 14 A.W.G. | |
| | | 200—400 | .081 in. | 12 A.W.G. | |
| Steel Sheet | ASTM - A93 | 1—80 | .0747 in. | 14 Mfrs. | Metal-arc, Oxy-acetylene, Inert Gas Sheilded Arc, Resistance |
| | | 80—200 | .1046 in. | 12 Mfrs. | |
| | | 200—400 | .125 in. | 11 Mfrs. | |
| Aluminized Steel | ASTM - A463 | 1—80 | .0785 in. | 14 Mfrs. | Metal-arc, Oxy-acetylene, Inert Gas Shielded Arc, Resistance |
| | | 80—200 | .1046 in. | 12 Mfrs. | |
| Terneplate Steel | ASTM - A308 | 1—35 | .0478 in. | 18 Mfrs. | Resistance |
| | | 35—50 | .0598 in. | 16 Mfrs. | |
| Aluminum | Alloy 5052 or 5053 or 5086 | 1—50 | .090 in. | —— | Inert Gas Shielded Arc, Resistance |
| | | 50—80 | .100 in. | —— | |
| | | 80—150 | .125 in. | —— | |
| Reinforced Fiberglass Laminates | —— | 1—60 | .187 in. | | Exclusive of core material used, if any |
| | | 60—120 | .250 in. | | |
| | | 120 + | .300 in. | | |

**PLATE 70 — Fuel tank construction specifications and materials recommendations.**

fabrication inside and out. However, diesel fuel tanks should never be galvanized, at least on the inside, since the galvanizing will react with the fuel. All steel tanks even if galvanized or otherwise coated, should be painted with a rust preventative paint on the outside.

Copper tanks must not be used with diesel fuel, and should be tin coated on the inside for gasoline use. The sulphur in diesel fuel oil reacts with copper and can cause deterioration of the tank. Some copper bearing alloys such as Monel make suitable tanks for diesel fuel, however, ordinary steel or so-called "black iron" is commonly used since it is much cheaper and entirely suitable. Copper tanks tend to be weaker than other metals, and consequently should be built stronger and so that unsupported surfaces (bottom, sides, and ends) do not exceed about 18″ in any direction.

Aluminum can be used for gasoline or diesel fuel tanks, but care in the welding by qualified aluminum welders is important. Aluminum tanks are both light in weight and corrosion resistant. Fiberglass fuel tanks are manufactured in cylindrical form using what is known as the filament wound process. Other fiberglass tanks which are made by the boatbuilder using "chopper gun" or hand lay-up processes can be suitable, but are often suspect due to quality control problems inherent with the fiberglass molding process. The same applies to fiberglass covered plywood tanks. While many amateur boatbuilders may attempt to build their own tanks from these two latter methods as a way to cut costs, such a practice is questionable. Fire retardant resin is advised

wherever resin is used in making tanks with fiberglass.

Stainless steel is often considered by many as one of the finest materials for tanks. However, there are many grades and types of stainless steel, with some more suitable to marine conditions than others. The choice can be confusing for the amateur, and picking the wrong grade could lead to disaster. Under certain conditions with certain types of stainless steel, crevice corrosion can occur. This type of corrosion can begin as a small pitted area on the outer or inner surface of a tank, and eventually trap moisture and corrode away in the most insidious manner, from the inside of the pitted area out to the metal surfaces. This can lead to a small hole that could allow fuel to leak making for a hazardous condition, especially if gasoline were used.

Regardless of the tank material, all fittings should lead through the top of the tank. On metallic tanks, clean-out plates should be fastened down with bolts spaced apart about seven times the thickness of the plate and a diameter about twice the plate thickness. A Neoprene or equal gasket should be used for a tight seal under the plate. Rubber gaskets should not be used as they will deteriorate. Corners at clean-outs should be radiused and the opening reinforced. While fittings should be located on top of all tanks, they must extend down into the tank almost (but not completely) to the bottom. Fill pipes should extend down into the tank so that fumes ignited in the fill pipe cannot explode in the tank proper. Fuel pick-ups should be near (but not directly on) the bottom of the tank so that virtually the entire contents of the tank can be pumped (see Plate 71).

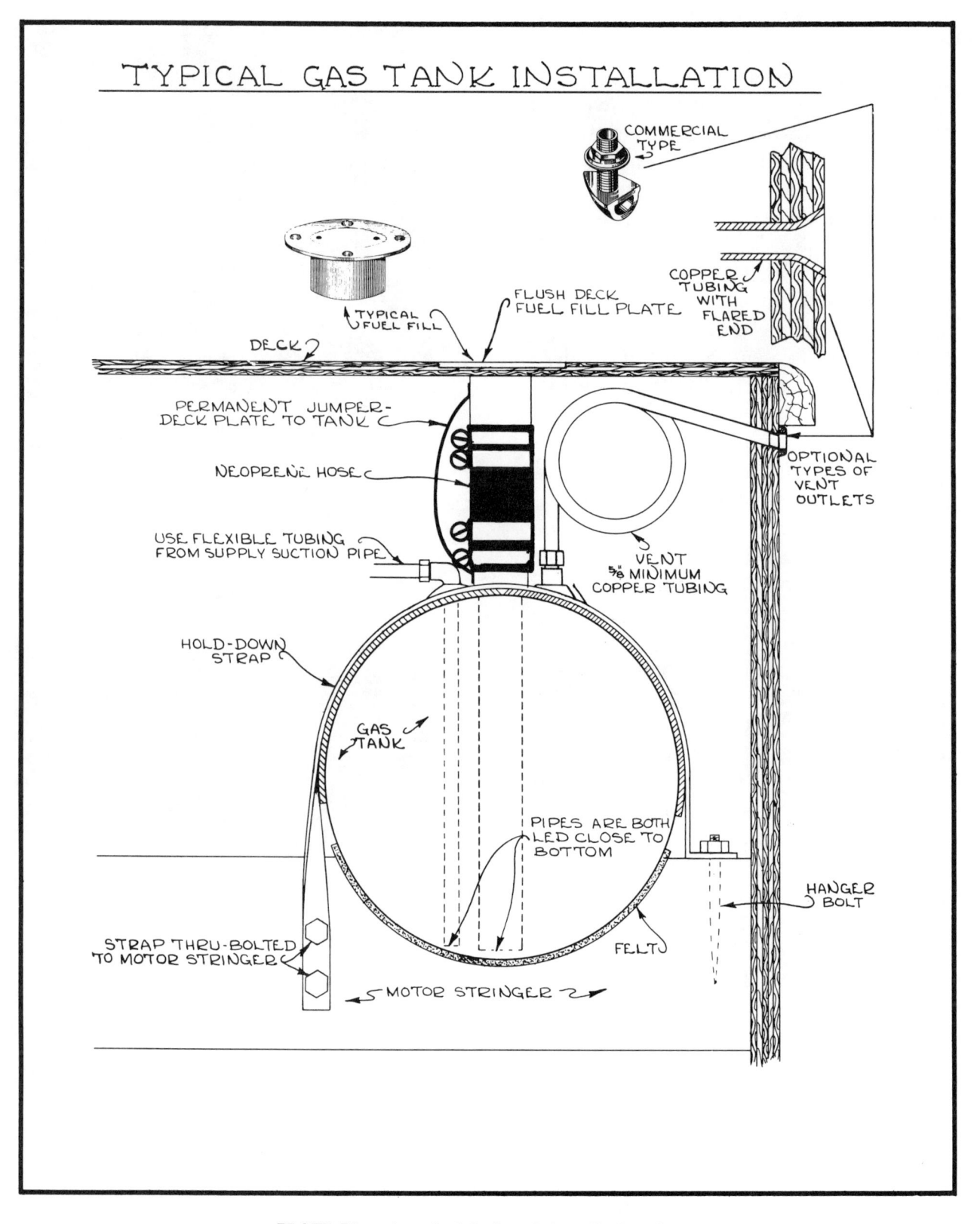

**PLATE 71 — A typical fuel tank installation showing the various components.**

213

## FUEL FILLS AND VENTS

Fuel fill pipes should be a nominal 1½″ (1¼″ min. I.D.) diameter, while a separate vent sized at least ⅓ the diameter and no less than a nominal ⅝″ (7/16 min. I.D.) diameter should be provided for each tank. The vent should not be taken from the fuel fill line. Fuel fill tubes usually lead to flush deck-mounted fill fittings which should be clearly marked for the type of fuel used (i.e., "GASOLINE ONLY" or "DIESEL ONLY"). Rigid fuel tanks should be connected between rigid fuel fill fittings by a length of Neoprene or equal hose, clamped with at least two ½″ wide stainless steel hose clamps on each end. Automotive-type spring clips should not be used. A metal conductor must be used to join the metallic fill to the metallic tank across the non-conductive flexible hose to prevent the possibility of sparks due to static electricity. Fuel fills should be located preferably on deck in such a manner that overflowing fuel cannot enter the cockpit or cabin. Ordinarily, the fill fittings are located outboard of any coamings or cabin sides, and often have raised lips to divert overflowing fuel overboard.

Fuel tank vents should lead from the tank to a high coiled loop just ahead of the overboard vent fitting. Such vent fittings should be well away from any hull opening as well as away from fuel or water fills. On powerboats, the vent opening is commonly located along the hull side as far above the waterline as possible with the vent facing aft in order to prevent spray from entering. On sailboats, consideration should be given in locating the vent fittings so that heeling of the boat will not allow

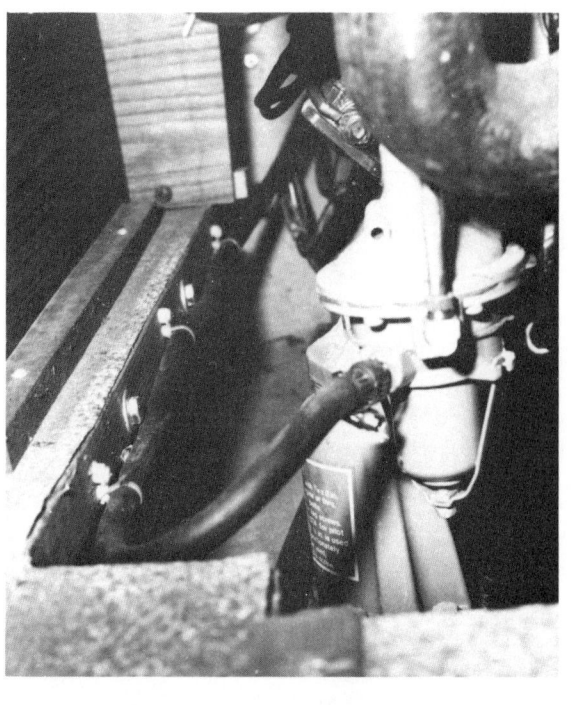

FIG. 17-4 — Straps are used to support non-rigid fuel lines spaced not over 14″ apart. (Courtesy of Tempo Product, Cleveland, Ohio)

FIG. 17-5 — Long runs of fuel fill hoses should also be supported to avoid stretching and other damage that could cause a fuel leak. (Courtesy of Tempo Products, Cleveland, Ohio)

water to enter. Consequently, the vent fitting should not be located along the hull sides. Depending on the tank shape with sailboats, more than one tank vent per tank may be required due to heeling of the boat underway. A flame arrestor screen of 30 x 30 non-corrosive metal mesh should be a part of every vent fitting. Tank vents are important as they prevent pressure from building up due to expansion and during filling, and allow pressure equalization as the fuel is pumped out. Therefore, avoid any kinking and abrupt changes in direction in the vent lines, and keep the runs as short as possible.

## FUEL LINES

Fuel lines can be made from iron or steel for diesel use, while gasoline systems usually use seamless annealed copper, nickel-copper, or copper nickel all with at least a .032″ thick wall. Rigid fuel lines must be connected with a flexible section of approved type to the engine to eliminate the effects of fatigue. Fuel lines should be securely fixed to the boat's structure with suitable clips that will not abrade or wear through the tubing. Fuel line supports for non-rigid line should be spaced no more than 14″ apart. At the junction with flexible sections, a clip should be provided within 4″ of the end of the rigid line. Metal sections of fuel line should also be grounded with the fuel system. Junctions should be kept to a minimum, and flare-type or other approved connections should be used. Never use ferrule-type fittings such as are used on some common copper tubing junctions in commercial use.

Shut-off valves should be provided

FIG. 17-6 — Rigid metallic fuel line requires a flexible "Neoprene" section at the end connected to the engine to absorb vibration. The line should not kink as shown, however, an easy-to-reach shut-off valve visible in the photo is a good idea. (Courtesy of Tempo Products, Cleveland, Ohio)

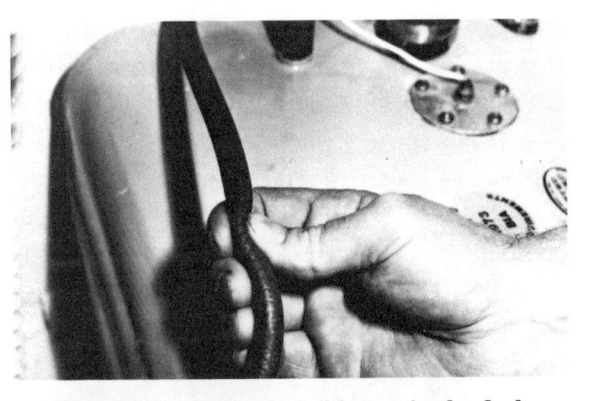

FIG. 17-7 — "Neoprene" hoses in the fuel distribution system should be checked periodically. If spongy, they should be replaced. (Courtesy of Tempo Products, Cleveland, Ohio)

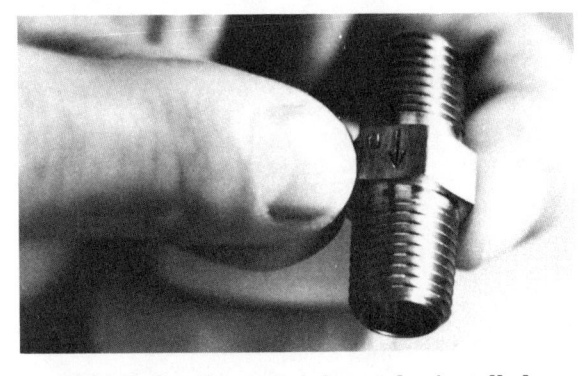

FIG. 17-8 — An anti-siphon valve installed in the fuel tank withdrawal fitting is good insurance against fuel draining into the boat if a line breaks. (Courtesy of Tempo Products, Cleveland, Ohio)

at both the tank and the engine. One valve should be readily accessible and operable from outside the compartment, preferably from the helm. If these are of the electrical type, they should be manually operable as well. All valves should be of the "packless" type to prevent leaks from occurring if the packing were to fail. Fuel lines should be located well above the bilges and slope continually up to the engine if possible. If the tank is below the engine level, a check valve should be placed in the line to prevent the fuel from draining back into the tank. Similarly, interconnected athwartship tanks should be fitted with check valves between to keep fuel from flowing from tank to tank when heeling, especially on sailboats. Shut-off valves should also be provided on either side of filters so these can be removed with-

out leaking fuel. To prevent syphoning of fuel into the engine carburetor in gasoline powered boats, the entire length of fuel line should be above the tank top. If this is not possible, then an anti-syphon device should be located in the line, or an electrically operated fuel stop valve installed that closes when the engine is stopped.

Copper lines or brass fittings should be separated from aluminum tanks since the metals are dissimilar. A galvanic barrier consisting of a section, coupling, or fitting, made from 300 series stainless steel or galvanized steel is suitable in this instance. Fittings on aluminum tanks are preferably type 6061-T6 aluminum or 300 series stainless steel. Filters in the fuel line must be supported by the boat's structure and should be of ample size marine types. The cheap in-line auto-

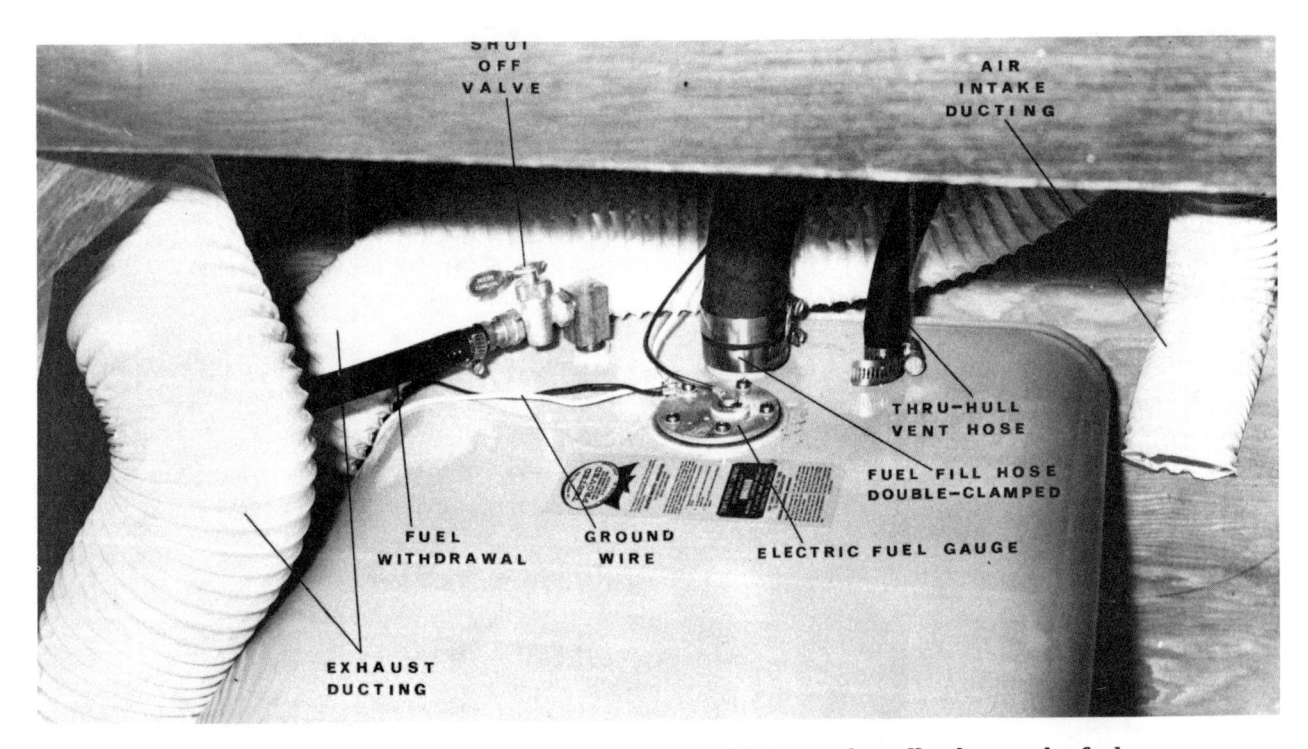

FIG. 17-9 — A proper fuel tank installation includes a shut-off valve on the fuel withdrawal, double clamped fuel fill hose, thru-hull vent hose, grounding wire, and adequate compartment ventilation. (Courtesy of Tempo Products, Cleveland, Ohio)

216

FIG. 17-10 — To prevent static sparks, the metallic fill fitting is fitted with a bared ground wire. (Courtesy of Tempo Products, Cleveland, Ohio)

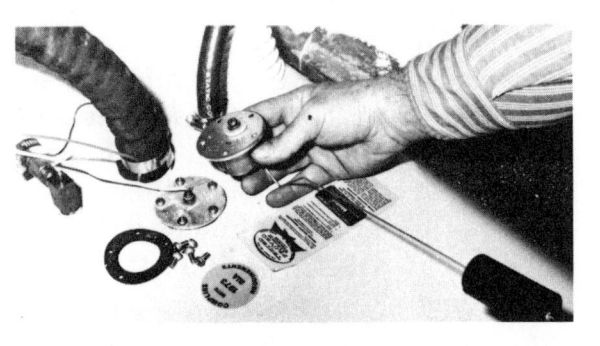

FIG. 17-12 — A fuel gage sender unit about to be installed into a fuel tank. (Courtesy of Tempo Products, Cleveland, Ohio)

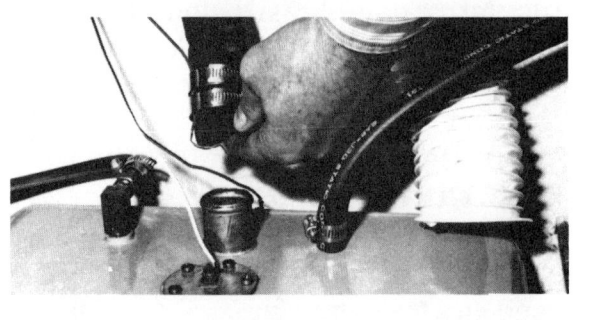

FIG. 17-11 — The other end of the tank fill ground wire connects to the metallic fuel fitting on the tank or fill neck, to ground the fill which ordinarily is separated from the tank by a non-conductive fill hose. (Courtesy of Tempo Products, Cleveland, Ohio)

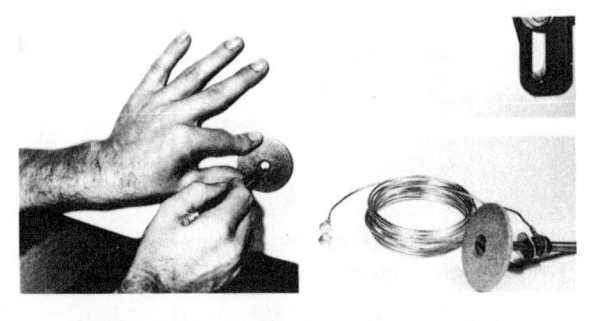

FIG. 17-13 — If the boat does not have a bonding system, the fuel tank can be bonded with a "kit" such as this. A wire from a terminal on the tank passes to the ground terminal through the hull below the waterline for protection against static electricity. (Courtesy of Tempo Products, Cleveland, Ohio)

FIG. 17-14 — A tank installation in a small runabout. Note the stainless steel straps securing the tank to the motor stringers and the coil in the vent line at the top center of the tank.

motive filters and similar components are suspect aboard boats and generally not acceptable. Filters should preferably not be located above the level of the tank as this will stop the gravity flow of fuel after changing filters. This can be especially bothersome with diesel engines where a primed line is necessary to keep the injectors operating. The problem can be helped, however, by installing a hand wobble pump in the line in order to purge the line of air and keep a head of fuel available to the engine. Note that with diesel engines, unlike gasoline engines, a return line must be provided from the engine back to the fuel tank to recover unused fuel from the injectors. Fuel pumps, other than transfer pumps, should be located within 12" of the engine. Electric fuel pumps should be ignition wired to stop pumping when the engine is shut down.

## TANK INSTALLATIONS

All tanks, together with all fuel system components, should be arranged for future removal so that a minimum of the boat's structure need be affected. Access should be readily available to the tanks and various components in the hull via hatches, access panels, and similar openings without first removing permanent structural members of the boat. Anchoring tanks in place to prevent movement is important, however, stress concentrations should not be allowed at any portion of any tank. There should be adequate space around all sides of tanks for inspection, maintenance, and ventilation. If straps are used for tank hold-downs, they should be fitted with Neoprene or equal insulators between the strap and the tank.

All tanks should be supported on bearers or chocks to prevent movement, and support the weight of the tank in such a manner that the stresses on the hull are transferred over as broad an area as possible. Small tanks can be hung from deck beams. Chocks for cylindrical tanks should be sized so that at least ¼ of the tank's circumference will bear on the chock. Several chocking methods for use with cylindrical tanks are shown by Plate 72. Insulative non-abrasive non-absorbant material should be used between the tank and all bearers or chocks.

## TANK CAPACITY AND FUEL CONSUMPTION

The chart given by Plate 73 can be used to estimate the capacity of tanks when various dimensions are known. Additional tank computations can be made assuming that a cubic foot of volume contains 7.48 gallons, while one gallon contains 231 cubic inches (or .134 cubic feet). A gallon of gasoline weighs about 6.2 lbs. per gallon and diesel oil weighs about 7.1 lbs. per gallon.

For those who wish to determine cruising range, there are several approximation methods that can be used. A rough rule-of-thumb for normal inboard powered cruising boats is to divide the horsepower used at a given speed by the number 10. For practical purposes, the horsepower at cruising speed may be considered to be 80% of that which the engine is rated. Therefore with a 100 HP engine, 80 HP would be used at cruising speed. By dividing this figure by 10, the gallons per hour would be 8. By knowing the

# TANK HOLD DOWNS

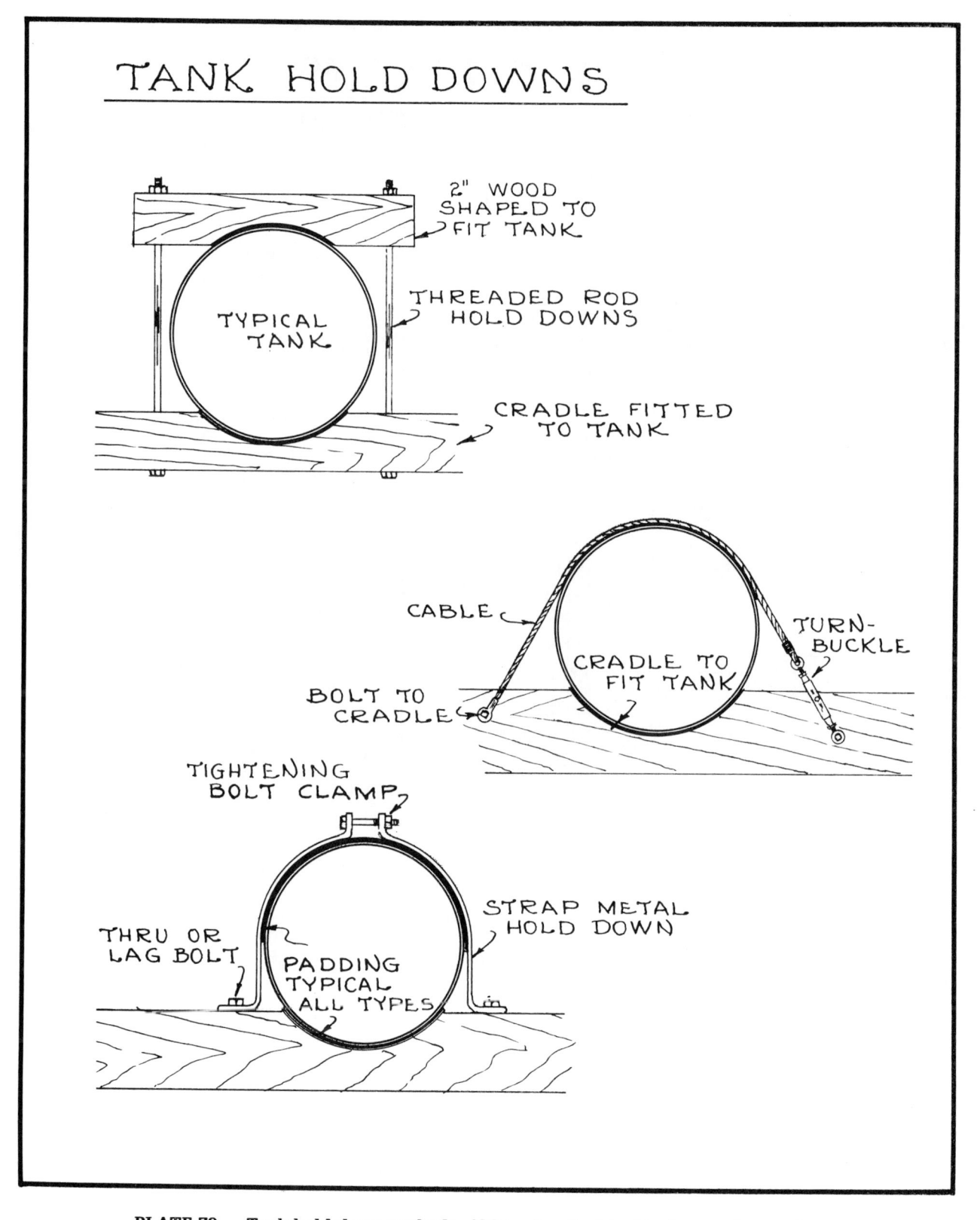

2" WOOD SHAPED TO FIT TANK

THREADED ROD HOLD DOWNS

TYPICAL TANK

CRADLE FITTED TO TANK

CABLE

CRADLE TO FIT TANK

TURN-BUCKLE

BOLT TO CRADLE

TIGHTENING BOLT CLAMP

THRU OR LAG BOLT

STRAP METAL HOLD DOWN

PADDING TYPICAL ALL TYPES

**PLATE 72 — Tank hold-down methods. Although cylindrical tanks are shown, these methods are often adaptable to tanks of other shapes.**

219

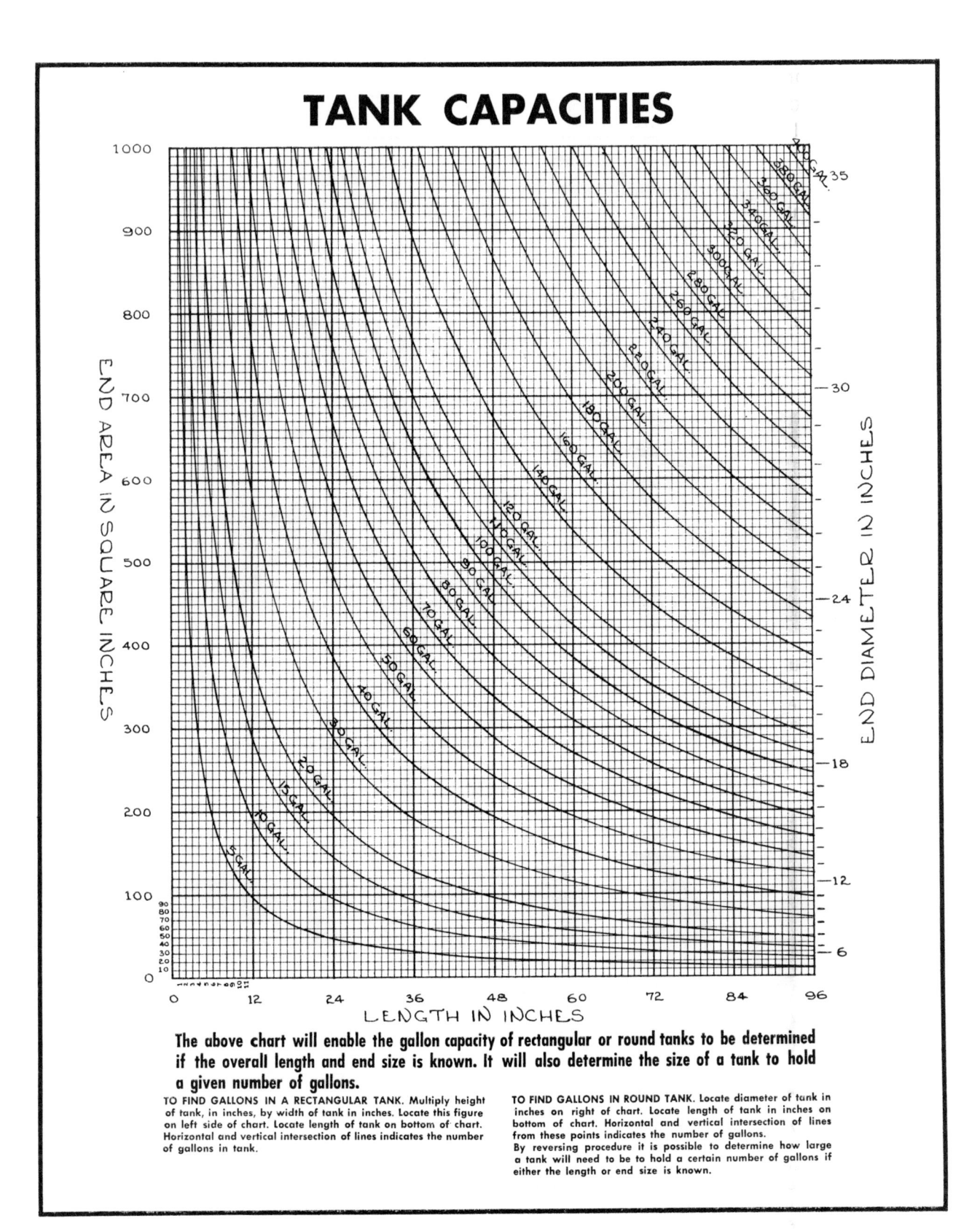

**PLATE 73 — Tank capacity reference chart.**

time elapsed between cruising points, a rough approximation of fuel used may also be obtained.

With diesel engines, another method that is fairly accurate can be used, since their fuel consumption is usually quite different from gasoline engines. On the average, a diesel engine will consume approximately .45 lbs. of fuel per brake horsepower/hour. In other words, if the engine is rated at 100

horsepower at cruising speed, it will consume 45 lbs. of fuel every hour. Divide this by the weight of the fuel (7.1 lbs per gallon), and the result is about 6.34 gallons of diesel fuel used per hour. Divide this figure into the total fuel capacity and you'll have the total number of hours that the boat will run (although some leeway should be allowed since most tanks can't be pumped dry). If you know the speed of

FIG. 17-15 — The vinyl coated metal tank cradles securely anchor the tank in place and raise the tank somewhat above the surface for air circulation. (Courtesy of Tempo Products, Cleveland, Ohio)

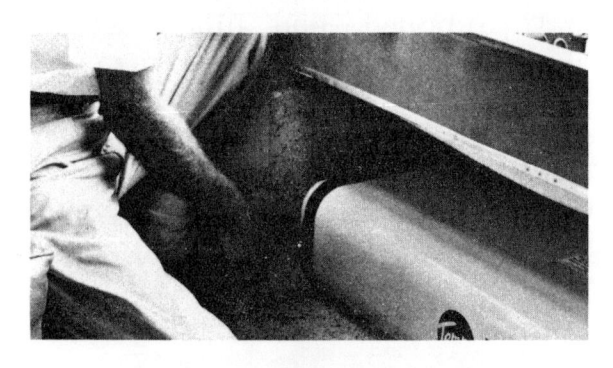

FIG. 17-16 — With the tank in the cradles, bolts are used to secure the tank in place and yet allow for easy removal. (Courtesy of Tempo Products, Cleveland, Ohio)

FIG. 17-17 — This prefabricated tank uses special hold-down clips that effectively raise the tank off the surface enough for air circulation. (Courtesy of Tempo Products, Cleveland, Ohio)

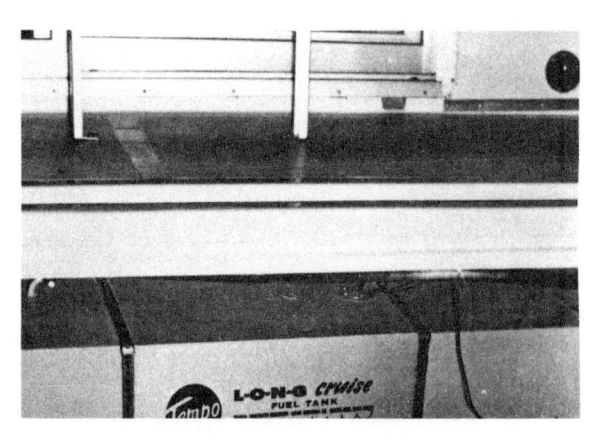

FIG. 17-18 — Large tanks require several hold-downs or straps, and adequate support underneath. Note the padding at corners under the strapping on this tank. (Courtesy of Tempo Products, Cleveland, Ohio)

the boat in knots per hour, you can then multiply the total number of hours, times the speed, and arrive at the range of the boat in nautical miles.

Nevertheless, there should be a means of checking the capacity of tanks. This is commonly done with fuel gages which may or may not be reliable. Where more positive accuracy is desired, sounding tubes or sounding "sticks" through the fill fitting should be used. Needless to say, these sounding sticks should be carefully marked and calibrated, and fills must be aligned for a direct lead into the tank. With diesel engines, sight gages consisting of glass tubes are often fitted directly on the tanks. These give a direct reading of the fuel in the tanks.

If sight gages are used, they should be fitted with valves to close off the tubes when not being checked.

Before operating any gasoline powered boats, always check for gasoline fumes, especially low down in the hull where they may settle, since they are heavier than air. While there are electronic "sniffers" that can be used to detect gasoline fumes, the human nose is still the best. The same applies to starting after refueling. Always raise the hatches and floor boards to air out any fumes which may collect, and don't start the engines unless you are sure that no volatile fumes are present! On long cruises, frequent checks of the below decks spaces are a prudent practice also.

# CHAPTER 18 — VENTILATION & INSULATION

An adequate and positive flow of air within an inboard powered boat is important for several reasons. First, the internal combustion engine must "breathe" to operate, and in so doing sucks in prodigious amounts of air. Considerable heat is given off, even though the motor is probably water-cooled. This heat must be dissipated in order to achieve maximum power output and thereby best operating efficiency for performance and economy. Wherever there is a fuel tank, fuel line, or other component in the fuel system, there is always a possibility of a fuel leak. To prevent a dangerous build-up of volatile fumes from such leaks if they occur, a positive movement of fresh air is necessary since these fumes are heavier than air and tend to settle to the low areas of the hull. To prevent mold, mildew, and rot, and to minimize the effects of condensation, air should be forced into all areas of the hull where stagnant conditions would otherwise prevail, and cause damage to the hull and its components. Battery boxes not located in the engine compartment, or otherwise separately enclosed, should also have fresh air directed over their tops in order to dissipate any explosive hydrogen fumes that can be given off during charging.

Unlike the typical automobile where an unlimited supply of fresh air is available, the motor in a boat is frequently concealed in a "box" or hidden down below a cockpit or cabin sole. While the engine on a boat may be out of sight, and therefore out of mind, it must nevertheless not be neglected in terms of adequate ventilation. To do so not only will affect the performance and longevity of the engine, but the safety and durability of the vessel as well.

How much air does an engine need to operate? This varies depending on whether the engine is gasoline or diesel powered. Generally, the diesel engine will require more air for operation than a gasoline engine, and a two cycle engine will require more air than a four cycle engine of comparable horsepower. Usually, the installation manual provided with the engine will specify the air intake requirements. If this is not available, a good rule-of-thumb with gasoline powered engines is to provide a net cross sectional area of about 20 square inches of vent opening per 100 horsepower. With diesels, the area should be increased to about 50 square inches per 100 horsepower. Note that these figures are for natural ventilation and are for NET areas. Screens, grills, or louvers over a vent opening will decrease the area and should be compensated for in figuring the opening area. If a powered blower is added in the ventilation system, the area can be decreased commensurate with the blower capacity. These figures are for four cycle engines, and consequently for two cycle engines, the figures may need a substantial increase. Note that these figures are just for the engine air intake irrespective of compartment ventilation and heat dissipating requirements.

For removing heat from the engine compartment, it may be that the air intake for the engine may be enough to provide adequate cooling. This is hard to know without actually testing the boat, however. Generally, if combustion air temperature entering the engine exceeds about 110 degrees, additional cooling ventilation should be provided. Combustion air should be as cool as possible for maximum engine efficiency. Since heat rises, the inlets should be located low down at the extremeties of the engine compartment (usually forward, one at each corner), and with the exhaust outlets next to the closest part of the engine (usually aft of the inlets and on each side of the engine).

As can be seen from the preceding, there would be two intake vents and two exhaust vents, and indeed this is the ideal minimum system. However, much depends on the size of the boat and consequently the size or volume of the area being vented. The listing given indicates some compartment volume sizes small enough for using just a single intake and single exhaust vent. However, whenever possible, dual intakes and dual exhaust vents are better.

Vents should be fitted with cowls or other devices to direct the air and deflect spray and water. Such cowls must not reduce the net area of the adjoining duct, however and screens are normally not used unless the area is in-

creased to compensate. Intake vents should face forward, while exhaust vents should face aft. The two should be well separated so that exhausted air cannot re-enter any vent. No vent should be located adjacent to a fuel tank vent either. Ideally, the intake vent cowls should be located at least 6" above the exhaust outlets, and as high above the water as possible. The location of vents should consider the many possible ways that water could enter, including spray, rain, waves, heeling (important on sailboats), reversing backwash, and even washing down the deck. Obviously, large amounts of water entering the vents can be dangerous.

Tank spaces, battery spaces, and engine compartments which are separated should preferably be individually vented. Spaces where fuel vapors could accumulate can be naturally ventilated, however, at least one powered exhaust blower should be provided in addition to natural ventilation in the engine compartment. If desired, the blower can be located in a natural exhaust air duct. The powered blower must be of the non-sparking arcless type, vapor-proof, and not exposed to spray. Furthermore, the blower should be installed at least 14" above the lowest point of the bilge to keep bilge water away from it. The blower should be operable from the helm, and run for a period of 2 minutes minimum before starting. The blowers should also be run during starting and while running below cruising speeds when insufficient air volume could result from slow speed operation.

Ducts from vent intakes and outlets can be made from non-ferrous or galvanized sheet metal, or high-temperature resistant non-metallic tubing. The exhaust ducts are ideally 50% bigger than the intake ducts to create a stronger suction affect, however, this is not always done. Ducting should lead low down in the hull, but well above any bilge water which would halt the flow of air. The intake ducting can be lead to the level of the carburetor on gasoline powered boats, while the exhaust ducts should be lower since fuel fumes settle lower in the hull than air. Ducting should have a minimum of bends. Cowls (especially for air intake) should be located outside of cabin sides, coamings, and cockpit openings. Cowls should not be located on transoms, since a vacuum is created here which can cause engine exhaust fumes to be sucked back into the boat. Cowl intakes should also not be located on the sides of motor boxes inside cockpit areas.

In building a new boat or changing the engine or compartment configuration on an existing boat, a check should be made with local governing bodies or the U.S. Coast Guard for current ventilation recommendations which can change from time to time. The following listing prescribes the ventilation areas based on compartment volume often used in the boating industry. They do NOT consider any extra air needed for engine operation requirements. While ordinary ducting is of a circular type, the net ducting area is also listed so that square or rectangular ducting can also be considered.

| Maximum Compartment Volume (cu. ft.) | Net Vent Opening Area - Each Vent | |
|---|---|---|
| | 1 Intake, 1 Exhaust | 2 Intake, 2 Exhaust |
| 12 | 2½" dia. (4.91 sq. in.) | — |
| 17 | 3" dia. (7.07 sq. in.) | 2½" dia. (4.91 sq. in.) |
| 23 | 3½" dia. (9.62 sq. in.) | 2½" dia. (4.91 sq. in.) |
| 30 | 4" dia. (12.57 sq. in.) | 3" dia. (7.07 sq. in.) |
| 80 | — | 3" dia. (7.07 sq. in.) |
| 110 | — | 3½" dia. (9.62 sq. in.) |
| 140 | — | 4" dia. (12.57 sq. in.) |
| 220 | — | 5" dia. (19.63 sq. in.) |

## INSULATION

Insulation with respect to the engine installation is used to reduce both heat and noise. The main consideration in selecting an insulating material is that it must be fire-proof and not absorb flammable materials such as oil, grease, solvents, or gasoline. While fiberglass batt-type insulation will not burn, it will absorb flammable materials and retain them, ultimately leading to a fire hazard. There are other insulating materials that are similar, and therefore should be avoided un-less protected with a barrier that will preclude the absorption of flammable materials.

The subject of noise insulation is a complex one and often beyond the grasp of the average person. While running, the internal combustion engine is inherently noisy, besides setting up additional noise through vibrations and resonance that can be transferred throughout the boat. Proper mounting and alignment practices can eliminate many undesirable vibrations and resonant situations. However, the noise from the engine when running can travel both through the air as well as through adjacent materials.

Consequently, sealing the engine to prevent noise through air transfer, and using proper materials or sound insulative barriers around the engine compartment, are the most important elements in reducing noise levels aboard inboard powered boats. Any opening or crack into the engine compartment should be sealed (except for the various ventilation ducts), and the locations of these should be carefully planned so that noise emanating through the cowls will be as remote from the ears of crew members as possible.

Materials used around the motor compartment or "box" such as plywood are naturally more sound-absorbent than, for example, fiberglass or metal. However, a well-padded upholstered motor box regardless of the material makes a very good sound-absorbent covering in the typical cockpit loca-

tion. On a cabin cruiser where the engine may be located under the cabin, one of the best sound insulators is a good thick carpet over a thick foam pad as long as they are of materials suitable for marine conditions. Various motor compartment liners can be used to further insulate the motor compartment both for heat and sound. Fire resistant rigid insulation tiles are commonly used, as is thin sheet lead linings specially available for marine installations. Special combination materials consisting of a layer of lead with polyurethane foam are also available. Heat from the engine is not only conducted through the air, but also radiated from the hot areas of the engine. Since radiated heat travels in a straight line, it can be reflected back to the engine by means of sheet metal shields covered on the outside (or cool side) with a thin sheet of asbestos. Wire screening can be used on the cold side of the asbestos to keep it from flaking and breaking off (see Plate 74).

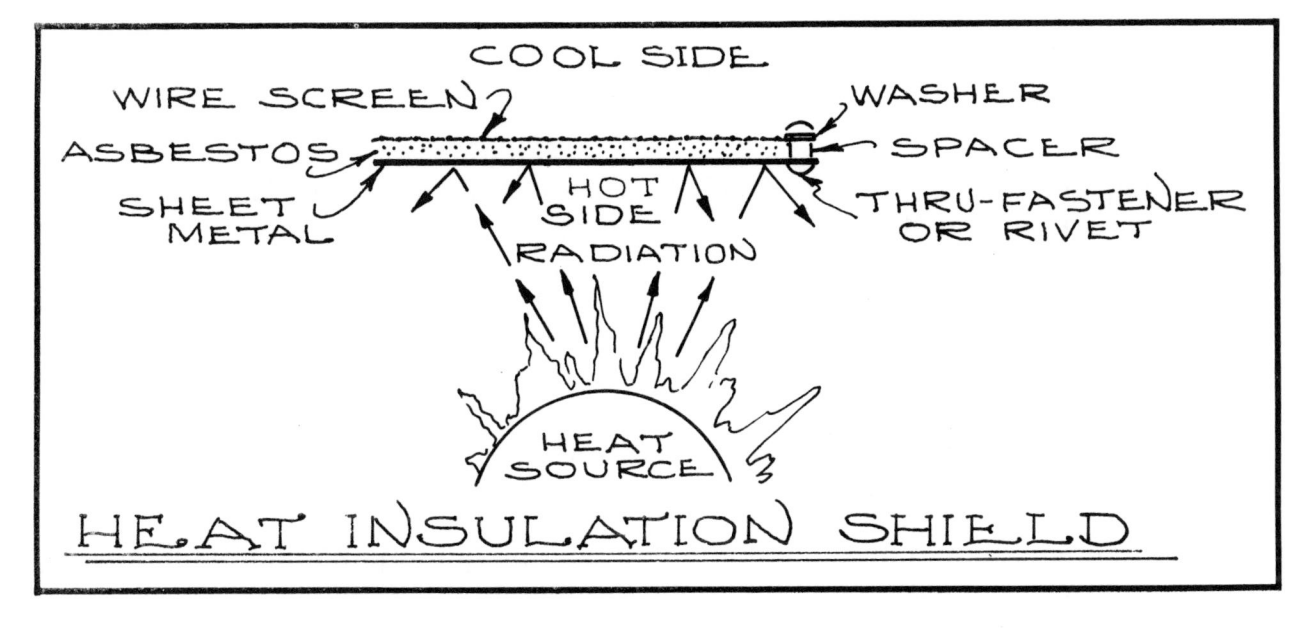

**PLATE 74 — A method for making reflective heat insulation.**

226

# CHAPTER 19 — ENGINE ELECTRICAL SYSTEMS

The average amateur installing his own engine or building his own boat often overlooks his boat's electrical system and wiring. Wires are often seen strung haphazardly from point to point, frequently laying in the bilge, with exposed or open junctions. Incorrectly sized wires and unsuitable fittings are often substituted in an attempt to cut costs. In short, there is a tendency for many individuals to "second rate" the electrical system. In truth, just the opposite should be the case, since the system should be second to none. The possible costs savings resulting from batteries with too little capacity, or undersized wires, or a minimum number of circuits being available, or minimal generating capacity, may be exceeded many times in the future by necessary changes, modifications, and corrections. In a production-type boat, these costs savings may make the difference between a profit and a loss. But, the individual doing his own installation who wants to avoid future headaches and problems will realize little savings between a minimum installation and one that is the best.

Electrical systems can be broken down into two categories or types of systems. One system (and the one which this book is concerned with) is the operational system, which is directly related to the operation of the engine and its related components.

The other system is the accessory system, which includes items such as lighting, appliances, and accessories not related to engine operation. All boats with an inboard engine will have some sort of an operational electric system, however, not all boats will have an accessory system. Depending on the type of boat and the owner's needs, the electrical requirements may be quite basic or perhaps exceedingly extravagant and complex. Some boats can get along with just a simple low voltage operational system, while other boats may have both operational and accessory systems in dual voltage or perhaps even three-way voltage systems serving many functions. If shore-side power is desired at all times, the system may be further complicated by the installation of a generator. To adequately cover all the various aspects of accessory electrical systems would require another entire book, and indeed such texts are already available on this subject. The reader who desires knowledge of electrical systems of this type should consult one of these texts and also check with the various standards organizations such as the National Fire Protection Association, American Boat and Yacht Council, and the U.S. Coast Guard for current wiring practices.

## ENGINE WIRING

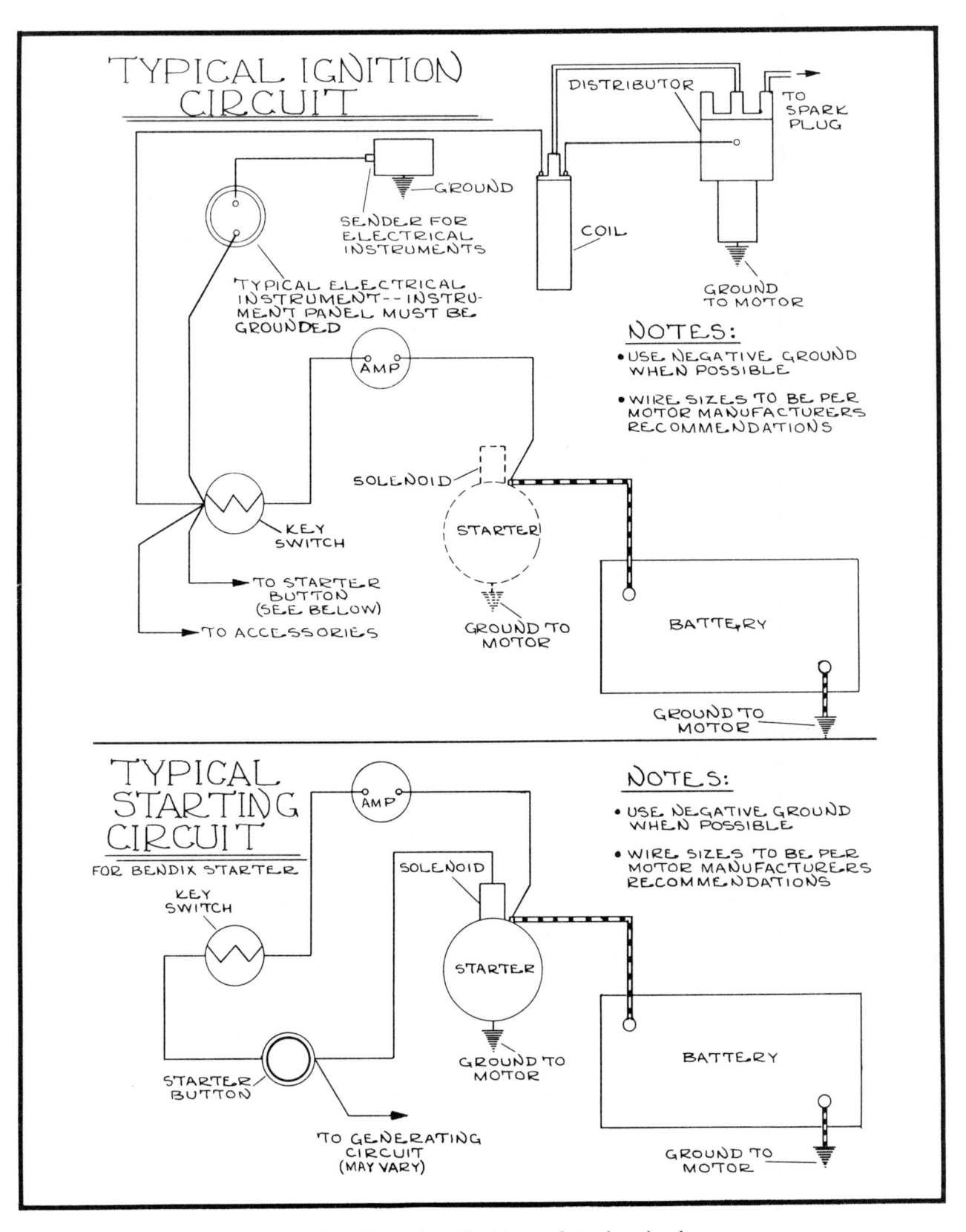

**PLATE 75 — Examples of ignition and starting circuits.**

228

Engine wiring is a low voltage direct current (D.C.) type of electrical system of either 12, 24, or 32 volts. By far the most common and virtually considered "standard" aboard pleasure boats is the 12 volt D.C. negative ground system. The 24 volt and 32 volt systems are sometimes used on larger yachts and commercial type boats.

If the engine is being purchased from a manufacturer, the engine will usually come with the necessary wiring together with wiring diagrams and installation instructions. If an automotive conversion is used, the wiring will be per the automobile manufacturer's recommendations, although some changes may be required for a marine installation. The wiring recommendations provided should be adhered to in all cases. For reliability and safety, the engine operational system used for starting and ignition should be kept separate from any other accessory circuits, and should have its own battery or bank of batteries.

All conductors or wires used should be of the stranded insulated copper type as opposed to the single wire or aluminum type, since they are less liable to fatigue and possible fracture. Unless approved-type harnesses are provided, all junctions should be of the solderless crimp-type since solders are subject to corrosion. Where it is necessary to run wiring through a part of the hull structure, the wiring should be fitted with grommets or other devices to protect against chafing. Color coding of all circuits is highly advised.

Note that wire sizes are listed by numbers which designate the wire diameter. The bigger this number, the smaller the wire is. For example, a #16 wire is smaller than a #14 wire. Each wire in a multi-conductor sheath or "bunch" of wires must be at least a #18 size, while if a separately installed conductor, the size must be at least a #16 wire to assure adequate strength in the conductor. Insulated clips or hangers should be used to support conductors throughout their lengths. Spacing of these supports should not be more than 18″ apart. All wiring should be lead above the bilges as high as possible. All wires should be protected or located away from physical damage although the use of conduit is not advised aboard boats. Closed-eye terminals are recommended at wire junctions. Where wires must be spliced, a terminal block should be used for the junction. Copper fittings should be used for all junctions and terminal fittings.

Low voltage direct current wiring systems aboard boats must be of the two-wire type with one wire going from the power source or battery, and a second wire returning to the negative or ground terminal. The "common ground" system used in automobiles is not suitable for boats. In a boat's system, each individual electrical component must have a separate return or "ground" wire. Bonding and grounding wires cannot be used for current carrying purposes. Note an important difference in terminology here. A return or "grounded" conductor carries current in returning it to the power supply or battery, whereas a "grounding" wire is used to bond the electrical component or system for the prevention of stray current corrosion, protection of crew members from electrical shock, and to minimize radio interference on those boats so equipped which will be discussed later. The two wires in a two

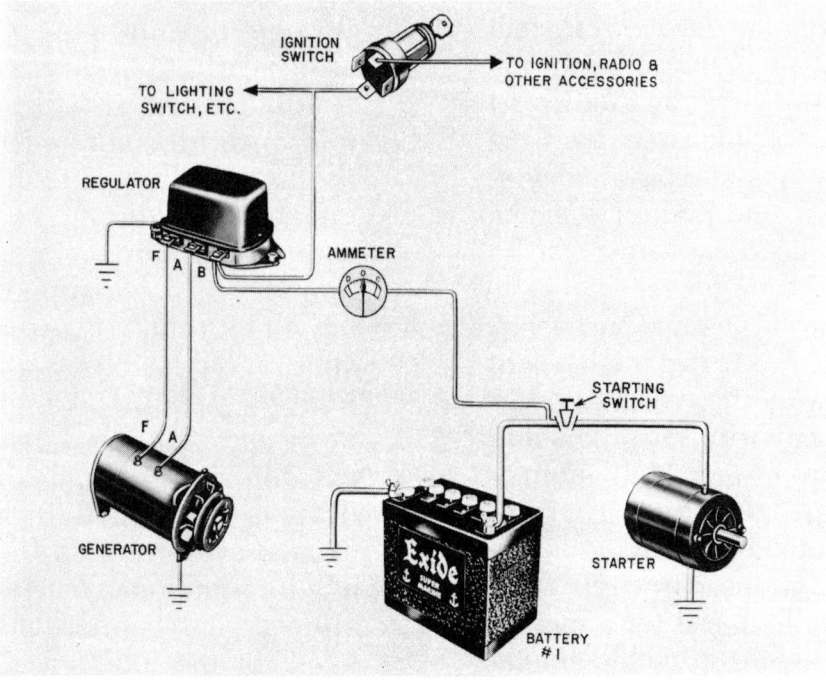

FIG. 19-1 — Generating circuit using a regulator-type generator with single battery.

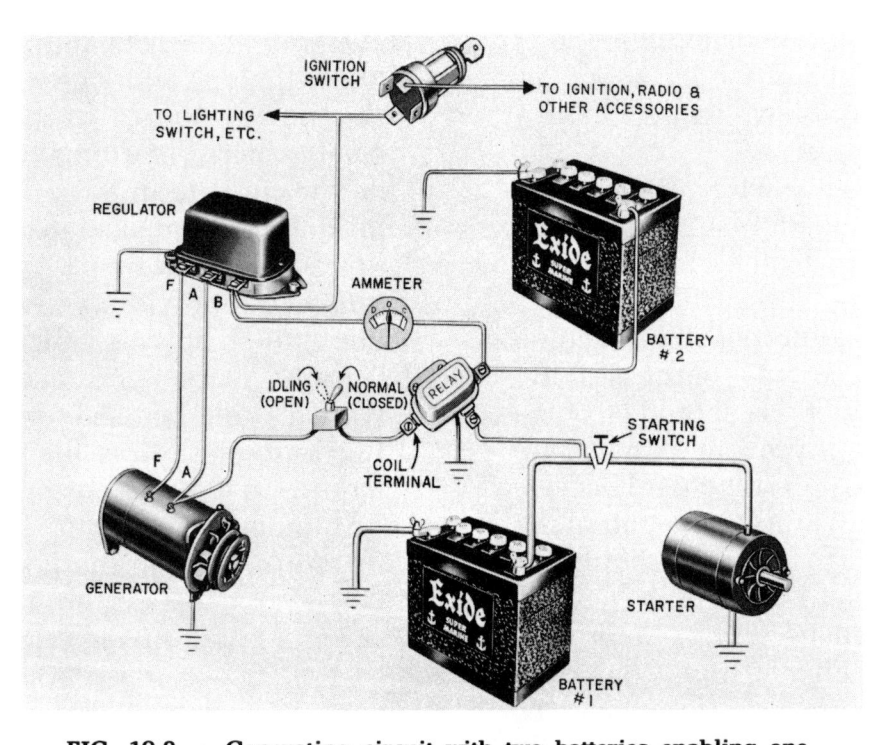

FIG. 19-2 — Generating circuit with two batteries enabling one battery to be reserved for starting use and the other for accessory use. Normal position of switch is for charging both batteries. If accessories are inadvertently left on, second battery may become discharged, but starting battery will remain fully charged.

230

wire circuit are usually twisted in pairs which cancels out their magnetic fields. The grounding wire, however, is kept separated from any current carrying conductors. Engine-mounted accessories may use the engine block as a common ground return, however, and do not need a return conductor.

All circuits must be protected from possible overloads, and this should be done by the use of circuit breakers at the power source. The use of fuses aboard boats is frowned upon since they are not reliable and do not have switching capabilities. Battery cables to the engine starter and the high voltage ignition wires, however, do not have overload protection. Battery power circuit breakers for protecting low voltage wires must be located within 6' of the battery measured along the conductor. All electrical switches and breakers should be of the approved marine explosion-proof type, and of suitable capacities to suit the conductors. Generators and alternators with outputs above 250 watts should also be protected from overload by suitable circuit breakers.

Ignition wiring should be of such a type that water will not become trapped or allowed to accummulate at junctions. All connections must have tight fitting caps, boots, or nipples that will not allow any hint of an electrical spark. Note that with diesel engines which have no ignition system, most of the concern with the electrical will apply to just the starting circuit from the battery. Another consideration is that if electronic communication and navigation equipment will be used, the distributor, coil, distributor leads, and spark plugs of the gasoline engine should be shielded to suppress noise interference. Most marine engine manufacturers supply engines with this equipment.

## BATTERIES

The heart of the electrical system on most inboard powered boats is the storage battery. Basically, the storage battery used on a boat is just like that used on an automobile, although there are batteries made especially for marine use with certain features and capabilities seldom required in automotive use. Battery selection, installation, and location are important matters in a boat and should not be taken lightly. The battery must be sized to provide ample electrical capacity. During charging, a battery will give off potentially explosive hydrogen fumes. Hence, the battery should have an ample supply of fresh air at all times. This does NOT mean, however, that the battery can be set loose in the open deep down in the bilge. All batteries must be securely mounted in acid-tight boxes so they won't move. Boxes can be made from wood with lead linings, or from heavy fiberglass linings, or one of the manufactured plastic types can be used. Easy access should be provided to all batteries so that routine checking and maintenance will be encouraged. Allow at least 1 foot clearance around the sides and tops of batteries. Although air should be allowed to circulate over the tops of the batteries, there should be a protective cover so that a metallic object dropped onto the batteries will not create an accidental spark.

Batteries can weigh a considerable amount, and therefore may have quite an effect on the trim or stability of the

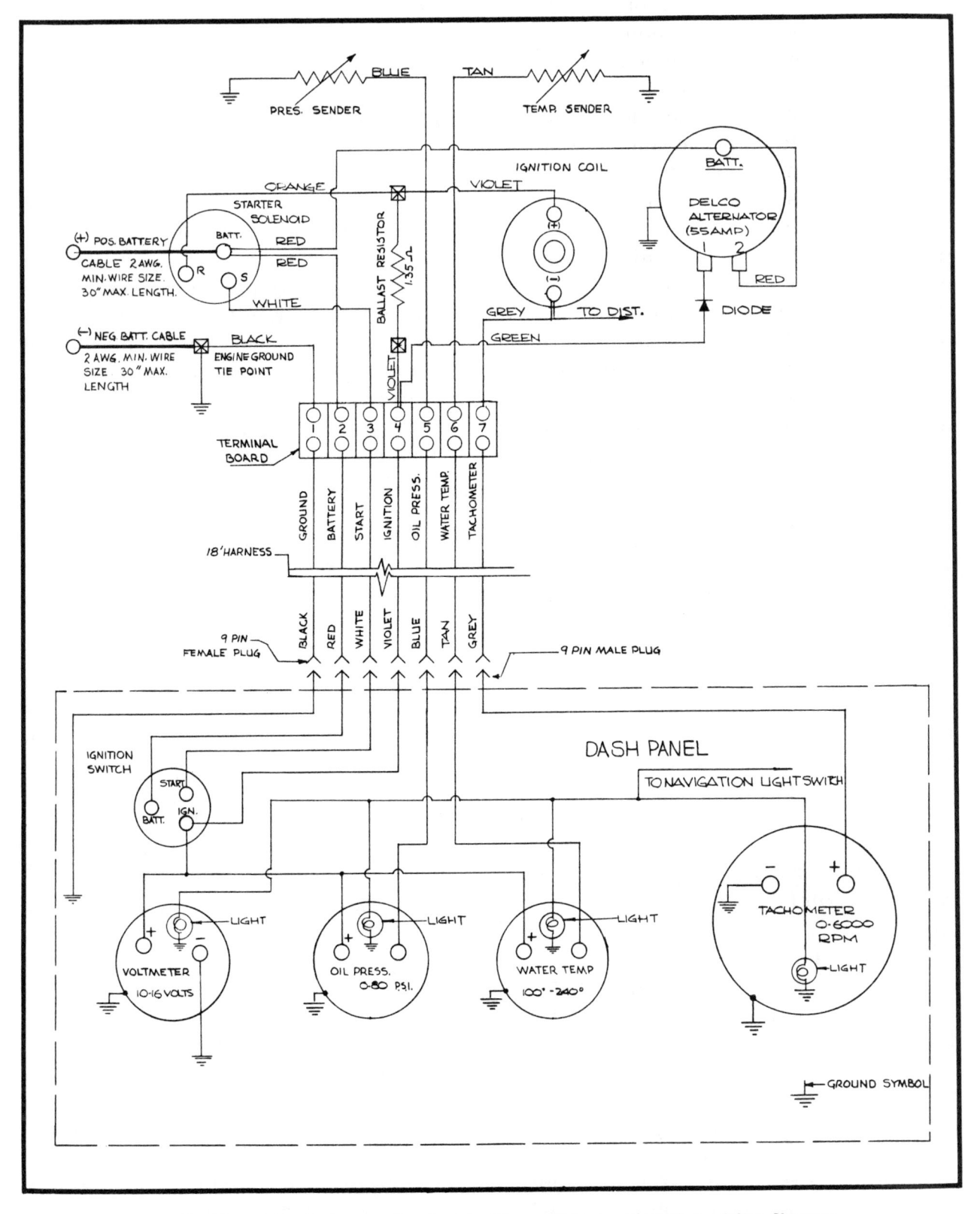

**PLATE 76 — A typical example of an ignition and instrumentation wiring diagram provided by a motor manufacturer. (Courtesy of Berkeley Pump Co., Berkeley, Calif.)**

boat in some instances. From a trim standpoint, the batteries should be located as close to the center of buoyancy as possible, however, the distance from the engine should not be too great due to possible voltage drop which would make the battery less efficient. Batteries should be located low in the vessel in order to have a positive effect on the boat's stability. However, the batteries must be well above the bottom of the boat so that bilge water cannot flood them out and render them useless at a time when they may be most needed. While the batteries should not be too far away from the engine, ideally they should not be

placed directly next to the engine since heat shortens the life of the battery and causes fluid loss in the cells. Fuel lines and fuel system components within about 1 foot of the battery should be electrically shielded or insulated.

Batteries are rated by amp hours; in other words, a battery with a 60 amp hour rating would provide 60 amps of power in an hour, or 30 amps for two hours, or 20 amps for three hours. However, at the end of these times, the battery would be virtually dead and would require recharging to restore its power. Even though a battery may be rated at a certain capacity, this does NOT mean that the battery will deliver

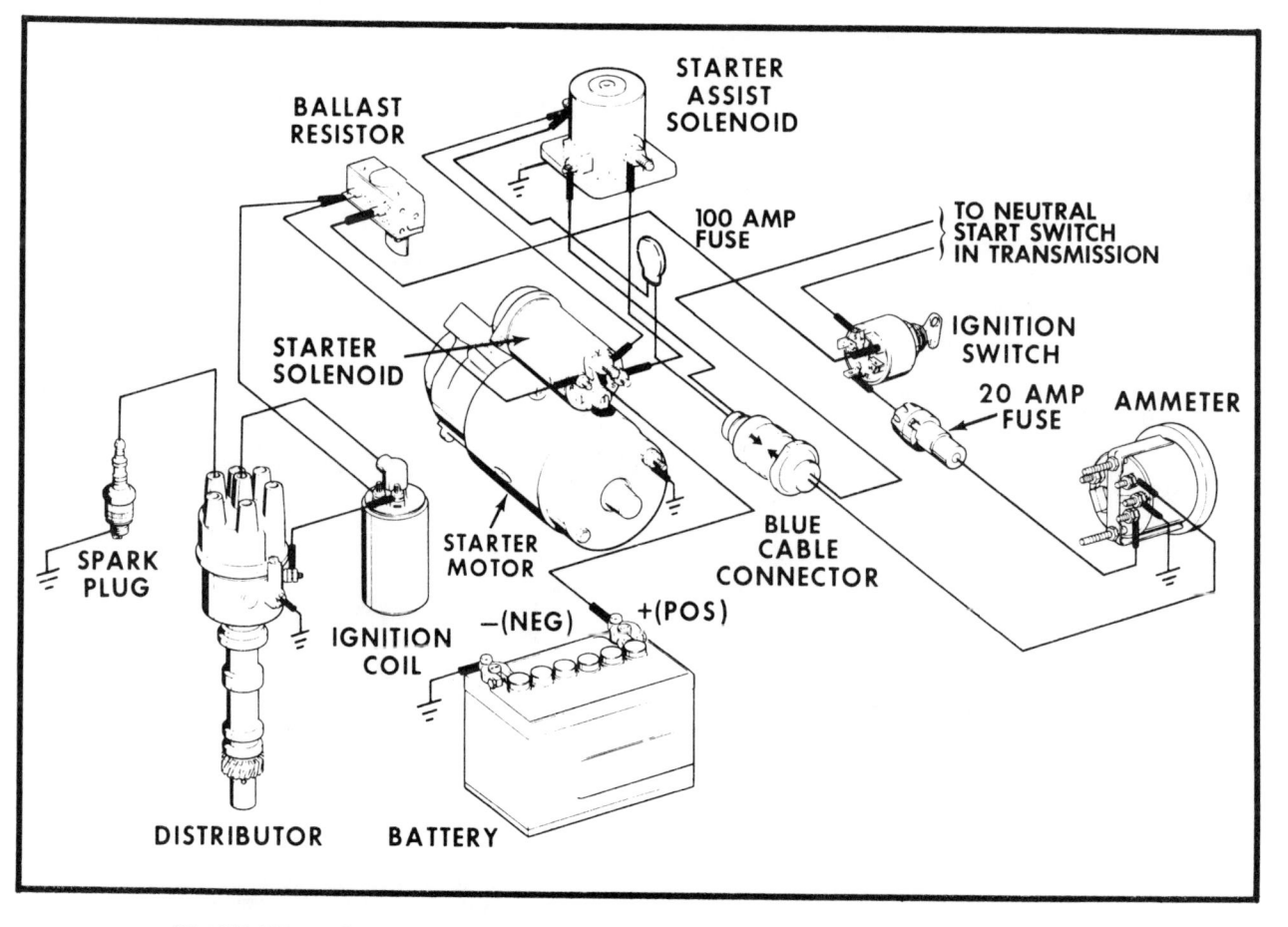

**PLATE 77 — A starting circuit diagram showing typical components as recommended by one engine manufacturer. (Courtesy of OMC, Waukegan, Ill.)**

the necessary power. The reason is that as the battery dissipates its power over a period of time, the voltage also begins to decrease. When this occurs, there may not be sufficient voltage to operate some components such as bilge pumps and other motor-driven appliances. So amp hour ratings

should be considered with this in mind. Another consideration is ambient temperatures. When it is cold, the battery may not be able to deliver the power that it is rated at. So when estimating electrical loads and what size battery will be necessary to meet the load requirements, allow some leeway

FIG. 19-3 — A marine-type storage battery. Wing nuts on the terminals allow quick and easy removal of the battery cables. Cell caps are available which allow the battery to tip and not leak, which can be valuable protection when the boat is heeling. (Courtesy of Surrette Storage Battery Co., Salem, Mass.)

FIG. 19-4 — A large capacity marine-type storage battery. Note the convenient lifting handles. (Courtesy of Surrette Storage Battery Co., Salem, Mass.)

FIG. 19-5 — Batteries may look pretty much the same on the outside. However, the so-called "bargain" batteries at left and center show about half as much actual material on the inside as the battery to the right. The full size plates in this battery assure extra capacity and power, and the battery will obviously weigh much more. (Courtesy of Surrette Storage Battery Co., Salem, Mass.)

so that the battery will not be totally drained.

In purchasing a battery you generally get what you pay for. All batteries may look pretty much alike, but there is no seeing what's inside (see Fig. 19-5). Generally, the more plates and the bigger their area, the higher will be the rating of the battery along with more weight. In fact, weight of a battery is one way to compare which one will have a higher rating. It is possible to get a battery that is too heavy. Ideally, the battery should be light enough for one person to remove and replace. But what do you do if the estimated power load is such that the battery capable of doing the job weighs too much?

If the electrical system is, for example, a 12 volt system, then two smaller 12 volt batteries can be used connected in parallel. Alternately, two smaller 6 volt batteries connected in series could be used. More connections, however, would be required. The 12 volt battery is the most common aboard pleasure boats, at least for starting batteries, however 24 volt and 32 volt systems are sometimes used. These larger voltage systems are often used on larger boats since a smaller amperage drain and therefore smaller wiring requirements are possible.

### MARINE WIRING COLOR CODE — DIRECT CURRENT SYSTEMS UNDER 50 VOLTS

| COLOR | ITEM | USE |
|---|---|---|
| Green (G) | | Bonding |
| White (W) or Black (B) | | Return, negative main |
| Red (R) | | Positive mains, particularly unfused. |
| Yellow w/Red stripe (YR) | Starting circuit | Starting switch to solenoid |
| Yellow (Y) | Generator or alternator field | Generator or alternator field to regulator field terminal |
| | Bilge blowers | Switch to blowers |
| Dark gray (Gy) | Navigation lights | Switch to lights |
| | Tachometer | Tachometer sender to gage |
| Brown (Br) | Generator armature | Generator armature to regulator |
| | Alternator charge light | Generator terminal/alternator auxiliary terminal to light to regulator |
| | Pumps | Switch to pumps |
| Orange (O) | Accessory feed | Ammeter to alternator or generator output and accessory switches |
| | Accessory common feed | Distribution panel to accessory switch |
| Purple (Pu) | Ignition | Ignition switch to coil and electrical instruments |
| | Instrument feed | Distribution panel to electric instruments |
| Dark blue | Cabin and instrument lights | Switch to lights |
| Light blue (Lt Bl) | Oil Pressure | Oil pressure sender to gage |
| Tan | Water Temperature | Water temperature sender to gage |
| Pink (Pk) | Fuel gage | Fuel gage sender to gage |

**FIG. 19-6 — A suggested wiring color coding system for direct current low voltage systems.**

Also, a series of lighter weight 8 volt batteries in series makes handling the batteries easier. A problem with these voltages, however, is that electrical parts are sometimes difficult to obtain in the suitable voltage.

In any boat which uses battery power for other than just engine starting and ignition, the use of dual batteries or two separate banks of batteries is highly recommended. Depending on the boat's electrical system, one battery may serve as a stand-by alternate, while the other serves starting and engine needs. When the system becomes more elaborate, one battery will be used for the engine, while the other will be used for accessory use. If an electrical generator will be used, still another battery should be installed for starting this item also. Switching between two or even three batteries of the same voltage can allow separate use of all for either engine starting or accessory use thereby adding some margin of reliability. Batteries are joined to one another and to the starter solenoid with standard battery cables.

**BONDING**

Bonding or "grounding" on a boat means the electrical connection of all exposed metallic non-current carrying parts to the negative or ground side of the direct current system. The function is similar to that in a house having a wiring system with a grounding or third wire conductor. On a boat, bonding is done not only for the safety of crew members from electrical shock, but also for lightning protection, minimizing corrosion caused by stray electrical currents, and minimizing radio interference. With the exception of metal boats, it is generally agreed that all boats should be bonded. The bonding system or "circuit" is normally non-current carrying and completely separated from the boat's other electrical systems, whether they are low voltage DC or high voltage AC types.

Common items aboard a boat that are bonded would include all propulsion and auxiliary engines, large metallic enclosures of all electrical equipment, motors, pumps, compressors, fuel tanks, fuel fills, thru-hull fittings, underwater fittings, metal spars, metal sail tracks on sailboats with wood spars, rigging chainplates on sailboats, metal piping or conduits, and all ground terminals on electrical units.

The bonding system is intended to provide a low resistance path to electricity, and consequently all conductors should make a direct lead to the bonding system. Furthermore, conductors must be able to do this even at voltages well in excess of normal, such as when lightning strikes. A typical bonding system includes a common bonding conductor that can be made from uninsulated copper or bronze strip, copper tubing, bare tinned-copper wire, or insulated copper wire, but should NOT be copper braid since it corrodes and is difficult to connect to. Where the metal strip is used, it should be at least 1/32" thick and ½" wide. If wire is used, it should be at least a #8 size, with #6 preferable. This bonding conductor usually runs fore and aft in the boat, preferably near the centerline but not located so that it will be in contact with bilge water. The individual bonding conductors attached to the main bonding conductor should be as short and direct as possible, and do not need to be insulated. They should be at least as big as the conductors leading to the equipment. The bonding conductor ultimately connects to a common single underwater ground which can be any metal with at least a surface area of one square foot, preferably copper. This exterior ground plate can be a radio telephone ground plate, or underwater fitting such as a rudder, or ballast keel, or metal centerboard if in contact with the water. If the boat is metal, no further ground is necessary.

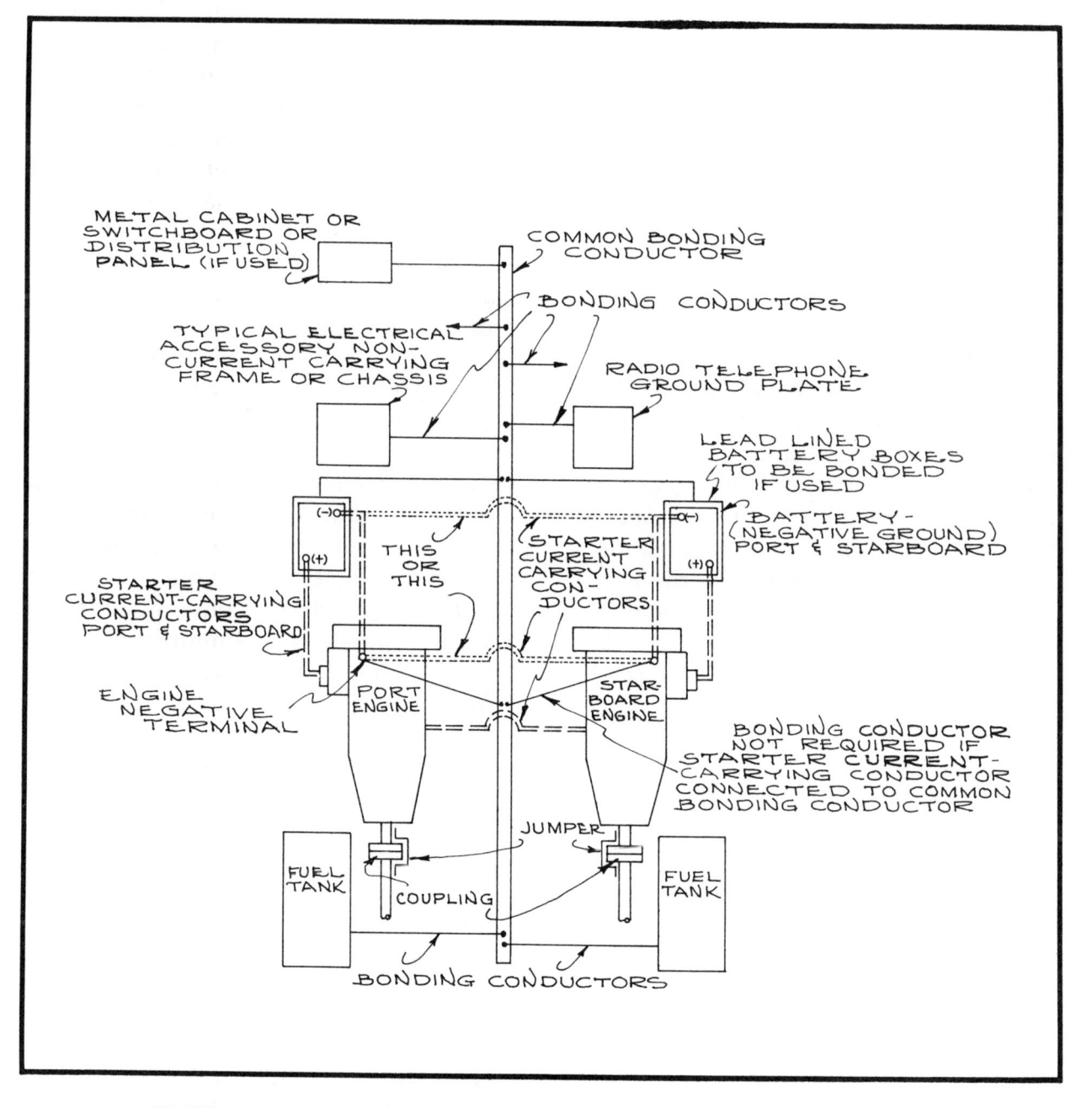

**PLATE 78 — An example of a bonding system aboard a larger twin screw powerboat. A single screw boat would be similar.**

# CHAPTER 20 — CONTROLS & INSTRUMENTATION

Together with the steering system, the controls are used to vary the speed and direction of the vessel. The various instruments monitor the condition and performance of the boat and its mechanical equipment. The types of controls and instrumentation will vary considerably with the boat and the owner's desires.

## THROTTLE & SHIFT CONTROLS

The controls used to control the throttles and shift can be either mechanically, hydraulically, or pneumatically actuated. In most pleasure boats, mechanical controls are commonly used of the push-pull cable type. Other types of controls are more costly, complex, and usually relagated to the larger yacht or commercial boat. When the push-pull cable is used, there should be as few bends as possible and routing should be direct. Any bends should be of as large a radius as possible. Sheathed cables must not be located adjacent to heat, and should always be located well away from, or shielded by insulation, when adjacent to exhaust manifolds.

The type of control to be used for the shift lever will depend on whether the transmission is a hydraulic or manual type, and on the relative position of the motor to the helm or control position. With hydraulic transmissions, a push-pull cable will suffice. However, the manual transmission may require some sort of mechanical linkage which can require considerable thought on the part of the installer. Normally the problem is one of transmitting motion in one plane to another by means of bell cranks and adjoining levers (see Plate 79).

Most manual transmissions have a given pull adjustment, or effort required to move the lever at a given distance, in pounds. The length of the lever arm is in direct proportion to the effort required, disregarding friction. This means that if a lever requires 15 lbs. to move 12" from the pivot point, a force of 7½ lbs. will be required when the effort is applied 24" from the pivot point. On the other hand, if the lever is 6" in length it would take 30 lbs. of effort to move.

By working out the radii of the various levers in the system, it will be possible to determine the amount of effort required to move the reverse mechanism. By the same method, distances of movement can be determined by laying out the various lever arms. Many of these arms have several holes for various lever arm distances from the fulcrum. In the installation of this type of system, great care must be taken to strongly and securely anchor each of the pivot or fulcrum points. Usually the connecting linkage is done with galvanized pipe or comparable material, with ½" being a minimum diameter.

In some cases, hydraulic control can be used to actuate manual transmissions. These are much less complex to install and easier to operate. Details for installation and the types available are provided by various manufacturers of hydraulic control products.

Most boats use hand levers for operation of throttle and shifting controls. Both single and dual lever types are available. With the single lever type, forward, neutral, and reverse directions together with throttle control are made with the same lever. With dual control levers, one lever is for the throttle, and the other for the shift. Certain recommendations are made as to the arrangement of dual lever controls. If used with a single engine, the right lever is used for the throttle and the left for the shift. When throttle and shift are not self-evident, the right lever would be red and the left black. With twin engines requiring two sets of dual lever controls, it is desirable to operate

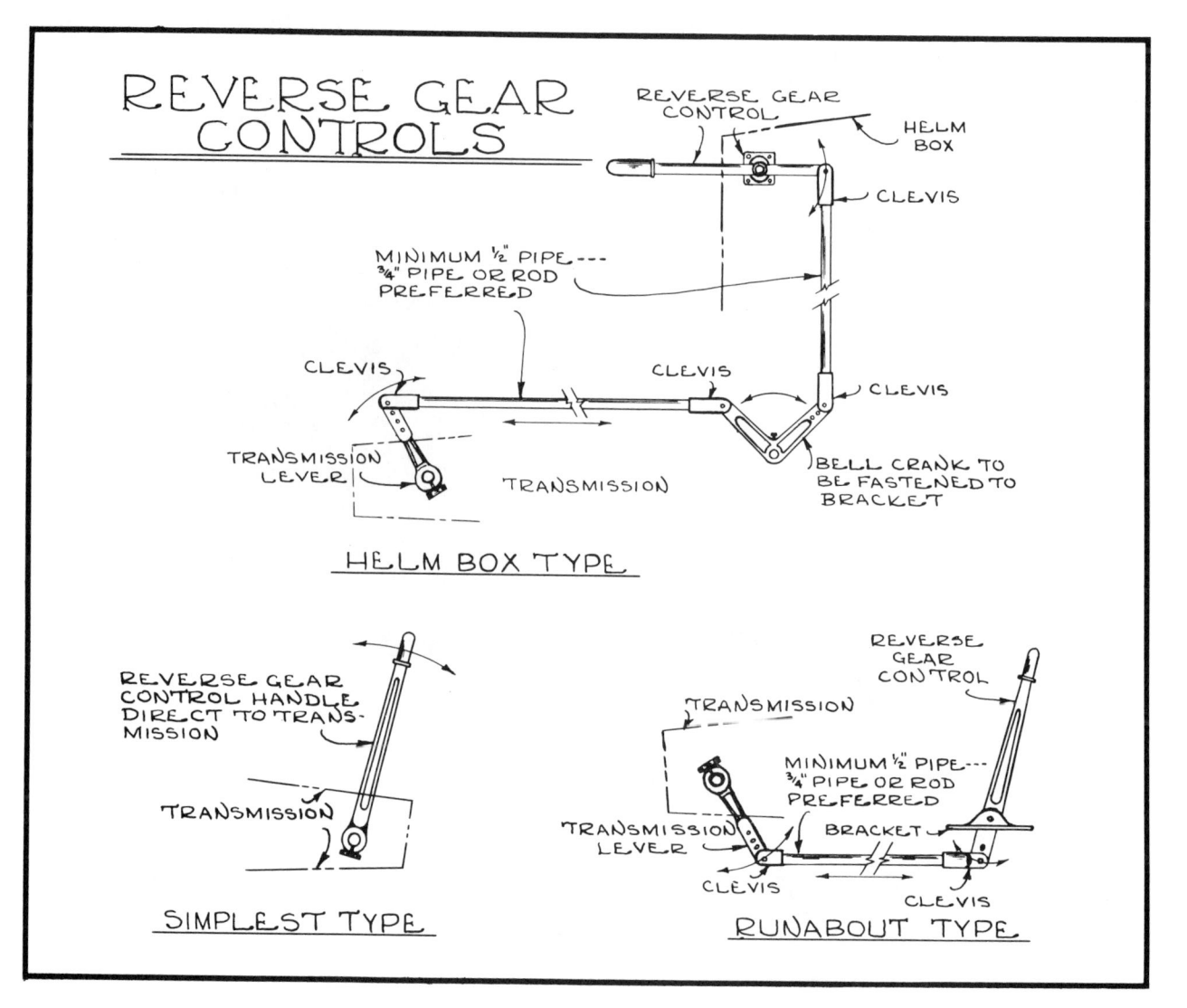

**PLATE 79 — Mechanical type linkage for reverse gear control.**

both throttles with one hand if need be. Often the throttle levers will be mounted close together or towards the center of the console, with the shift being outboard each side for each respective engine, port and starboard.

Throttle levers should be made to increase engine speed when pushed forward, and to reduce speed when pulled aft. Shift levers should activate forward gear when pushed forward, and reverse gear when pulled aft. Neutral should be at mid position, and there should be a safety interlock so that starting can only take place in this position. Throttle and shift controls of the lever type are available for use with dual control stations.

On certain types of boats, a foot throttle much like that used in the automobile is more suitable than the hand type (see Fig. 20-1). On high speed ski, sports, and competition craft, a spring loaded foot throttle provides better control and safety since hand control of the throttle is not necessary. On many boats of this type, a hand lever is used to control the cavitation plates or trim tabs (see Chapter 21), and a free hand is needed for this as well as the steering wheel. Hence, the standard hand lever control is not desirable. The so-called "dead man's" throttle, whether hand or foot operated, is a necessary safety feature on any racing-type boat where the driver could possibly be flipped out of the boat. As with shift levers, the standard push-pull cable type is the most common, although lever and rod types, and hydraulic types may be used.

FIG. 20-1 — A foot throttle is often used on high speed sport and ski boats for better control and safety. (Courtesy of Glenwood Marine Equipment)

240

## INSTRUMENTATION

The instruments used on a boat may be quite different from those used in an automobile, depending on the type of boat and its powerplant. There is also a wider variety of possible optional instruments available, and it is quite possible for a boat owner to become quite "gadget happy" in this area. Just how many of these various instruments will be of value depends on the boat, the owner's requirements, and conditions of use.

As a bare minimum just about all inboard powered boats should have for each engine in the boat, a tachometer to register the RPM's of the engine, an oil pressure gage that monitors the oil pressure within the engine, a water temperature gage to make sure that the cooling system is operating properly, and an ammeter that shows whether or not the boat's battery is being charged. Note that these are preferably gages, and not just "idiot lights" like those on many automobiles. The problem with idiot lights is that substantial damage could occur before such lights register. Of course, if the gages are supplemented with idiot lights to perform the function of an alarm or "attention getter", this is a good situation. However, the prudent skipper will keep a frequent glance on his instruments when underway.

Other instruments can be provided as a further aid in monitoring mechanical conditions. For example, an oil temperature gage as well as a transmission oil gage will indicate low oil level and improper cooling which could lead to damage. A vacuum gage is desirable on the gasoline powered boat to monitor engine efficiency, and to check the performance between engines on a twin installation. Even though the tachometer may register the same RPM's for both engines, the vacuum may be different between the engines indicating a possible problem in one of the engines. On a diesel engine, an exhaust temperature gage performs a similar function. If one engine is working more than the other, it will show up in the form of a higher exhaust temperature, and may indicate a problem in the engine, such as a defective injector.

Unlike an automobile, a boat engine does not have an odometer which measures the miles of operation. Instead, an hour meter is often used which operates while the engine is running. This provides a means of setting maintenance schedules as well as telling how much use an engine has. While speedometers are often included in boats, their accuracy is often questionable. Most types operate by a Pitot or impact tube suspended in the water or fixed to the bottom of the hull. As noted, the accurate way to know the speed of a boat is to time it both ways over a known measured mile course.

Similarly, fuel gages are often installed aboard boats, and these are not always accurate. Whenever possible, a sounding tube and calibrated stick are more accurate. A desirable safety device aboard any gasoline powered boat is a remote fuel shut-off located at the control station. Other convenience items may include a rudder angle indicator and engine synchronizers on twin engine craft. When installing controls and instruments always follow the instructions provided by the manufacturer.

# CHAPTER 21 — TRIM PLATES

Trim plates, which are also referred to as trim planes, trim tabs, after planes, and cavitation plates, are primarily used to adjust or "correct" the planing attitude of high speed boats. Trim plates can be likened to the ailerons on an airplane in that not only can they be used to alter the running trim of the boat by raising or lowering the bow, but some types can alter the trim of the boat from port to starboard underway as well. It was once considered that the addition of trim plates was an attempt to "correct" a boatbuilder's or designer's mistake, and indeed in the past when knowledge of high speed planing boats was limited, this was the case in many instances.

However, this attitude has changed considerably, and in fact the addition of trim plates on boats is often considered standard equipment. Older boats which suffer from trim problems underway can often have their performance greatly improved by the addition of trim plates. While trim plates should not be considered as a design short-cut or an excuse for a poorly designed hull, they can correct for a wide variation in loading conditions so common in modern powerboats. It is not possible for the designer to consider how many people will be aboard a given boat at a given time, nor can he control their locations underway or the variations in fuel and water loadings that can alter the trim and performance of the boat in operation.

While a bow-high attitude is generally frowned upon, there are times when such a trim condition is desirable. For example, a bow-high condition makes the boat safer when running before the seas, gives more positive steering, and quicker acceleration. However, if the boat operates in this condition of trim at all times, there will usually be a loss of speed, loss of fuel

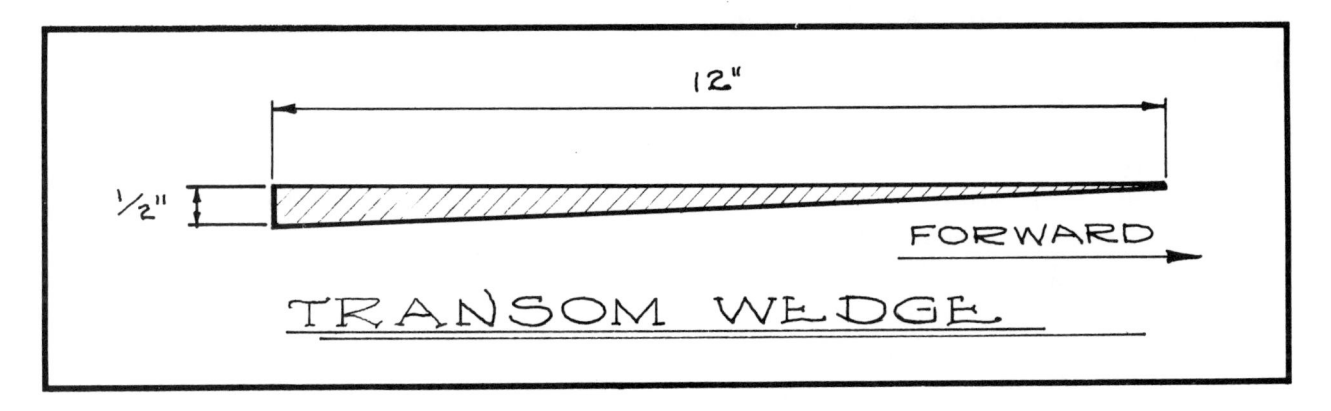

**PLATE 80 — Wedges or "shingles" are one type of trim plate device.**

FIG. 21-1 — The manually adjustable cavitation plate attaches to the transom of the boat and is adjusted with turnbuckles. (Courtesy of Glenwood Marine Equipment)

economy, poor visibility and more wear on the engine. Consequently, it is usually desirable to correct the trim of a vessel which rides with a bow-high attitude, or conversely one that "squats" at the transom.

There are many types of trim plate devices available, however, the first type that should be discussed is the somewhat primitive, but often effective, wedge or "shingle". A wedge or "shingle" as shown by Plate 80 is fitted to the bottom of the boat just forward of the transom with its thickest portion along the trailing edge. In effect, the wedge deflects the water down when

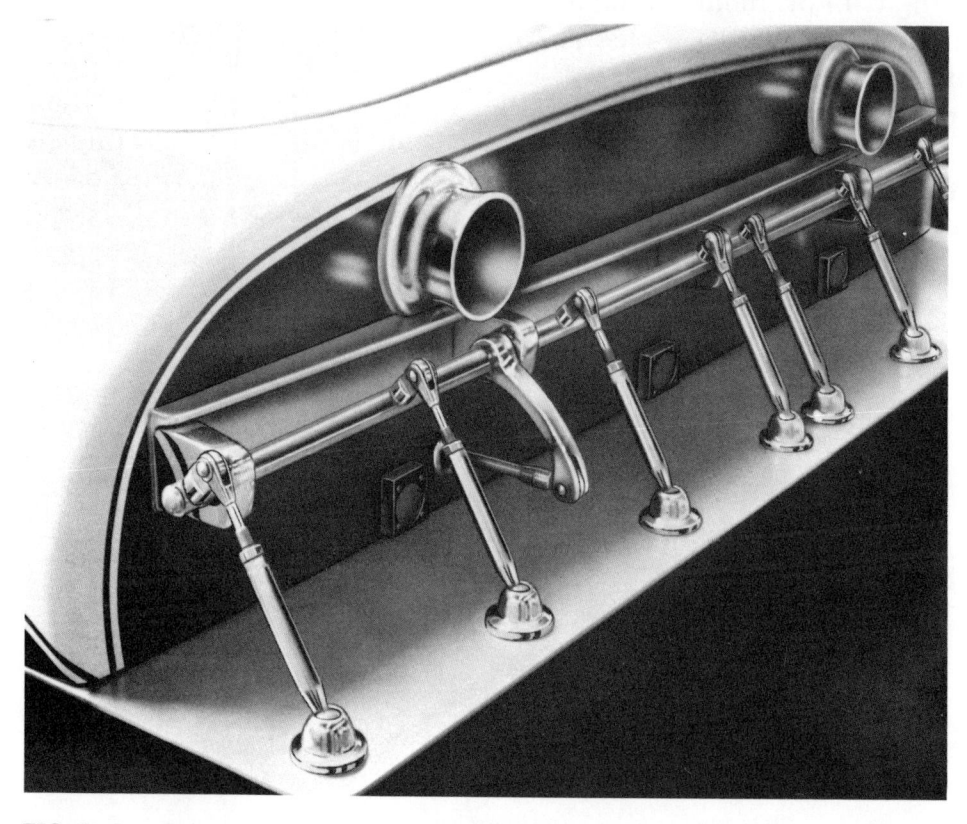

FIG. 21-2 — This cavitation plate is remotely adjustable from the cockpit. A lever arm connects a push-pull cable to an actuating rod linking the turnbuckles together. (Courtesy of Nicson Engineering, Santa Fe Springs, Calif.)

underway thereby lifting the stern of the boat and forcing the bow down. One of the problems with wedges is that nobody actually knows exactly how much wedge or taper is necessary for a given amount of correction on a given boat. It's usually a "by-guess and by-gosh" situation, but one that can be readily corrected by adding a bigger shingle or taking some off as the case requires. Another problem, however, is that the wedge offers no chance for adjustment even though some degree of correction may be good enough for many boat owners and is therefore more desirable and less expensive than purchasing ready-made trim plate units.

For those who want to try adding a wedge on the bottom of their boats to correct running trim problems, a basic beginning point for making a wedge is to start out with a taper ratio of ½" thickness to 12" of chord or fore-and-aft length. The wedge should be fitted across the entire bottom of the boat as much as possible. Generally speaking,

FIG. 21-3 — A typical turnbuckle used for the cavitation plate units shown in FIG. 21-1 and FIG. 21-2. (Courtesy of Nicson Engineering, Santa Fe Springs, Calif.)

FIG. 21-4 — Remotely controlled cavitation plates can be controlled either by foot or by hand with this dual controller. (Courtesy of Glenwood Marine Equipment)

the faster the boat, the less thickness required at the trailing edge and the shorter the chord length can be. Note that this is merely a starting point in what is admittedly a "seat-of-the-pants" trial and error situation. Another approach would be to discuss what others have done with their boats if they are of the same make or design. Often, the problem can be solved in other ways, such as relocating weights, changing propellers, or making other adjustments that can affect running trim. In short, don't go to the trouble of making a wedge before checking out the other elements that could affect the trim and be corrected more easily.

Other types of trim plates include those which are adjustable ready-made units that actuate by either mechanical or electro-hydraulic means. The type of trim plates which are mechanically adjustable are either adjustable at the trim plate device itself, or remotely via a mechanical linkage from the helmsman's position. The former type is similar to the fixed wedge to the extent that

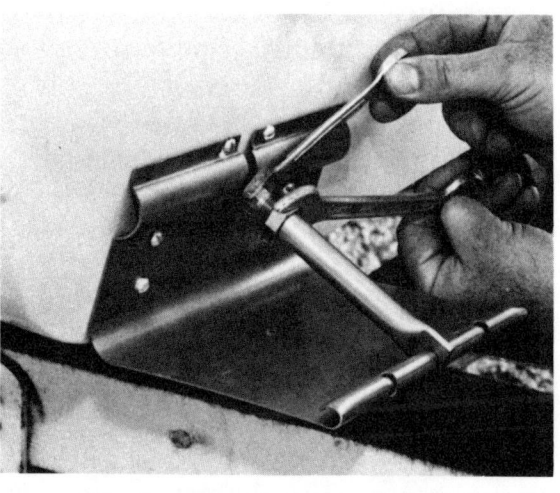

FIG. 21-5 — A manually adjustable trim tab for use on boats in the 17' to 20' range of the planing type. (Courtesy of Tempo Products, Cleveland, Ohio)

once they are set, they cannot be adjusted underway, even though they can usually be readjusted with the boat out of the water. A common type is called the standard cavitation plate as shown by Fig. 21-1. These consist of stainless steel or aluminum plates attached to the transom of the boat and braced at several points across the transom with

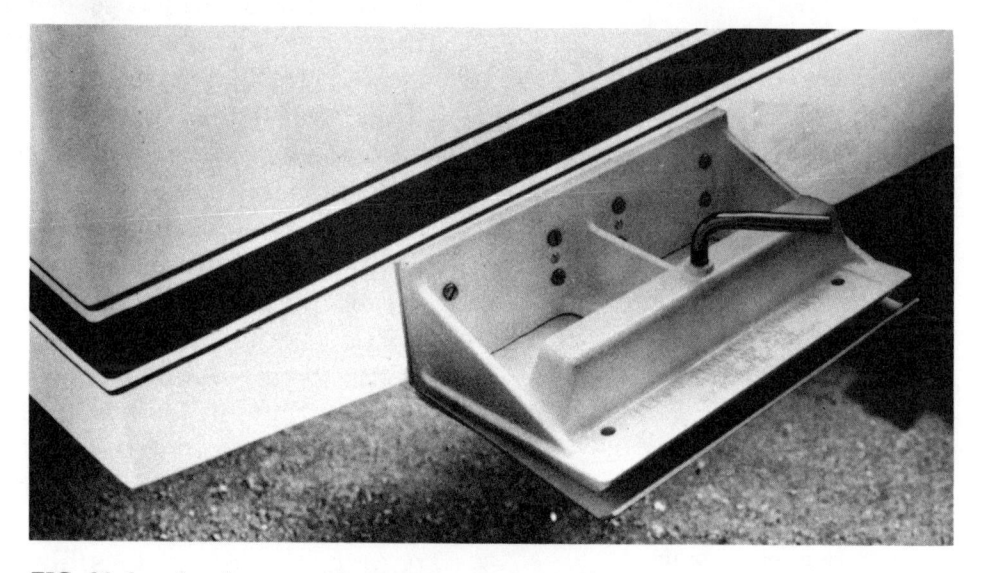

FIG. 21-6 — Another type of manually adjustable trim tab. This type can be used on planing boats to 23' and is available in several sizes. (Courtesy of Tempo Products, Cleveland, Ohio)

245

adjustable turnbuckles. The remotely controlled adjustable cavitation plate as shown by Fig. 21-2 is similar, but is an improvement over the standard cavitation plate since the helmsman can alter the adjustment either by means of a foot or hand control (see Fig. 21-4).

The so-called cavitation plate type of trim plate is commonly used on ski-type and competition boats where high horsepower engines and high speeds are typical. For competition use, the adjustable type is almost a necessity since the driver can place the plates in

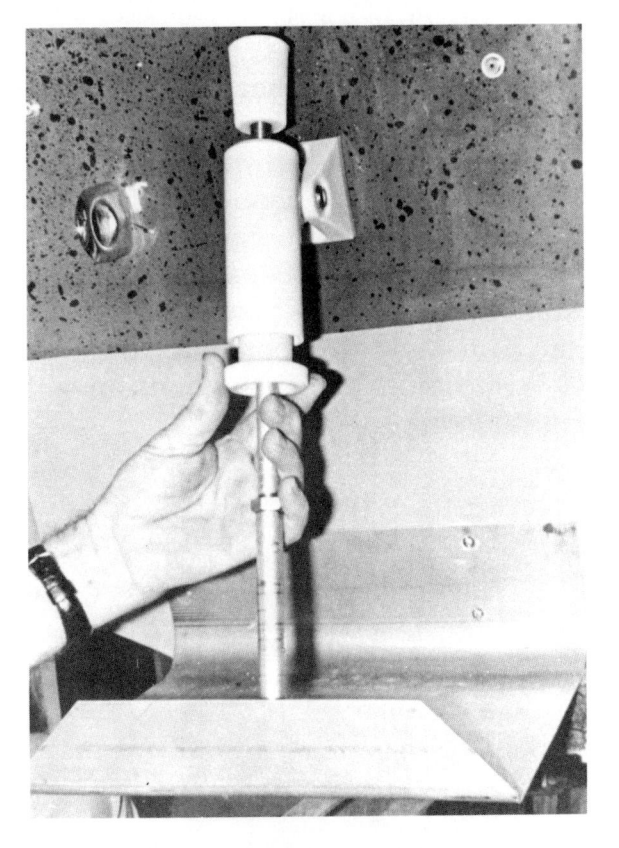

FIG. 21-7 — This trim tab is said to be automatically adjustable to suit varying conditions of speed and trim, and can be used on boats up to 25′ depending on the size unit selected. (Courtesy of Tempo Products, Cleveland, Ohio)

a down position and rapidly accelerate the boat from a standstill, keeping the bow down at the same time, thereby directing power most efficiently. As speed increases, he can change the angle of the plates infinitely for best speed and even include some degree of porpoising (which is ordinarily undesirable but which can increase the speed in these high speed boats as they break free of the water). However, at skiing speeds, such porpoising is not desirable, and consequently, the plates must be readjusted not only for skiing use, but to suit the number of skiers that will be towed. Another advantage of the cavitation plate type is that because each turnbuckle (see Fig. 21-3) is adjustable, it is possible to put a "hook" at one or both ends of the plate thereby changing the handling of the boat to suit specific conditions, or for "correcting" some aspect of the boat's nature.

On the larger cruiser type planing boats, the electro-hydraulic trim plate is often used. While similar to the cavitation plate units described above, these use hydraulic cylinders controlled from the helm to raise and lower the plates. Controls are available which electrically actuate the hydraulic cylinder of each plate either individually or in unison for a wide variety of adjustments underway. Proper trimming of the plates results in more speed, better fuel economy for most boats, better visibility from the helm, a better ride with less pounding; correction (at least to some degree) of torque reactions, steering, and porpoising; and reduced wake turbulence. Of course, it is often possible to overtrim this type of plate and aggravate some problems. The makers recommend that the operator exercise cautious use, at least in the beginning, until he gets used to his boat's reactions to various degrees of trim.

One type of electro-hydraulic trim plate system is shown by Fig. 21-8. This type mounts externally to the bottom of the boat extending aft beyond the transom. However, there are types that will mount to the transom itself, as well as those which are built into the hull (which are usually used on factory-built boats for the most part). Whichever type is used, the plates must be in line with the bottom of the boat; not below. Where an outdrive unit is installed, there should be at least 8″ clearance from the centerline on each side. On vee bottom boats, the plates should not be so closely mounted that they interfere with each other, so always allow some clearance. As a general recommendation, the longest span (distance from the centerline outboard to the chine or turn of the bilge) should be used. To check for ultimate trimming, a good gage is to observe the tach to see when the RPM's decrease. Also listen to the engine for a decrease in laboring, and check the wake.

Do all high speed planing boats need trim plates? Not necessarily; it all depends on the boat as well as the conditions of use and the owner's requirements. If your boat rides smoothly, handles easily, turns well both to port and starboard at normal operating speeds, has good fuel economy, and runs with the stern down by only a few degrees, then there is probably little need for trimming devices. However, if your boat does not measure up in even one of these categories of performance, then trim plates may help. Other than the expense and work of installation, the addition of trim plates cannot hurt your boat's performance.

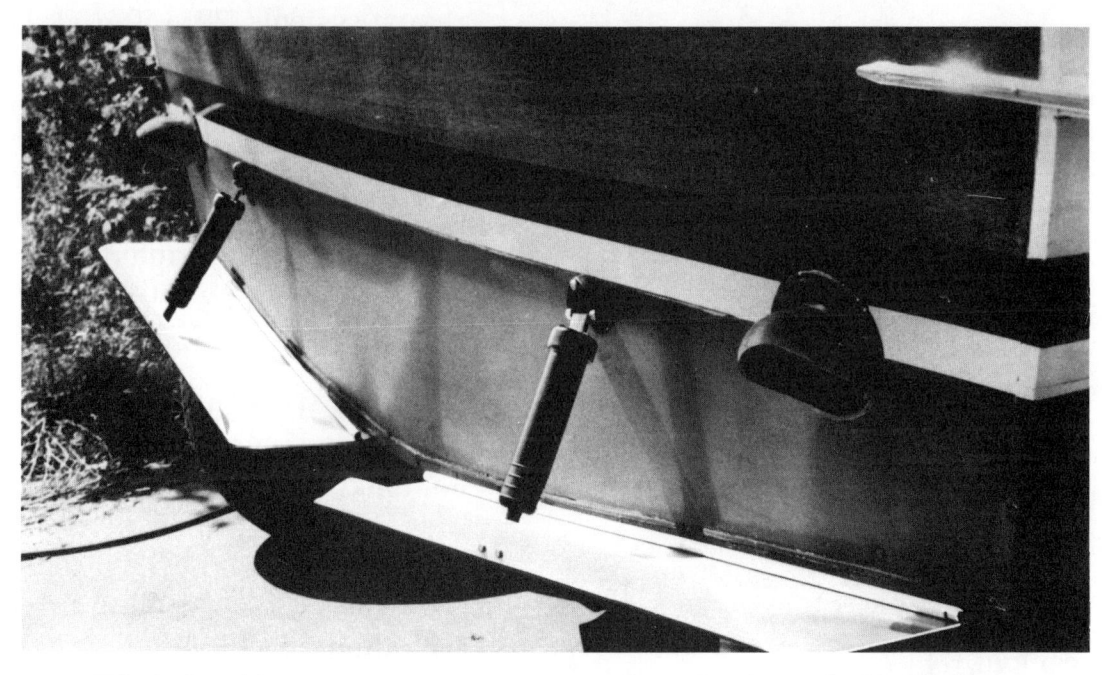

FIG. 21-8 — Adjustable trim planes are commonly used on large planing type boats such as this to improve performance and handling. (Courtesy of Bennett Marine, Deerfield Beach, Fla.)

# INDEX